Neurological and
Electroencephalographic
Correlative Studies
in Infancy

A CONFERENCE AND SYMPOSIUM

Sponsored by the World Federation of Neurology
and presented under the auspices of
Baylor University College of Medicine
with the support of
the National Institutes of Health and
Houston Endowment
October 2 and 3, 1963

Neurological and Electroencephalographic Correlative Studies in Infancy

Edited by PETER KELLAWAY
and INGEMAR PETERSEN

 GRUNE & STRATTON / New York and London

Library of Congress Catalog Card No. 64-15159

Printed in U.S.A.
(O/B)

Contents

Members

MARIA ROBERT DE RAMIREZ DE ARELLANO, *National Institute of Neurological Diseases and Blindness, National Institutes of Health, and University of Puerto Rico, San Juan, Puerto Rico.*

MURRAY B. BORNSTEIN, *Mount Sinai Hospital and Columbia University College of Physicians and Surgeons, New York, New York.*

JAN BUREŠ, *Institute of Physiology of the Czechoslovak Academy of Science, Prague, Czechoslovakia.*

WILLIAM CAVENESS, *Columbia University College of Physicians and Surgeons and Neurological Institute of the Presbyterian Hospital, New York, New York.*

STANLEY M. CRAIN, *Columbia University College of Physicians and Surgeons, New York, New York.*

C. DREYFUS-BRISAC, *Clinique Baudelocque, Maternity Hôpital Saint Antoine, EEG Department of the Hôpital de Pitie, Paris, France.*

ROBERT J. ELLINGSON, *Nebraska Psychiatric Institute, The University of Nebraska College of Medicine, Omaha, Nebraska.*

SIDNEY GOLDRING, *Washington University School of Medicine, St. Louis, Missouri.*

BERNICE GRAFSTEIN, *The Rockefeller Institute, New York, New York.*

PETER KELLAWAY, *Baylor University College of Medicine, Houston, Texas.*

ROBERT MAULSBY, *Baylor University College of Medicine, Houston, Texas.*

GIUSEPPE PAMPIGLIONE, *The Hospital for Sick Children and The Royal Free Hospital, London, England.*

INGEMAR PETERSÉN, *Sahlgrenska Sjukhuset, Göteborg, Sweden.*

JOHN STOBO PRICHARD, *The Hospital for Sick Children and University of Toronto, Toronto, Ontario, Canada.*

DOMINICK P. PURPURA, *Columbia University College of Physicians and Surgeons, New York, New York.*

D. SAMSON-DOLLFUS, *Laboratories d'EEG et Anatomie Pathologique du Centre Hospitalie Universitaire, Rouen, France.*

J. P. SCHADÉ, *Netherlands Central Institute for Brain Research, Amsterdam, The Netherlands.*

WILLIAM F. WINDLE, *National Institute of Neurological Diseases and Blindness, National Institutes of Health, San Juan, Puerto Rico.*

Guests

J. PRESTON ROBB, *Montreal Neurological Institute, Montreal, Quebec, Canada.*

GILBERT H. GLASER, *Yale University School of Medicine, New Haven, Connecticut.*

CHARLES E. HENRY, *Cleveland Clinic, Cleveland, Ohio.*

A. H. PARMELEE, JR., *University of California Medical Center, Los Angeles, California.*

E. C. ALVORD, JR., *University of Washington School of Medicine, Seattle, Washington.*

DORA HSI-CHIH CHAO, *The Blue Bird Clinic, Methodist Hospital, Houston, Texas.*

M. M. DESMOND, *Baylor University College of Medicine, Houston, Texas.*

RUDOLF ENGEL, *University of Oregon Medical School, Portland, Oregon.*

Preface

This book is a record of a Conference held in Houston from September 30 to October 3, 1963. The Conference was concerned with the ontogenetic evolution of the electrical activity of the brain and the correlation of this evolution with morphological and behavioral development.

The idea for such a Conference was first suggested in discussions with Dr. E. C. Alvord, Chairman of the Sub-Committee on Electroencephalography of the Perinatal Research Committee, the National Institute of Neurological Diseases and Blindness, and planned as an interdisciplinary "round table" which would bring together a wide range of specialists working with various aspects of the ontogenetic development of the brain.

During the last six to seven years, interest in maturation as a primary determinant of the character of electrographic phenomena has greatly intensified. The "Ontogenic Evolution of the Electroencephalogram in Man and in Animals" was one of the main topics chosen for discussion at the Fourth International Congress of Electroencephalography and Clinical Neurophysiology held at Brussels in 1957, but at that time the literature of the subject, especially in terms of fundamental electrophysiological studies, was comparatively meager. Since 1957, however, the number of papers directly or indirectly concerned with electro-ontogenesis has more than doubled, and the number of laboratories in which this is a subject of primary research interest has increased fourfold, with considerable activity centering in Amsterdam, Paris, Montevideo, New York, St. Louis, Los Angeles and Houston.

In order to allow a reasonable fluidity and freedom of discussion the Conference was limited to 28 members and guests. The sessions of Sept. 30th and Oct. 1 were conducted by a series of chairmen, each assigned a particular topic. Each chairman opened his particular session with a review of his own recent work in the field and a discussion of the essential problems requiring study. The chairmen's remarks served as a basis for an ensuing period of free discussion. The topics selected and the chairman responsible for leading the discussion were as follows:

Structure-Function Relationships in Immature Cerebral and Cerebellar Cortex—Dominick Purpura

Ontogenic Evolution of Evoked Cortical Response in Man and in Animals —Sidney Goldring

Cerebral Electrical Responses to Auditory and Visual Stimuli in Infancy— Robert Ellingson

Ontogenetic Evolution of Spontaneous Activity of the Brain during Sleep and Wakefulness—Peter Kellaway

Anoxia and Ischemia in the Pre- and Perinatal Period—William Windle

Hypoxia and Ischemia in Infancy and Early Childhood—Giuseppe Pampiglione

The twenty papers which constitute the chapters of this book have been arranged according to these main topics of discussion.

The editors wish to express their gratitude for the financial support which was provided for the Conference by the National Institute of Neurological Diseases and Blindness (Grant #NB 04511-01) and by Houston Endowment. We wish to acknowledge our debt to our associates, Dr. James D. Frost, Jr. and Dr. Meyer L. Proler, who not only monitored and recorded the entire proceedings of the Conference and Symposium but also undertook the major task of correcting and condensing the more than 400 pages of resulting type-script. The Conference Secretary, Mrs. Marilyn Ekeroot, was responsible for much of the detail of the organization and arrangements for the Conference, and to her and to Miss Linda Lawson who assisted us in enumerable ways we wish to express our appreciation.

PETER KELLAWAY AND INGEMAR PETERSÉN
Houston and Göteborg   June 1964

MORPHOLOGICAL DEVELOPMENT OF NEONATAL MOUSE CEREBRAL CORTEX IN TISSUE CULTURE*

MURRAY B. BORNSTEIN

Laboratory of Cellular Neurophysiology, Department of Neurology, The Mount Sinai Hospital, New York, N. Y.

The method of culturing mammalian cerebellum in the Maximow slide assembly (Bornstein and Murray, 1958) has been extended to include fragments of cerebral neocortex obtained from 1 to 5 day old mice. During their healthy, long-term *in vitro* existence, the cultures reveal somewhat different patterns of development and maturation from those previously observed in the cerebellar fragments. Their additional inherent interest for other experimental studies leads to this description of their tissue culture characteristics.

Although it is a demanding, arduous technique, the Maximow slide method is favored in our laboratory since it offers the tissues a favorable environment for maturation processes. At the same time, it presents the cultures to the investigator for daily, direct observation by high power microscopy as well as for relatively easy experimental manipulations and control. At any time during the course of an experiment, active and reactive phenomena may be observed and recorded photographically. Also, morphologically apparent events at the cellular level, such as various stages of development, can be selected by direct observation and the tissue may then be submitted to other forms of laboratory analysis or examination, as the micro-electrophysiological studies of Dr. Stanley Crain will demonstrate.

Methods

The previously described methods (Bornstein and Murray, 1958; Bornstein and Appel, 1961) have been applied to the cerebral tissues with only slight modifications. The success of this extension to cerebral tissues probably results more from the gradual accumulation of small improvements in the preparation and sterilization of glassware and media and the consequent elimination of toxic and contaminating factors rather than from any major change in technique. The fragments are prepared in the following manner: The cerebral hemispheres are removed from etherized 1 to 5 day old mice. After the meninges are removed, the fragments are prepared from slices of the anterior portions of each hemisphere (Fig. 1). The individual fragments measure about 2 mm. by 0.5 mm. along the surface of the cortex and 1 mm. deep, into the substance of the hemisphere. Care is taken to assure that the fragments do not in-

---

*This work was supported by Grant NB 01913 from the National Institute of Neurological Diseases and Blindness and Grant 246 from the National Multiple Sclerosis Society.

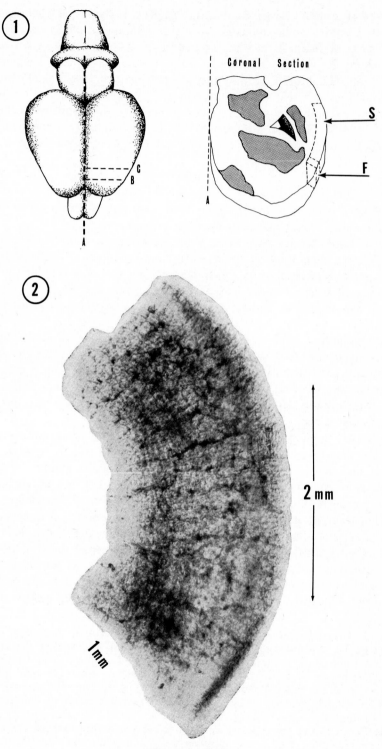

Figs. 1 and 2

clude other systems of neuronal tissue, such as thalamus. Each fragment is explanted onto a collagen-coated coverslip (Bornstein, 1958) and is fed a single drop of "natural" medium consisting of 40% human placental or fetal calf serum; 25% bovine serum ultrafiltrate; and 35% Simms' balanced salt solution at pH 6.9 to 7.1 with a glucose supplement to yield a final concentration to 600 mgm. %. No antibiotics are used. The cultures are sealed into the Maximow assembly and are maintained in the lying-drop position in the incubator at 34–35° C. and are removed to room temperature for their daily microscopic examinations. The feeding solution is changed twice a week.

Observations

Over 650 cultured fragments of mouse cerebral neocortex and its underlying tissues have been observed for periods of time ranging from a few days to over 2 months. Most were maintained for at least a month.

The cultured tissues have been obtained mainly from 1–3 day old mice. Younger fragments seem to suffer more from the shock of explantation and lose a great number of cells. Older ones do not flatten well which not only decreases their translucency and observability, but also tends to produce a central necrosis due to inadequate nourishment or oxygenation in the deeper-lying areas.

The explants assume a characteristic crescent shape (Fig. 2) with the original uncut surface of the cortex being convex and the previously deep-lying sub-cortical layers forming a parallel concavity. This orientation is maintained during the entire period in culture so that the observer can usually state which edge of the explant represents the original uncut surface and which the underlying, deeper layers.

Practically no outgrowth can be seen during the first 2 days after explantation, but soon thereafter a prolific growth of neurites extends from the uncut surface and the cut edges of cortex (Fig. 10). A smaller number of neurites extend from the deep, concave edge where neuroglial and microglial cells appear in greater numbers than from the surface convexity. The dense, almost felt-like, layer of neurites not only extends out from the fragment in the horizontal plane, but these collateral extensions also grow above, below, and within the main mass of the cellular elements composing the fragment itself (Fig. 11). These intertwining nerve filaments are probably important for the development of inter-neuronal relationships. The various cell bodies are easily visualized, however, as they lie densely packed and closely nestled into the

---

Fig. 1. **Diagrammatic representation of the dissection used to prepare cerebral fragments for explantation.** On the left, the cerebral hemispheres, having been stripped of meninges, are to be separated along dotted line "A". Each hemisphere is cut along lines "B" and "C" to prepare the coronal section, 2 mm. thick, as represented at the right. A slab, "S", 1 mm. deep, is cut from the coronal section. The individual fragments, "F", are prepared by serial sections of the slab—each section being cut 0.5 mm. thick.

Fig. 2. **An actual fragment of newborn cerebrum at the time of explantation. The dimensions, cf. Fig. 1, are approximate.** Photograph taken at 100 diameters magnification.

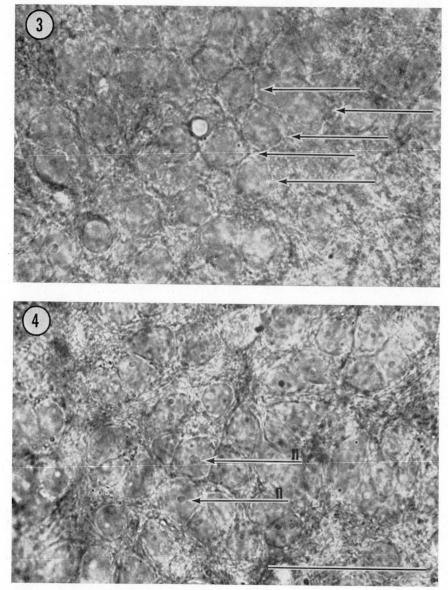

Fig. 3. Culture M66-3, 3-day-old mouse cerebrum, 5 days *in vitro* (DIV). Many closely packed neurons, some of which are designated by arrows, are already visible. X600. Scale equals 100 microns.

Fig. 4. Culture M6-8, 1-day-old mouse cerebrum, 20 DIV. The neuron somas are well delineated. Note small, occasionally multiple, nucleoli (arrow - "n"), relatively large nuclei and scanty cytoplasm. X600. Scale equals 100μ.

fibrillar surround. This dense neuropile, by the way, acts somewhat like a ground glass and offers some interference for high quality photography.

After about 4–5 days *in vitro*, neuron cell bodies become recognizable (Fig. 3). Their appearance differs according to their location in the fragment. Along the uncut surface of the cortex, the neurons are numerous and densely

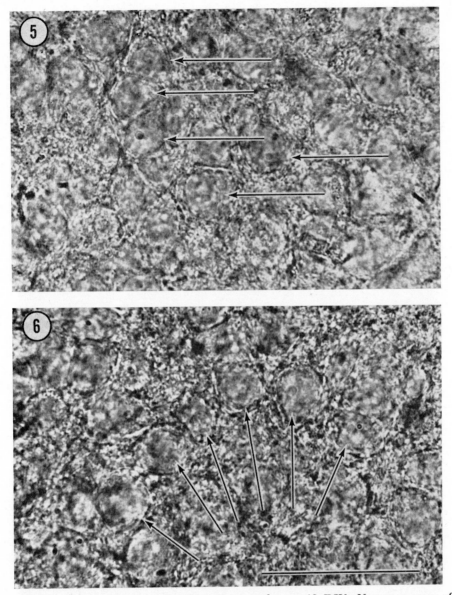

Fig. 5. Culture M60-8, 3-day-old mouse cerebrum, 46 DIV. Neurons, some of which are designated by arrows. X600. Scale equals 100μ.

Fig. 6. Culture M60-8, same as in Fig. 5 but after 62 DIV. Neurons, some of which are designated by arrows. Note slight granularity due to accumulated cytoplasmic Nissl and lipid material. X600. Scale equals 100μ.

packed one next to the other and frequently piled up 2 to 3 cell layers thick (Fig. 3, 4, 5, 6). The individual somas look alike, being rather small, about 15–20 microns in diameter, with small nucleoli, relatively large nuclei and a rather scanty cytoplasm. In the "depths" of the fragment, the neurons are less numerous, being separated by the thick meshwork of neuropile. They are also less uniform in size and tend to be larger than those at the surface (Fig. 7).

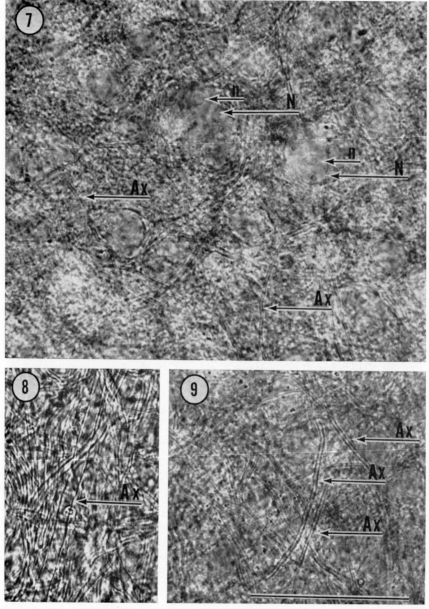

Fig. 7. Culture M60-10, 3-day-old mouse cerebrum, 50 DIV. Photograph of the "deep" area of the culture where larger neurons (arrow - "N") and their larger nucleoli (arrow - "n") are less numerous and are separated by a thick neuropile in which myelinated axons (arrow - "Ax") run in and out of focus. X600. Scale equals 100μ.

Fig. 8. Culture R23-16, newborn rat cerebellum, 22 DIV. Myelinated axons, to compare with those in Fig. 7 and 9, of variable diameter. A particularly thick axon is designated by the arrow. The myelin sheaths are also more evident than those of the cerebrum. X600. Scale equals 100μ.

Fig. 9. Culture M60-10. Same as in Fig. 7, but a different region to demonstrate other axons, their relative uniformity after 50 DIV and their relatively thin myelin sheaths. X600. Scale equals 100μ.

Some reach diameters of 30–35 microns. Their nuclei and nucleoli are correspondingly larger, particularly the nucleoli. It is here that neuroglial cell bodies can occasionally be visualized, but they are usually hidden by the dense neuropile. In the outgrowth, however, where all the tissue elements are less compact, their presence is abundantly apparent. The neuron somas change little in appearance during the following months in culture (Fig. 5, 6). The cytoplasm may assume a granular appearance due to the accumulation of basophilic (Nissl) and lipid materials.

During the 2nd. to 3rd. week *in vitro,* many of the cultures may be observed to develop myelinated axons (Fig. 7, 9). These differ in a number of ways from those previously studied in cultured cerebellar fragments (Fig. 8). First, they occur almost exclusively in the "deep-lying" portions of the explant, i. e. those areas corresponding to or approaching the sub-cortical white matter. Only rarely has a myelinated axon appeared in the neuronally populated surface areas of the fragment. Secondly, the axons remain fine, about 1 micron in diameter, as compared to the cerebellum where they vary from 1 to 5 microns. Third, the amount of myelin is thin when compared to the thick sheaths about the cerebellar axons. Finally, their course through the tissue is entirely different. The cerebellar axons seek the tissue-collagen interface, accumulate in that plane, and run a more or less straight or slightly bending two-dimensional course so that their appearance was originally compared to railroad tracks. The fine, lightly myelinated cerebral axons, however, run in no particular plane of the culture, but wander in and out, around and about the various cell bodies. To follow the previous metaphor, they are more like a meandering New England back country road. These characteristics make photographs less spectacular, but may well be important in terms of neuronal functional inter-relationships.

A number of histological and histochemical procedures are being applied to cultures selected and fixed during various stages of development so that the patterns of maturation and complexity may be more fully documented. The Bodian silver impregnations (Fig. 10, 11) reveal the dense neuritic growth as well as characteristic neuronal configurations. It should be mentioned that Dr. George Pappas of the Anatomy Department of Columbia University, College of Physicians and Surgeons, has been examining selected cultures by means of the electron microscope (unpublished observations). The usual cellular and sub-cellular constituents are abundantly present. Of major importance is the fact that the cultured fragments contain both axo-dendritic and axo-somatic synapses, the post-synaptic spine apparatus, and desmosomes between neuroglial cell membranes—all evidence of *in vitro* differentiation and maturation.

Discussion

This conference is not the place for an exhaustively detailed review of culture studies' contributions to the understanding of central nerve tissue. Except for R. G. Harrison's (1906–08) pioneering studies, most of the work is relatively recent and reveals an interesting trend of development itself.

Understandably, many of the earlier studies of Murray and Stout (1940, 1942, 1947), Hogue (1947, 1949, 1950, 1953), and Costero and Pomerat (1951)

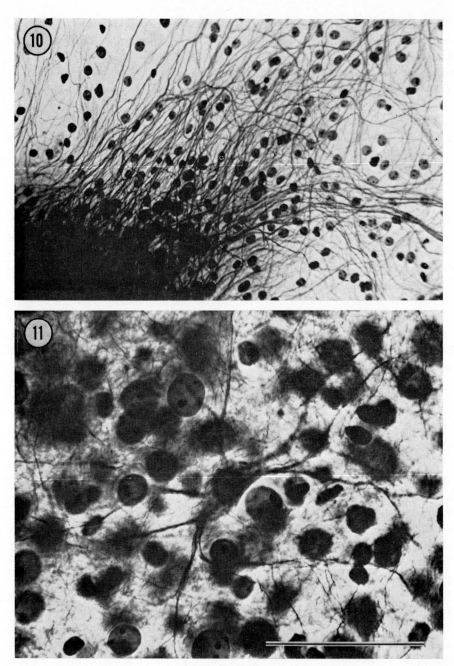

Fig. 10. 3-day-old mouse cerebrum fixed after 14 days *in vitro* and stained with Bodian's silver impregnation to demonstrate neurites. The dark mass at the lower left represents the edge of the explant itself. The dense neuritic outgrowth and the sparse neuroglial migration are clearly evident. X150. Scale equals 400 microns.

Fig. 11. 2-day-old mouse cerebrum fixed after 21 DIV and stained with Bodian's silver impregnation. Neurons and heavy neuritic network demonstrated. X1350. Scale equals 40 microns.

were concerned with the identification and characterization of various cell types—neurons, neuroglia, microglia, ependyma, choroid plexus—as they occur in culture. As a result of this necessary emphasis, the observations were directed primarily toward the outgrowth zones where the individual cells were more easily seen. It was not immediately apparent in these early studies that isolated cells in the outgrowth zones might assume bizarre and misleading shapes. Later, the community of cells which remained in the original explant area attracted attention (Pomerat and Costero, 1956) and occasionally served to correct some of the earlier impressions of what constituted a neuron in culture.

The importance of cellular inter-relationships received a strong statement in the description by Peterson and Murray (1955) of myelin sheath formation in cultures of avian spinal ganglion, peripheral nerve tissue. Hild's (1957) application of roller tube techniques to kitten cerebellum first demonstrated *in vitro* myelin formation in the mammalian central nervous system. Some of his interpretations concerning the mechanism of central myelinogenesis, e. g. that the axoplasm proper might form myelin without neuroglial cell assistance or that an area of swelling of the myelin sheath represented an area of myelination, yielded to the greater detail supplied by serial observations of the process in kitten and rat cerebellum maintained in the Maximow slide assembly (Bornstein and Murray, 1958) and to the electron microscopic examination of the cultures (Ross, Bornstein and Lehrer, 1962).

Occasionally, there appear unwarranted conclusions from inadequately controlled experiments which may misinform the uninitiated reader about the limits of applicability of known methods to the study of nerve tissues. Geiger's studies (1957; 1958 a, b; 1960) are energetic but, unfortunately, her conclusions are based on the misinterpretation of altered cells as normal neurons. As studies of glia, they might be interesting. The persistent interpretation of the data in terms of normal neurons suggests an ignorance of, or disdain for, recent available advances and information as well as an unwillingness to submit the unrecognized error to proper controls.

In studies directed toward eliciting possible evidence of functional relationships in cultured cerebellum, Hild and Tasaki (1962) found electrophysiological activity but no manifestations of synaptic, interneuronal relationships. They suggested that cultured mammalian central nervous tissue simply did not develop to this degree. In this regard, Cunningham's recent (1962) electrical recordings from cultured avian telencephalon are suggestive. The word "neuron," however, is carefully avoided and is replaced by circumlocutions, such as "all the cells expected in embryonic chick telencephalon." Moreover, no actual data concerning the histology of the fragments has been published. The suggestive electrical recordings would be of much greater interest and relevance with some firm anatomical support. Other recent studies suggest, however, that significant neuronal inter-relationships do develop in cultured mammalian spinal cord (Peterson, Bornstein and Crain, 1962; Crain and Peterson, 1963).

This study, therefore, of the mammalian cerebral neocortex in tissue culture simply represents an additional step in the application of these techniques to the analysis of the great complexity of nerve tissues. And yet, this work represents but an introduction.

ACKNOWLEDGMENTS

The author acknowledges with appreciation and thanks the assistance of Dr. Lilian Breitbart, Miss Rachel Monzain, Miss Annelies Herrmann and Mrs. Berthe Puteaux.

REFERENCES

BORNSTEIN, M. B. Reconstituted rat-tail collagen used as substrate for tissue culture on coverslips in Maximow slides and roller tubes. *Lab. Invest., 1958,* 7:134–137.

BORNSTEIN, M. B. and APPEL, S. H. The application of tissue culture to the study of experimental "allergic" encephalomyelitis. I. Patterns of demyelination. *J. Neuropath. Exper. Neurol., 1961,* 20: 141–157.

BORNSTEIN, M. B. and MURRAY, M. R. Serial observations on patterns of growth, myelin formation, maintenance and degeneration in cultures of new-born rat and kitten cerebellum. *J. Biophys. Biochem. Cytol., 1958,* 4:499–504.

COSTERO, I. and POMERAT, C. M. Cultivation of neurons from the adult human cerebral and cerebellar cortex. *Am. J. Anat., 1951,* 89:405–467.

CRAIN, S. M. and PETERSON, E. R. Bioelectric activity in long-term cultures of spinal cord tissues. *Science, 1963,* 141: 427–429.

CUNNINGHAM, A. W. B. Qualitative behavior of spontaneous potentials from explants of 15 day chick embryo telencephalon *in vitro. J. Gen. Physiol., 1962,* 45:1065–1076.

GEIGER, R. S. *In vitro* studies on the growth properties of brain cortex cells of adult individuals. *Progr. Neurobiol., 1957,* 2: 83–99.

GEIGER, R. S. Subcultures of adult mammalian brain cortex *in vitro. Exp. Cell Res., 1958a,* 14:541–566.

GEIGER, R. S. Effect of adrenalin on neurofibril formation in adult mammalian cortical neurons in tissue culture. *Nature, 1958b,* 182:1674–1675.

GEIGER, R. S. The effects of LSD-25, serotonin, and sera from schizophrenic patients on adult mammalian brain culture. *J. Neuropsychiat., 1960,* 1:185–199.

HARRISON, R. G. Observations on the living developing nerve fiber. *Anat. Rec., 1906–1907,* 1:116–118. *Soc. Exp. Biol. Med. 1906–1907,* 4:140–143.

HILD, W. Myelogenesis in cultures of mammalian central nervous tissue. *Zschr. Zellforsch., 1957,* 46:71–95.

HILD, W. and TASAKI, I. Morphological and physiological properties of neurons and glial cells in tissue culture. *J. Neurophysiol., 1962,* 25:277–304.

HOGUE, M. J. Human fetal ependymal cells in tissue cultures. *Anat. Rec., 1947,* 99: 523–529.

HOGUE, M. J. Human fetal choroid plexus cells in tissue cultures. *Anat. Rec., 1949,* 103:381–399,

HOGUE, M. J. Brain cells from human fetuses and infants, cultured *in vitro* after death of the individuals. *Anat. Rec., 1950,* 108:457–476.

HOGUE, M. J. A study of adult brain cells grown in tissue cultures. *Amer. J. Anat., 1953,* 93:397–427.

MURRAY, M. R. and STOUT, A. P. Schwann cell vs. fibroblast as the origin of the specific nerve sheath tumor; observations upon normal nerve sheaths and neurilemomas *in vitro. Amer. J. Path., 1940,* 16: 41–60.

MURRAY, M. R. and STOUT, A. P. Characteristics of human Schwann cells in vitro. *Anat. Rec., 1942,* 84:275–293.

MURRAY, M. R. and STOUT, A. P. Adult human sympathetic ganglion cells cultivated *in vitro. Amer. J. Anat., 1947,* 80: 225–273.

PETERSON, E. R., BORNSTEIN, M. B. and CRAIN, S. M. Development, myelination and function in cultures of mammalian spinal cord. *Excerpta Med.*, 1962, 16 (Sect. 1):813.

PETERSON, E. R. and MURRAY, M. R. Myelin sheath formation in cultures of avian spinal ganglia. *Amer. J. Anat.*, 1955, 96: 319–355.

POMERAT, C. and COSTERO, I. Tissue cultures of cat cerebellum. *Amer. J. Anat.*, 1956, 99:211–247.

ROSS, L. L., BORNSTEIN, M. B. and LEHRER, G. M. Electron microscopic observations of rat and mouse cerebellum in tissue culture. *J. Cell Biol.*, 1962, 14:19–30.

DISCUSSION

DR. WELLS: Dr. Pomerat has shown that axons would not grow unless glial elements were present. I noticed in yours there were not or didn't appear to be too many glial elements in these long axons that were growing out of the slab. Could you explain that?

DR. BORNSTEIN: Do you mean in the outgrowth zone?

DR. WELLS: Yes.

DR. BORNSTEIN: I don't believe that Dr. Pomerat has ever suggested that axons may not grow out of cultured fragments of cerebellum or cerebrum. Axons may exist *in vitro* without the necessity of contacts with neuroglial cells. However, myelin will not be formed along axons which are not intimately surrounded by glia. One of the reasons for the difficulty of visualizing neuroglia in these photographs is simply the plane of focus at which the picture was taken. We may have been focused, for example, on the neuron somas or on the myelinated axons which would then be most apparent. There are, however, many glia populating the cultures.

DEVELOPMENT OF BIOELECTRIC ACTIVITY DURING GROWTH OF NEONATAL MOUSE CEREBRAL CORTEX IN TISSUE CULTURE*

STANLEY M. CRAIN†

Departments of Anatomy and Neurology, College of Physicians and Surgeons, Columbia University, New York, N. Y.

Introduction

Electrophysiologic studies of cultured spinal ganglia and spinal cord fragments have demonstrated that neurons may maintain, for months *in vitro*, not only the capacity to propagate impulses along their neurites (Crain, 1956) but also a remarkable degree of functional organization resembling the activity of synaptic networks of the central nervous system (Crain and Peterson, 1963). The potentialities for close correlation of nerve cell structure and function have been well illustrated in Hild and Tasaki's work with cultured cerebellar tissue (1962), although their experiments were limited to conductile properties within individual neurons. Extension of these studies to cultured mammalian cerebral cortex (Crain, 1963 a, b; Bornstein, 1963 a, b) offers promise as a valuable supplement to *in situ* investigation of brain function. This work may be considered to be a further development of the pioneering bioelectric experiments carried out by Libet and Gerard (1939) on freshly isolated, adult frog brain. They showed that isolated olfactory bulb fragments, as small as 0.1 mg. in mass, could still generate rhythmic electric waves, at a frequency of about 30 per sec., for several hours *in vitro*. Spontaneous rhythmic bioelectric activity has also been recorded, more recently, from fragments of chick embryo brain maintained in culture for up to 2 weeks (Cunningham *et al.*, 1960; Cunningham, 1962). In our experiments, however, emphasis has been directed towards demonstration of characteristic neuronal responses to electric stimuli, using microelectrode techniques under direct microscopic observation of the cells. This approach should provide a firmer basis for analysis of the variety of spontaneous bioelectric activities which may occur in cerebral tissue.

It should be emphasized, however, that a cultured cerebral explant is a deafferented, neuronally (as well as chemically) isolated fragment, involving less than 1 cu. mm. of tissue. Its functional properties must obviously be

---

*This work was supported by grant NB-03814 from the National Institute of Neurological Diseases and Blindness.

†PHS Research Career Development Fellow (Award NB-K3-2904 from the National Institute of Neurological Diseases and Blindness).

altered as compared to the same tissue *in situ*. Nevertheless, our experiments demonstrate that sufficient preservation of basic CNS organization can be maintained in cerebral cultures to warrant their use as experimental models. To the extent that a cultured cerebral fragment shows any bioelectric activity resembling that of its *in situ* counterparts, we can utilize the unique geometry of the tissue culture array (Bornstein, this symposium) to gain additional insights into biophysical and biochemical mechanisms underlying this activity. Extremely flattened sheets of neural tissue would be ideal for serious correlative cytologic and bioelectric studies. We have found, however, that CNS explants maintained at a thickness of at least several cell-diameters show much greater functional integrity. Our present experiments have, therefore, been a compromise between these two factors. Although many cytologic details of the neuron perikarya and glia can be seen in the thicker explants with ordinary optics (Bornstein, this symposium), we have not yet been able to utilize phase-contrast optics to clearly resolve the contours of the somas and dendrites during microelectrode placements. The bioelectric studies to be described constitute, therefore, a foundation upon which experiments can be designed to obtain correlative data regarding cerebral structure and function at a level unobtainable *in situ*. Such experiments will become increasingly fruitful as improvements in culture technique and in optical systems permit greater resolution of the neurons and glia during functional investigation of organized networks of these cells.

Methods

The bioelectric experiments were carried out (at 36° C.) in a moist chamber attached to the mechanical stage of a compound microscope (Fig. 1). The culture coverglass was mounted as a "hanging-drop" preparation. Microelectrodes were inserted through holes in the side walls of the chamber and brought up to the tissue by micromanipulators (details in Crain, 1956). Platinum or chloridized silver electrodes with 10 to 25 μ tips were generally used. One electrode was positioned (under direct visual control) against or inside the tissue, while an indifferent electrode was placed in the fluid nearby. A chloridized silver wire in the periphery served as a ground elctrode. Electric stimuli, 0.1 to 0.3 msec. in duration and up to 100 μ amp. in strength, were applied locally through 10 to 15 μ pipettes filled with saline. Bioelectric signals were recorded with differential-input preamplifiers and an oscilloscope. With this experimental setup, reproducible activity has been maintained in the cerebral explants for more than 8 hours after transfer from the Maximow-slide culture chamber, even though no special precautions were taken to preserve sterility during this period.

Results

A. EARLY SPIKE RESPONSES IN VITRO

Only simple spike responses could be evoked in cultured cerebral tissue during the first 2 or 3 days after explantation from one-day-old mice.[*] Fig. 2

---

[*]The cerebral cultures were prepared by Dr. Murray B. Bornstein at the Laboratory of Cellular Neurophysiology, Neurology Department, The Mount Sinai Hospital, New York. (See Bornstein, this symposium, for culture technique and morphologic development.)

Fig. 1. Moist chamber attached to mechanical stage of compound microscope. Coverglass forms roof of chamber with tissue culture mounted as "hanging-drop" preparation. One pair of microelectrodes enters each side of chamber through tunnels in walls. Microelectrodes (bent upwards near tips) are brought up to tissue by micromanipulators located on each side of microscope. Electric stimuli are applied through one pair of electrodes and bioelectric signals are recorded through the other. Tubing entering chamber in right foreground permits alteration of culture medium during experiment.

shows a typical electrode arrangement used in these experiments. The action potentials in Fig. $3A_1$ were recorded simultaneously from loci "1" and "2" in response to a brief stimulus applied at "3." In analogy with recordings *in situ*, loci near the original surface of the cortex, e. g. "1," will be referred to as "superficial" in contrast to loci at greater "cortical depths," e.g. "2" or "3." The diphasic responses in Fig. $3A_1$ indicate propagation of impulses towards the cortical surface, one group arriving at the deep recording locus (lower record) after a latency of about 1 msec., and another at the more superficial locus (upper record) after 1.8 msec. The duration of the negative phase of these spikes is about 2–3 msec. and their amplitudes may reach 600 μV. Both responses are shown superimposed in Fig. $3A_2$. Only crude estimates of conduction velocity along these neurites can be made at present, due to lack of data on the actual pathways traversed. The values appear to be of the order of 0.4 m./sec. which agrees with data obtained for conductile elements in neonatal cerebral cortex *in situ* (Purpura *et al.*, 1960; Grafstein, 1962). Attempts to evoke responses at these loci ("1" and "2") by application of stimuli near the original cortical surface were ineffective at this stage *in vitro*.

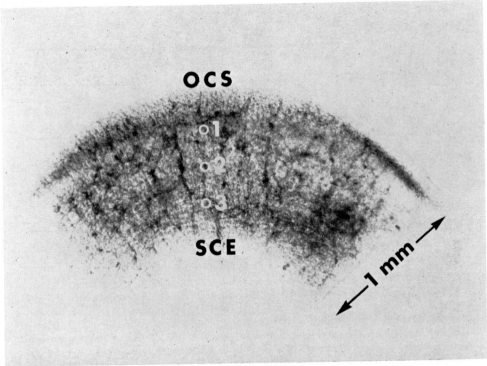

Fig. 2. Typical arrangement of microelectrodes in cerebral explant, as seen through microscope. (Thickness of tissue about 0.5 mm. at explantation.) OCS: original cortical surface; SCE: subcortical edge. Focal recording electrodes were often positioned, in contact with the tissue, at "1" and "2," and a cathodal stimulating lead placed at "3." "Indifferent" electrodes were located near each active electrode, in fluid just below tissue. Distance of locus from original cortical surface (OCS) will be referred to as "cortical depth (see text)."

Stimuli at 1 per sec. resulted in little or no attenuation of these responses (Fig. 3B). At 5–10 per sec. the potentials began to decrease in amplitude after the first few shocks, but still further stimulation at this rate led to restoration of the original amplitudes. Application of dual stimuli shows that these action potentials arise in conductile neural elements which display characteristic refractoriness following electric excitation. The amplitude of both superficial and deep responses is clearly attenuated when the test stimulus is applied 7 msec. after the conditioning stimulus (Fig. $3C_2$ vs. C_1) and refractoriness is almost complete with a test interval of 3.3 msec. (Fig. $3C_3$). The records in Fig. 3D show that these potentials are due to the summation of spikes from groups of synchronously active neurons. Gradual increase in stimulus strength (Fig. $3D_1$ to D_3) results in corresponding increase in response amplitude. The action potentials occur, at times, spontaneously and resemble repetitive unit-spike activity seen in cultured cerebellum (Hild and Tasaki, 1962). During the first 2 or 3 days *in vitro*, however, the bioelectric activity of the cerebral explants shows no clearcut signs of long-lasting excitatory phenomena or other complexities indicative of synaptic interactions.

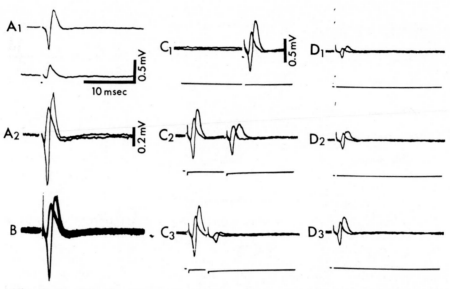

Fig. 3. Simple spike responses evoked by electric stimuli in cerebral cortex tissue cultured for 3 days after explantation from one-day-old mouse. A_1: Simultaneous records obtained with recording electrodes at "cortical depths" of about 200 μ (upper) and 400 μ (see Fig. 2). Stimulus (0.1–0.2 msec.) was applied near subcortical edge of explant (about 800 μ from original cortical surface). A_2: Superimposition of the records in A_1, at higher gain. Note longer latency of negative phase of superficial as compared to deep response. B: Superimposition of a series of responses as in A_2 at stimulus rate of 1 per sec. C_2: Application of dual stimuli under same recording conditions as in A. Note attenuation in amplitude of both superficial and deep spike responses with test interval of 7 msec. (vs. responses to single stimulus in C_1). C_3: Reduction of dual stimulus interval to 3.3 msec. reveals almost complete refractoriness to test stimulus. D: Graded-amplitude responses (under same recording conditions as in A) produced by increasing stimulus strengths (D_1 to D_3). Lower record in C_1–C_3 and D_1–D_3 shows stimulus signals. Time and amplitude calibrations apply to all succeeding records unless otherwise noted; upward deflection indicates negativity at active recording electrode (in this and all subsequent figures).

B. Onset of Complex Response Patterns in Vitro

Within 3–4 days after explantation much more complex response patterns can be evoked in some of the cerebral cultures (Fig. 4). At the slow sweep rate of records $4A_1$ and A_2 the short-latency spike potentials shown in Fig. 3 are not visible, but a long-duration negativity gradually arises with a latency of about 100 msec. after the early "superficial" spike (Fig. $4A_1$, upper record) and a long-duration positivity arises with a still greater latency after the early "deep" spike (Fig. $4A_1$, lower record). The long-duration (about 400 msec.) responses are much smaller in amplitude than the early spikes, ranging from 50 to 100 μV, whereas the latter may reach 600 μV (cf. Fig. $4A_2$). In these cultures, as well as in explants maintained for longer periods *in vitro* (Figs. 7B and 8A, B), the slow waves recorded from superficial loci are generally negative in polarity, while those of deep loci are positive (even when the

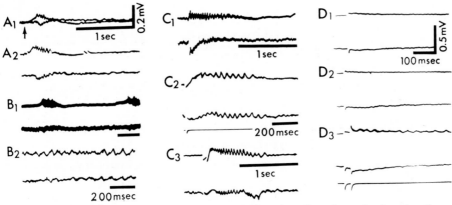

Fig. 4. **Early signs of complex response patterns in cultured cerebral cortex tissue (same explant as in Fig. 3).** A_1: Same recording and stimulus conditions as in Fig. $3A_2$, but at much slower sweep rate. Note long-duration negativity (shown alone in upper record of A_2) which arises gradually with a latency of about 100 msec. after the early superficial spike (see Fig. $3A_1$–upper); also note long-duration positivity (shown alone in lower record of A_2) which develops with a still longer latency after early deep spike (see Fig. $3A_1$–lower). Arrow indicates onset of shock artifact in record A_1. Small-amplitude repetitive potentials can be seen on falling phase of the slow-waves. Responses in A_2 were evoked by dual stimuli spaced 50 msec. apart (i.e., 60 and 110 msec. after start of sweep), resulting in decreased latency as compared to A_1. Note that second pair of stimuli in A_2, applied 1 sec. after first pair, is ineffective. B_1: Spontaneous bursts of 10–20 per sec. potentials lasting about 1 second. B_2: Single spontaneous burst at faster sweep. C: Responses evoked after strychnine (10 μg./ml.). Note increased duration of evoked barrage (C_1 and C_3 vs. A_2) and greater degree of synchrony between superficial and deep potentials (C_2, C_3). D_3: Facilitation with dual stimuli at 30 msec. test interval produces repetitive discharge (as in A_2), whereas single stimuli (at this amplitude) are ineffective (D_1 and D_2). Note lower gain in D vs. A–C. Lowest record in C_2 and D_3 shows stimulus signals.

stimulus is applied to more superficial regions). Careful probing at various cortical depths in some of the cerebral explants indicates that the polarity of the long-duration responses reverses at a critical depth, generally around 400 μ. Displacement of the microelectrode by less than 10 μ (in depth) may lead to polarity reversal. This indicates maintenance of at least some of the laminar organization of neural elements parallel to the original surface of the cerebral cortex, analogous to phase-reversal patterns characteristic of cerebral cortex *in situ* (Li *et al.*, 1956).

Still smaller oscillatory potentials (15–20 per sec.) can be seen superimposed on the falling phase of the long-duration responses. The potentials in Fig. $4A_2$ were evoked by the facilitating effect of dual stimuli, spaced 50 msec. apart (i.e., 60 and 110 msec. after the start of the sweep). Note the decreased latency of the responses in Fig. $4A_2$ as compared to $4A_1$. Single shocks of this strength were often much less effective. This is illustrated in Fig. $4D_3$ where dual stimuli at a 30 msec. test interval facilitate to produce a repetitive discharge (as in Fig. $4A_2$), whereas single stimuli of this amplitude are ineffective (Fig. $4D_1$

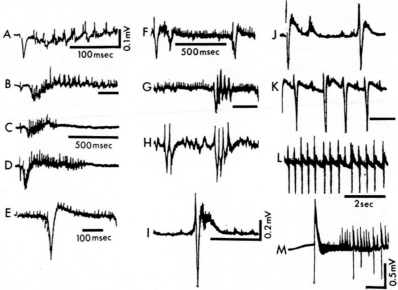

Fig. 5. **Complex spike and slow-wave patterns in cultured neonatal cerebral cortex tissue after 14 days *in vitro*.** A–D: Long-duration barrage responses to single stimulus applied about 200 μ from recording site. Note spike potentials superimposed on slow waves. E–I: Spontaneous slow-waves with repetitive spikes. J–L: Successive sweeps showing much longer barrage response following single stimulus applied at beginning of record J (note decrease in sweep rate in K and L). M: Similar sequence at still slower sweep rate. Note sudden appearance of spikes more than 2 seconds after large, early-latency evoked potential.

and D_2). In contrast to the early spike responses the slow waves are quite labile and are frequently blocked at stimulus frequencies greater than 1 per 5 sec. (note ineffectiveness of the second pair of stimuli in Fig. $4A_2$, applied 1 second after the first pair).

The long-duration responses of Fig. 4A resemble those evoked in neonatal cat cerebral cortex, *in situ*, by an electric stimulus applied nearby (Purpura *et al.*, 1960). Even more striking is the similarity of the 15–20 per sec. repetitive discharge pattern (see also Fig. 6) to those characteristic of neuronally isolated slabs of neonatal cat cerebral cortex (Purpura and Housepian, 1961). In contrast to the cat, the "direct cortical response" does not develop in rat cerebral cortex, *in situ*, until 3–5 days after birth (Schadé, 1957, 1964). The onset of these evoked responses in mouse cerebral explants after 3–4 days *in vitro* is in good agreement with the rat studies *in situ*.

The slow waves and superimposed repetitive discharges may occur spontaneously (Fig. $4B_1$), lasting about 1 second and occurring sporadically several times per minute. The rhythmic pattern of the potentials in these bursts is seen more clearly in Fig. $4B_2$. Whereas strychnine (10 μg./ml.) had no effect on cerebral explants less than 3 days *in vitro*, it appeared to enhance the activity in older cultures (Fig. 4C; see also Fig. 7). The barrage responses could be evoked with smaller stimuli and they often continued for longer periods (Fig. $4C_1$ and C_3 vs. A_2), with indications of greater synchrony between superficial and deep potentials (Fig. $4C_2$ and C_3).

C. FURTHER ORGANIZATION OF COMPLEX BIOELECTRIC ACTIVITY IN VITRO

1. *Spike and Slow-Wave Barrages.* During the following week *in vitro*, the responses of the cerebral explants to electric stimuli become larger in amplitude (up to 1 mV.), longer in duration, and more complex (Fig. 5). Rapid bursts of short-duration spikes are frequently superimposed on the slow-waves, both in evoked (Fig. 5A-D) as well as in spontaneous sequences (Fig. 5E-I). The latter occur sporadically, varying greatly in different regions of the explants, and are often difficult to distinguish from long-sustained barrages triggered by electric (Fig. 5J-M) or mechanical stimuli. Fig. 5J-L shows successive records during the development of an unusually rhythmic discharge (at 2–3 per sec.), lasting more than a minute following a single stimulus applied at the beginning of record J. This repetitive sequence shows interesting similarities to 3 per sec. spike and wave activity recorded in neuronally isolated cat cerebral cortex (Ingvar, 1955, Fig. 4). Fig. 5M shows an even more complex response pattern in which large repetitive discharges appear, suddenly, more than 2 seconds after an early evoked potential. Some of the patterns of the spontaneous and evoked discharges in this cerebral explant (e.g., Fig. 5I and J) also resemble focal microelectrode recordings in epileptic cortex, *in situ* (e.g., Schmidt *et al.*, 1959). The triphasic, initially negative, complex in Fig. 5I, for example, is remarkably similar to the "paroxysmal abnormal wave" in Fig. 4 of Schmidt *et al.'s* paper, including the characteristic superimposition of "epileptic unit potentials." The durations of the three phases of the complex in Fig. 5I are about 50, 25 and 200 msec., while the corresponding values in the epileptic record are about 40, 25 and 65 msec. The large amplitudes and the regularity of pattern of these complex potentials in cerebral explants suggest marked synchronization of activity through organized synaptic networks. Electron-micrographic evidence of numerous axodendritic synapses in the cerebral tissue after 14 days *in vitro* (Pappas, 1964) provides a valuable correlate to this interpretation of the bioelectric activity in the explants. Ephaptic interactions must also be kept in mind as a possible factor in synchronizing the activity of these closely packed neurons (Bennett *et al.*, 1963).

2. *Characteristic Repetitive Afterdischarges.* Whereas many of the cerebral explants showed simpler response patterns with smaller amplitudes than those of Fig. 5, the 15–20 per sec. repetitive discharge sequence, seen as early as 3 days *in vitro* (Fig. 4), was often evoked in older cultures with much larger amplitude, greater rhythmicity, and somewhat lower frequency (Fig. 6). Examples from 4 cerebral explants after 2 to 4 weeks *in vitro* are shown in Fig. 6A, B, D and E. Each sequence was evoked by a single stimulus, located several hundred micra from the recording site, and generally required a critical stimulus strength. The repetitive afterdischarge consists of 3–6 large diphasic (or triphasic) potentials, each lasting 25–50 msec., and occurring at a rate of about 10 per sec. The positive phases of these potentials are fre-

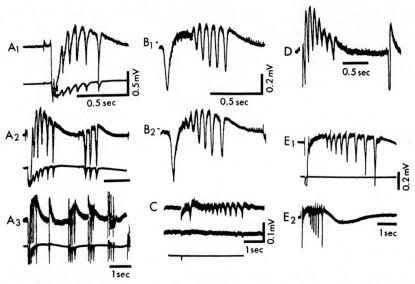

Fig. 6. Characteristic repetitive afterdischarges (at about 10 per sec.) evoked in 4 cerebral explants, after 2–4 weeks *in vitro*, by a single stimulus applied several hundred micra from recording site (A, B, D and E). Note variations in pattern of response to stimuli applied at 1 per sec. (A_2, A_3). Lower record in A_1–A_3 and C shows simultaneous recording from nearby region of explant. Note variation in latency of onset of repetitive discharge following initial, positive evoked potential (B_1 and B_2). Response in D is from same explant used in Fig. 5 (cf. record H). Note large positivity appearing in E_2 at end of series of potentials with gradually increasing amplitudes. C: Repetitive after-discharge evoked by single stimulus in spinal cord tissue (0.5 mm. cross-section) cultured for 3 months after explantation from 6-week human embryo. Note similarity between this complex response pattern and those evoked in the cerebral explants. (Lowest record in C shows stimulus signal.) (Fig. 6C from Crain and Peterson, 1963.)

quently much larger than the negative phases and the amplitudes often increase as the discharge progresses. Simultaneous recordings from other regions of the explant (100–400 μ away) indicate that the repetitive discharges involve synchronous activity over large areas of the explant (Fig. 6A and 8B). As in Fig. 5M, a long delay often occurs between the initial evoked potential and the repetitive sequence (Fig. $6B_1$, B_2, E_1 and E_2). The variability of these response patterns when evoked at a rate of 1 per sec. is shown in Fig. $6A_2$ and A_3. At stimulus rates below 1 per 5 sec., however, the responses are often quite reproducible.

The resemblance of the properties of the repetitive discharges in the cerebral explants to those characteristic of neuronally isolated slabs of cerebral cortex in the neonatal cat (Purpura and Housepian, 1961) has been pointed out in connection with Fig. 4. It should be noted that the cultured fragments are more than 100 times smaller in mass than the cortical slabs *in situ*. Maintenance of such functional integrity in a 1 cu. mm. explant of cerebral cortex, *in vitro*, sets limits to estimates of the degree of structural complexity required to produce these bioelectric phenomena *in situ*. Furthermore, a remarkably similar pattern can be evoked in cultured spinal cord tissue under the same recording and stimulating conditions. Fig. 6C shows a record obtained from a spinal cord cross-section (about 0.5 mm. thick) cultured for 3 months after explantation from a 6-week human embryo (Crain and Peterson, 1963). Although the frequency of this cord after-discharge is lower (5–6 per sec.), the pattern closely resembles that of the cerebral explants, including occurrence of an early evoked potential, followed by a long delay, and then a series of diphasic potentials of increasing amplitude. Purpura and Housepian (1961) have suggested that the hyperexcitability of neuronally isolated slabs of neonatal cerebral cortex is due to extensive axon-collateral sprouting that occurs during the regeneration of pyramidal neurons after the surgical isolation procedure. These collaterals are considered to be "the major factor responsible for the increase in excitatory synaptic drives that are reflected in evoked repetitive bursts." Similar axon collateral sprouting certainly occurs in the cerebral and spinal cord explants (Bornstein, this symposium; Peterson, E. R., personal communication). Further analysis of the structure and function of CNS explants may help to clarify the role of collateral sprouting, as well as that of "denervation supersensitivity" (Stavraky, 1961), in accounting for hyperexcitability of deafferented CNS tissues.

3. *Effects of Strychnine.* In addition to the strychnine effects illustrated in Fig. 4, much larger amplitude strychnine "sharp waves" may be elicited in cerebral explants after 3 days *in vitro.* Fig. $7A_3$ shows such a spontaneous, negative wave, over 600 msec. in duration and about 400 μV. in amplitude. Prior to strychnine treatment, evoked (Fig. $7A_1$) and spontaneous (Fig. $7A_2$) potentials at this recording site showed amplitudes of less than 100 μV. The strychnine waves occurred irregularly, at about 1 per min., and were quite similar to those evoked in 4-day rat cerebral cortex, *in situ,* by topical application of strychnine (Crain, 1952). No data is available on strychnine effects in neonatal mice, *in situ,* but it is of interest that even with huge doses of pentylenetetrazol (Metrazol) no spontaneous electrical activity could be detected from 4-day-old mouse cerebral cortex (Kobayashi *et al.,* 1963). Spike discharges could not be evoked with pentylenetetrazol until 7 days after birth.

Spontaneous strychnine sharp-waves evoked in a 6-day culture are shown in Fig. $7B_2$ and B_3. Prior to strychnine, simultaneous recordings near the cortical surface (Fig. $7B_1$–upper record) and in depth (Fig. $7B_1$–lower record) showed negative and positive evoked responses respectively, after latencies of more than 100 msec., but no spontaneous activity was detected. In comparison with the strychnine wave seen at 3 days, *in vitro,* the amplitude of those in the 6-day culture was much larger, about 800 μV., and their duration was much shorter—less than 300 msec. They occurred as often as 8 per min. and were followed, at times, by additional repetitive potentials which appeared synchronously in superficial and depth recordings (Figs. $7B_2$ and B_3). These changes in the strychnine sharp-waves with age in culture resemble the ontogenetic trend in rat cerebral cortex, *in situ* (Crain, 1952) and provide further indication of the increasing degree of synchronization of bio-

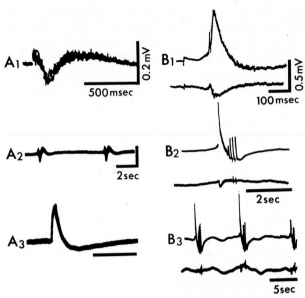

Fig. 7. **Effects of strychnine on activity of cultured cerebral tissue.** A: 3 days *in vitro.* A_1: Long-duration triphasic response including barrages of spikes, evoked by single stimulus located 400 μ away (prior to strychnine). A_2: Spontaneous bursts similar to evoked response in A_1, but at lower gain and slower sweep rate (prior to strychnine). A_3: Large spontaneous, negative "sharp-wave" after strychnine (10 μg./ml.), lasting more than 600 msec. and followed by a 2 sec. positivity. B: 6 days *in vitro.* B_1: Simultaneous records at "depths" of about 100 μ (upper) and 400 μ showing responses with about 100 msec. latency after stimulus applied at depth of about 700 μ (before strychnine). B_2: Spontaneous wave, similar to that evoked in B_1, but involving bursts of short-duration, negative potentials during the long positive phase (B_2–upper). Note two spikes in lower record of B_2 occurring synchronously with spikes in superficial record. B_3: Spontaneous bursts similar to B_2, at slower sweep rate.

electric activity in cerebral explants as they develop *in vitro.* It should be noted that strychnine (4 μg/ml.) greatly enhanced the amplitude of spontaneous rhythmic bioelectric activity recorded from explants of 15-day chick embryo telencephalon after 2 days in culture. Cunningham and Stephens, 1961). No data have been reported, however, regarding development of this activity as a function of age *in vitro.*

4. *Effects of d-Tubocurarine.* Dramatic pharmacodynamic effects of d-tubocurarine, seen as early as 10 days in *in vitro,* may be useful in clarifying the mechanisms underlying some of the complex bioelectric activities of cultured cerebral tissue. Simultaneous superficial and depth recordings prior to drug administration showed well-developed negative- and positive-evoked responses (as described earlier in Figs. 4A and 7B), followed by a series of 10–20 per sec. repetitive potentials, also with opposite polarities (Fig. 8A). After d-tubocurarine (10 μg./ml.), the evoked responses showed greater complexity, with spikes of increased amplitude (Fig. $8B_1$). This effect resembles the increased repetitive spike response to a peripheral stimu-

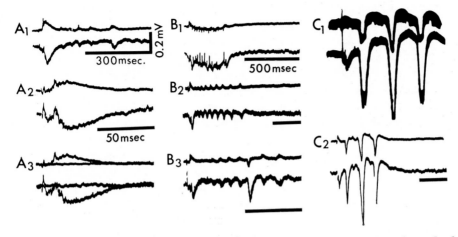

Fig. 8. Development of paroxysmal, repetitive discharges in cultured cerebral tissue (10 days *in vitro*) following d-tubocurarine. A_1: Simultaneous records at "cortical depths" of 250 μ (upper) and 650 μ showing complex responses following single stimulus applied at depth of 700 μ (but 300 μ from deep recording site). Note 60 msec. negative evoked response in superficial region and similar positive response in deep zone. Small amplitude repetitive potentials at 10–20 per sec. follow both of these responses and are also of opposite polarities. A_2 and A_3: Same as A_1 but at faster sweep rate (and with superimposed baselines in A_3). Note that positive evoked (deep) response is of longer duration and occurs after greater latency than negative evoked (superficial) response. B_1: After d-tubocurarine (10 μg./ml.) evoked responses are more complex, with spikes of increased amplitude. B_2: d-tubocurarine increased to 100 μg./ml. Note greater regularity of repetitive discharge pattern. B_3: Sudden increase in amplitude of one of the positive potentials in deep response (lower) and reversal of polarity of corresponding potential in superficial response. C_1: Large increase in amplitude of all positive potentials in deep response (within one minute after record B_3) and reversal of polarity of all corresponding potentials in superficial response (as well as increase in their amplitude). Note marked decrease in frequency of repetitive discharge. C_2: Decrease in amplitude of the large paroxysmal waves (shortly after record C_1).

lus, obtained with microelectrode recording in cat cerebral cortex, *in situ*, following topical application of d-tubocurarine (Morlock and Ward, 1961). Further increase to 100 μg./ml. led to a more rhythmic, repetitive after-discharge pattern (Fig. 8B_2 and B_3). Of particular interest in Fig. 8B_3 is the sudden, large increase in amplitude of one of the positive repetitive potentials in the deep response. Concomitantly, there occurred a reversal of the polarity of the corresponding potential in the superficial record, suggesting increased synchronization of the activity in these two regions (400 μ apart). Within 1 minute, the amplitude of all of the positive repetitive potentials increased greatly, from less than 100 μV. to as much as 800 μV. (Fig. 8C_1–lower record). Simultaneously, all of the corresponding superficial potentials reversed to positive polarity, also with relatively large amplitudes (Fig. 8C_1—upper record). Furthermore, the frequency of the paroxysmal waves in both regions decreased synchronously from about 10 per sec. to 3–4 per sec. Shortly thereafter, the amplitude of these large paroxysmal waves began to decrease toward normal levels (Fig. $8C_2$), and finally the response pattern returned to that of Fig. $8B_2$. Several times during the ensuing hour, the responses suddenly shifted back to the configuration of Fig. $8C_1$, the amplitudes of some of the depth potentials reaching up to 2 mV. It should be noted that along with the development of these large slow-waves, the threshold for evoked responses steadily increased after curarization of the explants.

The records of Fig. 8C show interesting similarities to the rhythmic bursts of large positive waves obtained by Chang (1953–Fig. 6) from rabbit cerebral cortex following intravenous injection of d-tubocurarine (3.5 mg./kg.). The paroxysmal cortical discharges *in situ* also occurred concomitant with an increase in threshold for evoked cortical potentials. It is tempting to speculate that the large positive waves evoked under curare may be due to selective block a large fraction of the negative excitatory post-synaptic potential component of the response, thereby unmasking a corresponding part of the membrane-hyperpolarizing, inhibitory post-synaptic potential component. The rhythmicity of these positive waves in the cultures may be based on recurrent-collateral inhibitory networks similar to those recently proposed as a "phasing device" for the development of various synchronized, rhythmic bioelectric activities in cerebrum, *in situ* (Anderson and Eccles, 1962). The long "silent periods" between the early latency, evoked potential and the 10 per sec. repetitive discharge in Figs. 5M and 6B, C and E may also be due to predominance of inhibitory post-synaptic potentials during these intervals. Although the data from cerebral explants is not yet adequate to firmly support such interpretations of the response patterns, it will be of great interest to investigate these problems by further experiments with cultured tissue.

In view of the essentially two-dimensional distribution of the cerebral cortical "layers" in an explant, these preparations may be quite useful for experimental analysis of the factors involved in synchronization of neuronal activity. Large numbers of microelectrodes can be accurately positioned (under direct microscopic control) throughout the explant, at all "cortical depths" (Fig. 2), without the injury problems associated with electrode penetration through the cortical surface, *in situ*. Further development of this approach, including simultaneous intra- and extracellular microelectrode recording, should provide significant data for the determination of the role of synaptic and ephaptic processes, as well as of more generalized electric fields, in the production of the complex bioelectric activity of the cerebral explants. The significance of glial cell potentials (Galambos, 1961; Svaetichin *et al.*, 1961; Hild and Tasaki, 1962) may also be clarified by analysis of their properties in these cerebral cultures. Ontogenetic studies will be facilitated by construction of special culture chambers permitting continuous electrophysiologic recording during critical periods of growth and differentiation. We believe that this method will prove to be an extremely useful supplement to *in situ* studies of CNS function at the cellular level.

Summary

Electrophysiologic studies have been made during the growth and differentiation of neonatal mouse cerebral cortex fragments isolated in tissue culture. During the first 2–3 days after explantation, only simple spike potentials can be evoked by electric stimuli. By 4 days *in vitro*, complex, long-duration responses can be detected. The latter show facilitation effects at long test intervals and can be augmented by strychnine. During the following week in culture, bioelectric responses increase in amplitude, complexity and regularity. Barrages of spikes superimposed on slow-waves often occur sporadically as well as in response to electric stimuli. Evoked-potential patterns suggest maintenance of laminar organization of neural elements parallel to the original surface of the cerebral cortex. The bioelectric properties of cultured cerebral explants appear to be remarkably similar, in many respects, to those of neuronally isolated slab preparations in immature cerebral cortex, *in situ*. Application of this method to problems of cerebral function at the cellular level are discussed.

REFERENCES

ANDERSON, P. and ECCLES, J. Inhibitory phasing of neuronal discharge. *Nature, 1962*, 196:645–647.

BENNETT, M. V. L., ALJURE, E., NAKAJIMA, Y. and PAPPAS, G. D. Electrotonic junctions between teleost spinal neurons: electrophysiology and ultrastructure. *Science, 1963*, 141:262–264.

BORNSTEIN, M. B. Morphological development and differentiation of mouse cerebral neocortex in tissue culture. *Excerpta Med., 1963a*, 18 (Sect. I):XI.

BORNSTEIN, M. B. Morphological development of cultured mouse cerebral neocortex. *Trans. Amer. Neurol. Assn., 1963b*, 88:22–24.

CHANG, H. -T. Similarity in action between curare and strychnine on cortical neurons. *J. Neurophysiol., 1953*, 16:221–233.

CRAIN, S. M. Development of electrical activity in the cerebral cortex of the albino rat. *Proc. Soc. Exper. Biol. Med., 1952*, 81:49–51.

CRAIN, S. M. Resting and action potentials of cultured chick embryo spinal ganglion cells. *J. Comp. Neurol., 1956*, 104:285–330.

CRAIN, S. M. Bioelectric activity of mouse cerebral neocortex tissue during growth and differentiation *in vitro*. *Excerpta Med. 1963*, 18 (Sect. I):XI.

CRAIN, S. M. Development of complex bioelectric activity during growth and differentiation of cultured mouse cerebral neocortex. *Trans. Amer. Neurol. Assn., 1963, in press.*

CRAIN, S. M. and PETERSON, E. R. Bioelectric activity in long-term cultures of spinal cord tissues. *Science, 1963*, 141: 427–429.

CUNNINGHAM, A. W. B. Qualitative behavior of spontaneous potentials from explants of 15 day chick embryo telencephalon *in vitro*. *J. Gen. Physiol., 1962*, 45:1065–1076.

CUNNINGHAM, A. W. B. and STEPHENS, S. G. Qualitative effect of strychnine and brucine on spontaneous potentials from explants of telencephalon. *Experientia, 1961*, 17:569–571.

CUNNINGHAM, A. W. B., DOUGHERTY, M. and RYLANDER, B. J. Spontaneous potentials from explants of brain tissue in culture. *Nature, 1960*, 186:477–478.

GALAMBOS, R. A. Glia-neural theory of brain function. *Proc. Natl. Acad. Sci., 1961*, 47:129–136.

GRAFSTEIN, B. Postnatal development of the transcallosal evoked response in the cerebral cortex of the cat. *J. Neurophysiol., 1963*, 26:79–99.

HILD, W. and TASAKI, I. Morphological and physiological properties of neurons and glial cells in tissue culture. *J. Neurophysiol., 1962*, 25:277–304.

INGVAR, D. H. Electrical activity of isolated cortex in the unanesthetized cat with intact brain stem. *Acta Physiol. Scandinav., 1955*, 33:151–168.

KOBAYASHI, T., INMAN, O., BUNO, W. and HIMWICH, H. E. A multidisciplinary study of changes in mouse brain with age. *Recent Adv. Biol. Psychiat., 1963*, 5:293–308.

LI, C. -L., CULLEN, C. and JASPER, H. H. Laminar microelectrode analysis of cortical unspecific recruiting responses and spontaneous rhythms. *J. Neurophysiol., 1956*, 19:131–143.

LIBET, B. and GERARD, R. W. Control of the potential rhythm of the isolated frog brain. *J. Neurophysiol., 1939*, 2:153–169.

MORLOCK, N. and WARD, A. A., JR. The effects of curare on cortical activity. *Electroenceph. clin. Neurophysiol., 1961*, 13: 60–67.

PAPPAS, G. *1964*, in preparation.

PURPURA, D. P., CARMICHAEL, M. W. and HOUSEPIAN, E. M. Physiological and anatomical studies of development of superficial axo-dendritic synaptic pathways in neocortex. *Exp. Neurol., 1960*, 2:324–347.

PURPURA, D. P. and HOUSEPIAN, E. M. Morphological and physiological properties of chronically isolated immature neocortex. *Exp. Neurol., 1961*, 4:377–401.

SCHADÉ, J. P. *Electro-area-grafie van de Cortex Cerebri*. Amsterdam, F. v. Rossem, *1957*, p. 102.

SCHADÉ, J. P., W. A. HIMWICH and H. E. HIMWICH (Editors) *The developing brain. Progress in Brain Research, Vol. 9*. Elsevier, Amsterdam, *1964*, in press.

SCHMIDT, R. P., THOMAS, L. B. and WARD A. A., JR. The hyper-excitable neurone; microelectrode studies of chronic epileptic foci in monkey. *J. Neurophysiol., 1959*, 22:285–296.

STRAVRAKY, G. W. *Supersensitivity following Lesions of the Nervous System; An Aspect of the Relativity of Nervous Integration*. Univ. of Toronto Press, Toronto, Canada, *1961*, p. 210.

SVAETICHIN, G., LAUFER, M., MITARAI, G., FATEHCHAND, R., VALLECALLE, E. and VILLEGAS, J. Glial control of neuronal networks and receptors. In R. JUNG and H. KORNHUBER (Editors) *The Visual System: Neurophysiology and Psychophysics*. Springer-Verlag, Berlin, *1961*: 445–456.

DISCUSSION

DR. GOLDRING: Do you have any records showing responses to repetitive stimulation?

DR. CRAIN: Not in this series, but in several other cerebral cultures stimulated at 5–10/sec. I have obtained records showing a successive increase in response amplitude for the first 3–5 responses and then a gradual diminution again.

SPREADING DEPRESSION AND MATURATION OF SOME FORE-BRAIN STRUCTURES IN RATS

J. BUREŠ, EVA FIFKOVA AND P. MARES

Institute of Physiology, Czechoslovak Academy of Sciences,
Prague, Czechoslovakia

Development of the central nervous system is characterized both by maturation of individual elements and by appearance of interaction between them, ranging from synaptic transmission to neuroglial relationships. In the present paper, it has been attempted to correlate the development of some properties of individual neurons with the appearance of a remarkable interaction phenomenon—Leão's spreading depression (Leão, 1944).

Spreading depression is a reaction of certain brain structures (cerebral cortex, hippocampus, striatum) to direct physical and chemical stimulation. When enough neurons in the area of stimulation are depolarized, the local increase of potassium concentration in the extracellular space may cause the depolarization of adjacent neurons, and the reaction starts spreading as a concentric wave moving with a velocity of 3 millimeters per minute in all directions (Grafstein, 1956; Marshall, 1959; Brinley *et al.*, 1960; Krivánek and Bureš, 1960). This humorally mediated process is accompanied by clear-cut electrophysiological manifestations (Fig. 1), namely, 1) depression of spontaneous and evoked EEG activity (hence the term spreading depression), 2) depression of unit activity, and 3) a striking slow potential change, a negative wave attaining up to 10 mV in amplitude, followed after 1 to 3 minutes by lower positivity. Complete recovery of the depressed EEG is attained only after some 10 to 15 minutes.

Spreading depression can be evoked in the cerebral cortex of many laboratory animals, including cats and monkeys, but it is most readily elicited in the lissencephalic cortices of rodents—rats, guinea pigs and rabbits. It was demonstrated also in several non-neocortical structures—in hippocampus and caudate of mammals, and in striatum of birds and reptiles. Since excellent reviews on spreading depression are available (Marshall, 1959), it is enough to stress here that from the anatomical point of view spreading depression does not depend on a particular cytoarchitectonic arrangement of neurons. Myelinated axons and probably also glial cells do not actively participate in the spreading depression process, white matter bands and glial scars preventing spreading. The assumption seems to be justified, therefore, that spreading depression can be evoked only in structures in which the surface of somatodendritic membranes (S_m) attains a definite minimal area per unit volume of tissue. Other important factors are the net outflux of potassium from unit area of depolarized membranes per one spreading depression wave (m_K), the

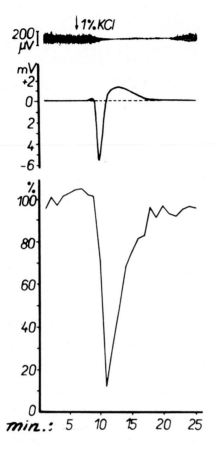

Fig. 1. Electrophysiological manifestations of spreading depression. Above:
EEG. Middle: Slow potential change
(surface negativity downwards). Below:
Spontaneous unit activity in 1 minute
intervals (100 per cent is the average
firing rate during the 10 minute pre-
depression interval). Arrow indicates application of 1 per cent KCl to the cortical surface.

volume of the extracellular space (V_e) in a unit volume of tissue, and threshold
concentration of extracellular potassium (K_t) required to start the autore-
generating process of depolarization.

In a very simplified way it can be assumed that spreading depression may
be evoked only when

$$\frac{S_m \, m_K}{V_e} \geq K_t \tag{1}$$

Let us now analyze from the above point of view the ontogenetic development of spreading depression. Data available for three species indicate that
spreading depression is already present in newborn guinea pigs (Bureš, 1957a),
that it appears (Fig. 2) between 10 and 15 days in rats (Bureš, 1957a; Tuge
et al., 1960; Fifková, 1963) and between 24 to 30 days in rabbits (Schadé,
1959). Especially in the last two species the period of spreading depression appearance is well-defined and can be easily correlated with other signs of brain
maturation. Since spreading depression is connected with changes of spontaneous EEG activity, appearance of adult type of EEG was considered first.
According to Crain (1952) and Schadé (1957) this happens between 8 and

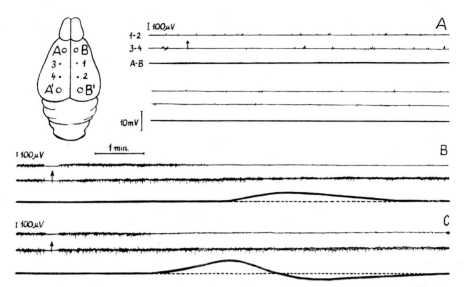

Fig. 2. Spreading depression in 10 (A), 15 (B), and 20 (C) day-old rats.
1–2, 3–4: Electrical cortical activity recorded with steel needle electrodes. A-B:
Slow potential change recorded with calomel cell electrodes between A and B. An
upward deflection indicates increased negativity of A. The arrow indicates application of 1 per cent KCl solution on area A in all records. Calibration: 100 mV for
EEG, 10 mV for record of slow potential change. (From Bureš, 1957a).

11 days in the rat, and according to Schadé (1959) between 10 and 15 days
in the rabbit. In both cases this is considerably prior to the appearance of
spreading depression. It must be pointed out, however, that the presence of
spontaneous EEG is not a necessary prerequisite of spreading depression
which can be elicited in adult animals with electrocortical activity completely
suppressed by deep pentobarbital anesthesia. The presence of spreading depression is then indicated by the slow potential change only, which represents
a transitory change of cortical polarization. In an attempt to find the relationship between the onset of spreading depression and the level of cortical
polarization, the latter was measured as a potential difference between the
cortical area damaged by thermocoagulation and normal cortical surface
(Bureš, 1957a). This potential rapidly increases between 10 and 15 days, when
it exceeds 50 per cent of adult amplitude. Close relationships between cortical
steady potential and spreading depression are indicated by experiments with
sublethal NaCN poisoning in adult rats (Bureš, 1957b). No spreading depression can be elicited after the cortical steady potential has been reduced to
approximately 50 per cent of the original level.

The main source of the cortical injury potential is the potential difference
between the damaged and normal membrane of the same cell. The potential
difference is generated, therefore, at the boundary between the normal and
damaged tissue, with decisive participation of cells which acutely survive
damage of some of their long processes. Similarly, as in muscles or nerve
bundles, the demarcation potential (E_d) is proportional to the average mem-

brane potential (E_m), the proportionality constant being the so-called short-circuiting factor, relating the internal impedance of the source R_i to the external impedance of the conducting medium R_e according to the equation

$$E_d = E_m \frac{R_e}{R_i + R_e} \qquad (2)$$

The close relationship between the injury potential and the average membrane potential was recently confirmed (Mares, 1964) by direct measurements of cortical membrane potentials in curarized rats. Using a hydraulic microdrive, glass microelectrodes (tip diameter of less than 0.5 microns and resistance ranging from 10 to 50 megohms) filled with 3.0 M KCl were gradually inserted into the cortex and underlying hippocampus or striatum. The microelectrode was connected through a unity gain Bak type cathode follower to a cathode ray oscilloscope. Characteristic potential jumps due to impalement of cells were recorded on continuously moving film and amplitudes exceeding 3 mV were measured. Cumulative histograms of potential distribution were plotted in 10 m V steps for neocortex, hippocampus and caudate and for age groups 10, 15, 20 and 90 days (Fig. 3). Each histogram was based on 100 to 300 individual measurements.

The adult data for neocortex are similar to those obtained with the same technique by Li and McIlwain (1957) in the guinea pig; the histogram is shifted by approximately 10 m V to the lower values, however. Whether this difference is due to smaller volume of cortical cells in the rat or to a different technique of recording remains an open question. In any case, histograms obtained in animals of increasing ages display a continuously decreasing incidence of low potentials, best expressed between 10 and 20 days of postnatal life. Average membrane potentials show a linear increase in the same period closely resembling the increase of the average injury potential (Fig. 4). The E_d/E_m ratio (approximately 0.8) cannot be directly identified with the short-circuiting factor, however, since it is not probable that all parts of the examined cell-population contribute to the injury potential in the same way.

Since in adult rats spreading depression can be evoked not only in neocortex but also in striatum and hippocampus, it is possible to use the appearance of spreading depression as an indicator of postnatal development of these three structures (Fifková, 1963). Experiments were performed in anesthetized rats with controlled body temperature. Deep spreading depression was elicited by micro-injections of less than 0.5 microliters of 25 per cent KCl into the dorsal hippocampus or into the head of caudate nucleus. Record'ng capillary electrode was placed at a distance of 2.0 millimeters from the tip of the injection needle. The results are summarized in Fig. 5, giving examples of the typical findings in different age groups. While cortical spreading depression appeared in some animals already at 12 days, it was observed only 2 days later in striatum and hippocampus. Average amplitude of the slow potential change rapidly rose to values found in adult animals, the incidence of spreading depressions becoming quite regular at 16 to 18 days. These results are illustrated by Fig. 6, the

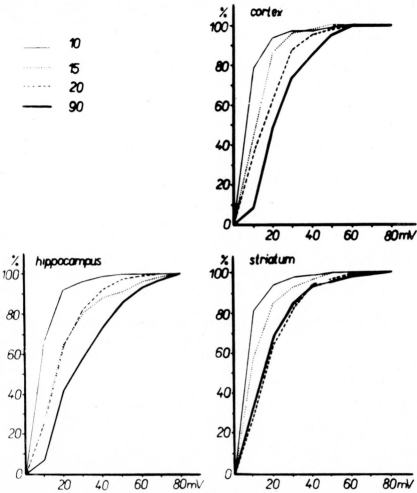

Fig. 3. Cumulative histograms of membrane potential distribution in neocortex (frontal and parieto-occipital regions), hippocampus and caudate in rats aged 10, 15, 20 or 90 days. Each ordinate indicates the incidence of potentials, the amplitude of which is lower than the corresponding abscissa. The histograms for the 4 age groups are based on 360, 363, 421 and 228 measurements in the cortex; on 234, 133, 259 and 115 measurements in the hippocampus; and on 308, 349, 354 and 302 measurements in striatum.

lower part of which gives the percentages of effective KCl applications. In the upper part of this figure, the average amplitude of the negative slow potential is compared with the average membrane potential in the corresponding structure. It is apparent that cortical and striatal spreading depression appears in approximately the same phase of membrane potential development, which seems to follow a similar time course in these two structures. In hippocampus, on the contrary, spreading depression appears at a somewhat higher level of membrane potential. There is no increase of hippocampal mem-

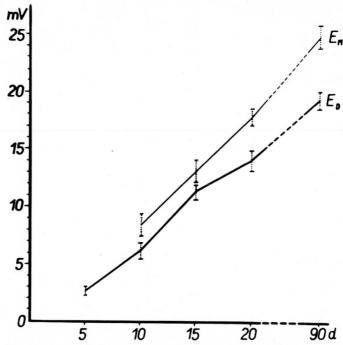

Fig. 4. Development of the injury potential (E_d) and of the average membrane potential (E_m) in the cortex during the ontogenesis of rats. Abscissa: age in days. Ordinate: potential in mV.

brane potential between 15 and 20 days, although the adult level is not yet attained. The different time course of membrane potential development in hippocampus and caudate is also illustrated by histograms in Fig. 3.

The main result of the present study is the correlation established between the membrane potential level and the spreading depression onset in three prosencephalic structures. This correlation is not absolute, however, since other important variables involved in the spreading depression process are changing at the same time. Thus the packing density of cell bodies (expressed as the cell/grey coefficient) rapidly decreases during the first 18 days of postnatal life, the decrease being due to growth of axons between days 6 to 12 and to development of dendrites between days 12 to 18 (Eayrs and Goodhead, 1959). Expansion of the dendritic field considerably increases the somatodendritic membrane surface and creates thus one of the necessary conditions of spreading depression initiation. Spreading depression may also be facilitated by alteration of the extracellular space which is high in newborn rats but seems to be reciprocally related to the growth of cellular processes and to maturation of metabolic activities maintaining the ionic gradients between the extracellular and intracellular compartments. Rapid loss of brain water (Donaldson, 1924) between days 10 to 20 coincides with increase of cortical vascularity (Craigie, 1925) and of oxygen consumption (Himwich et al., 1941).

The resting membrane potential probably reflects the other two variables:

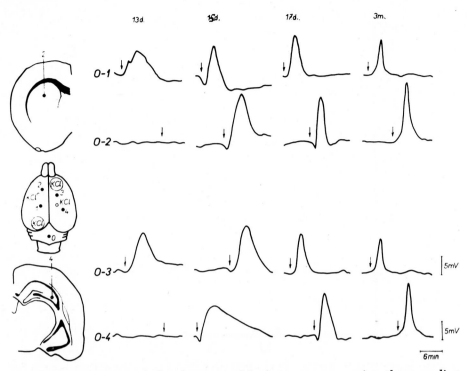

Fig. 5. Appearance of the slow potential change accompanying the spreading depression in neocortex, caudate and hippocampus during the ontogenetic development of rat. Above: Recordings from cortex and caudate. Below: Recordings from cortex and hippocampus. Arrows indicate application of KCl onto the cortex or into the corresponding structure. Positions of the recording electrodes and points of KCl application are shown in the inset brain schemata.

The potassium outflux and the threshold concentration of potassium. The membrane potential is determined by the ionic gradients, by relative membrane permeabilities for various ions, and by the intensity of metabolic ion transport. It seems that changes of the Ki/Ko ratio cannot account for the increase of membrane potentials observed between days 10 to 20, which is probably due to decreased sodium permeability of the membrane. The Ki/Ko ratio may be nearly normal even in 10-day-old rats, as indicated by direct measurements of potassium outflux into the isotonic sucrose solution washing the cortical surface. As shown by Krivánek and Bureš (1960), addition of 2, 4-dinitrophenol into the washing fluid causes nearly the same increase of potassium outflux in 10-day-old-rats as in adult animals (72 per cent as compared with 91 per cent), although no spreading depression can be evoked at this age. It seems, therefore, that increase of membrane potential indicates gradual development of membrane properties typical for the adult animal. Such a conclusion is supported by the finding that between 10 and 20 days there appears the ability in brain slices (Himwich *et al.*, 1942) to respond to increased KCl concentration in the medium with increased oxygen uptake. This reaction, which was shown to be a metabolic counterpart of spreading depression (Bureš, 1956;

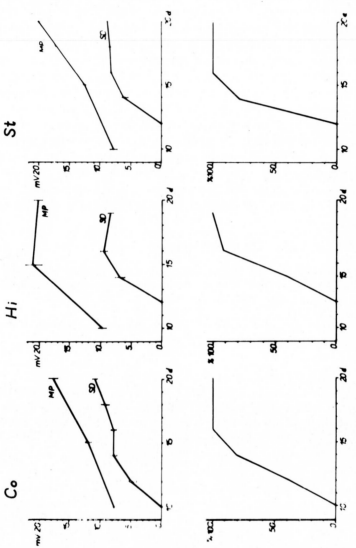

Fig. 6. Correlation between the development of the average membrane potential (MP), average amplitude of the negative slow potential (SD) (above) and relative incidence of spreading depression (below) in neocortex (Co), hippocampus (Hi) and striatum (St) of rat.

Hillman *et al.*, 1963), depends on the integrity of cellular membranes and cannot be elicited in homogenized brain tissue.

Spreading depression appears when the product of all variables on the left side of equation (1) attain the threshold value. Hippocampal spreading depression develops on a higher membrane potential level than the cortical or striatal one, probably because the other factors (especially the membrane surface) may be less developed at this developmental stage. Thus, in spite of the rapid development of the average membrane potential, the hippocampus reaches the spreading depression threshold at the same time as striatum.

At the age when spreading depression appears, neurons are still far from being mature. Dendritic growth continues up to 30 days and myelinization is not completed even then. The average membrane potential scarcely exceeds 60 per cent of the adult value. Some cortical functions (e.g., cortical postural reflexes) appear between 14 and 18 days, but learning and retention are still much poorer at this age than they are in adult rats (Campbell and Campbell, 1960). Nevertheless, the appearance of spreading depression marks an important point in development when interaction between individual elements of the given structure becomes strong enought to create a qualitatively new mass reaction, and may be used, therefore, as an indicator of a specific stage of cerebral maturation.

REFERENCES

BRINLEY, F. J., KANDEL, E. R. and MARSHALL, W. H. Potassium outflux from rabbit cortex during spreading depression. *J. Neurophysiol.*, 1960, 23:246–256.

BURES, J. Some metabolic aspects of Leão's spreading depression. *J. Neurochem.*, 1956, 1:153–158.

BURES, J. The ontogenetic development of steady potential differences in the cerebral cortex in animals. *Electroenceph. clin. Neurophysiol.*, 1957a, 9:121–130.

BURES, J. The effect of anoxia and asphyxia on spreading EEG depression. *Cesk. Fysiol.*, 1957b, 6:467–471.

CAMPBELL, B. A. and CAMPBELL, E. H. Retention and extinction of learned fear in infant and adult rats. *J. comp. physiol. Psychol.*, 1962, 55:1–8.

CRAIGIE, E. H. Postnatal changes in vascularity in the cerebral cortex of the male albino rat. *J. comp. Neurol.*, 1925, 39:301–324.

CRAIN, S. M. Development of electrical activity in the cerebral cortex of the albino rat. *Proc. Soc. exp. Biol.*, 1952, 81:49–51.

DONALDSON, H. U. *The Rat.* Philadelphia, The Wistar Institute, 1924.

EAYRS, J. T. and GOODHEAD, B. Postnatal development of the cerebral cortex in the rat. *J. Anat.*, 1959, 93:385–402.

FIFKOVA, E. Morphological aspects of Leão's spreading depression. Thesis. Prague, 1963.

GRAFSTEIN, B. Mechanism of spreading cortical depression. *J. Neurophysiol.*, 1956, 19:154–171.

HILLMAN, H. H., CAMPBELL, W. J. and McILWAIN, H. Membrane potentials in isolated and electrically stimulated mammalian cerebral cortex. *J. Neurochem.*, 1963, 10:325–339.

HIMWICH, H. E., BERNSTEIN, A. O., FAZEKAS, J. F., HERRLICH, H. C. and RICH, E. The metabolic effects of potassium, temperature, methylene blue and paraphenylenediamine on infant and adult brain. *Amer. J. Physiol.*, 1942, 137:327–330.

HIMWICH, H. S., SYKOWSKI, P. and FAZEKAS, J. F. A comparative study of excised cerebral tissues of adult and infant rats. *Amer. J. Physiol.*, 1941, 132:293–296.

KRIVANEK, J. and BURES, J. Ion shifts during Leão's spreading cortical depression.

Physiol. Bohemoslov., *1960*, 9:494–503.

Leão, A. A. P. Spreading depression of activity in the cerebral cortex. *J. Neurophysiol.*, *1944*, 7:359–390.

Li, C. L. and McIlwain, H. Maintenance of resting membrane potentials in slices of mammalian cerebral cortex and other tissues *in vitro*. *J. Physiol. (Lond.)*, *1957*, 139:178–190.

Mares, P. Ontogenetic development of membrane potentials in neocortex, hippocampus and caudate of rats. *Physiol. Bohemoslov.*, *1964 (In Press)*.

Marshall, W. H. Spreading cortical depression of Leão. *Physiol. Rev.*, *1959*, 39:239–279.

Schadé, J. P. *Electro-area-grafie van de cortex cerebri.* Amsterdam, F. V. Rossen, 1957.

Schadé, J. P. Maturational aspects of EEG and of spreading depression in rabbit. *J. Neurophysiol.*, *1959*, 22:245–257.

Tuge, H., Kanayama, Y. and Yueh, C. L. Comparative studies on the development of EEG. *Jap. J. Physiol.*, *1960*, 10:211–220.

DISCUSSION

DR. PURPURA: Dr. Bureš' laboratory, now, is probably most intensely investigating this problem and he probably knows more about spreading depression than anyone here. I would question one thing. In your presentation of the membrane potential relationship some of these cells looked to have such low resting potentials that I can't conceive of them having regenerative activity or at least, if they do, such spikes would be abortive.

DR. BUREŠ: I think that it is not too difficult to answer this question. We are sampling every potential which the electrode penetrates, and the figures which are given here are figures for the average of this. We cannot even be sure that these cells I am speaking about are all neurons. Maybe some part of these are glia cells which probably may have some quite low potentials. According to the new data it seems that the average potential of glia cells, even in adult animals, probably is around 20 millivolts. So, I agree with you that these data are, of course, somewhat difficult to interpret from this point of view because maybe there are two populations of cells which we cannot so far differentiate but, nevertheless, we consider this average potential to be in some way related to development. There appears to be a quite good correlation between this average membrane potential on one hand and the time that the spreading depression appears on the other.

ON THE CONTRIBUTION OF NEUROGLIA TO THE FUNCTION OF THE CEREBRAL CORTEX*

J. P. SCHADÉ

Netherlands Central Institute for Brain Research
Amsterdam, The Netherlands

Introduction

In our present thinking regarding the genesis of spontaneous electrical potentials in the brain we are still inclined to assume that the neuron is its main source. During the last three decades various properties of neurons and neuronal aggregates have been regarded as being responsible for the occurrence of the spontaneous potentials, viz., reverberating potentials in nerve networks, the summation of spike potentials or of postsynaptic dendritic potentials and prolonged hyper- and depolarization of dendritic membranes.

Microphysiology and microchemistry have, however, opened new fields for the investigation of small parts of the neuron and the relationship of neurons to the surrounding neuroglia. The various forms of glial elements were pulled from the dark, as it were, and placed into focus, with the result that many diverse functions are now being attributed to the astrocytes and oligodendrocytes, (Aladjalova, 1964; Galambos, 1961; Gerschenfeld *et al.*, 1959). Svaetichin *et al.* (1961), working on the functional relationships of nerve cells and supporting cells in the retinae of fishes, concluded that the excitability of the neuronal elements is dependent upon the state of these glial satellites. Hydén and coworkers (Hydén and Lange, 1962; Hydén and Pigon, 1960; Hydén *et al.*, 1958) investigated the effect of vestibular stimulation of Deiters' cells and the surrounding glia. Various reciprocal changes were observed in nerve cells and neuronal glia with respect to both cytochrome oxidase and anaerobic glycolysis. They therefore concluded that these two components form a functional metabolic unit. One of Hydéns' pupils, Hamberger (1961, 1963), made an extensive study on what he calls neuronal and capillary glia. The latter, due to its close relation with the vascular endothelium, is regarded as being of great importance in the transport of material between the blood and the brain.

Van Harreveld and Schadé (1959, 1960, 1962), Schadé (1963) and Collewijn and Schadé (1962, 1963) have studied the shifts of water and ions between neurons and the surrounding tissue. They suggest that although the astrocytes are cellular, at least a part of them seem to function as a sort

*This research was supported in part by research grants from the National Institutes for Health (B3048) and the Netherlands Organization for Pure Research (563-15).

of extracellular space in the brain, containing a pool of water, electrolytes and nutrients. Impedance measurements were used to show the movements of water and ions. The impedance of the cerebral cortex has become a subject of considerable interest lately, since it was demonstrated that the parameters of this impedance are related to the functional state of the cerebral cortex (Aladjalova, 1955, 1964; Adey *et al.*, 1962; Van Harreveld and Schadé, 1962). Since particularly the apical dendrites were involved in electrolyte movements, it was suggested that these structures play a special role in maintenance of the ionic homeostasis of the cerebral cortex (Van Harreveld and Schadé, 1962; Schadé, 1963).

This report will present the results of impedance measurements under various physiological conditions and data on the mechanism of electrolyte movements between apical dendrites and neuroglia. It will be shown that the apical dendrites and the astroglia constitute a functional entity. The astroglia may thus play a role in modulating activity of the apical dendrites or the whole neuron. It is therefore interesting to consider the possibility that small ionic shifts between these constituents may actually be responsible for at least part of the spontaneous electrical potentials in the cerebral cortex.

Results*

1. *Impedance changes, electrolyte movements and cellular changes during anoxia*

The impedance of the cerebral cortex increases shortly after cortical anoxia. For about 3 to 4 minutes a very slow increase is seen, probably due to the emptying of cortical vessels; since blood is a relatively good conductor this will increase the cortical impedance. Also cooling of the cortex will contribute to this effect. Following the initial slow rise there is a sudden and marked increase (Fig. 1), which does not last more than one minute, after which the slow impedance rise is resumed. During this sudden increase 30 to 40 per cent of the cortical conductivity may be lost. If the rise is due to transport of extraneuronal electrolytes into cells and fibers of the cortex a change in the concentration of certain ions can be expected in these structures. In most neuronal tissues the abundant extracellular ions are sodium and chloride, and it seems likely that this is also true for the central nervous tissue. It has been possible to show with our histochemical method for chloride ions (Van Harreveld and Schadé, 1959, 1960) that a transport of chloride (and probably other anions) takes place, mainly into the apical

---

*For the various methods we refer the reader to the following publications: Collewijn and Schadé, 1962 (movement of potassium ions); Collewijn and Schadé, 1964 (changes in the size of astrocytes and oligodendrocytes during anoxia and spreading depression); Van Harreveld, 1957–1958 (changes in the volume of cortical neurons during anoxia and spreading depression); Van Harreveld and Schadé, 1959, 1960 (movement of chloride ions in the cerebral cortex); Van Harreveld and Schadé, 1962, (impedance changes during seizure activity); Schadé, 1959 (recording of electrical activity in immature cerebral cortex).

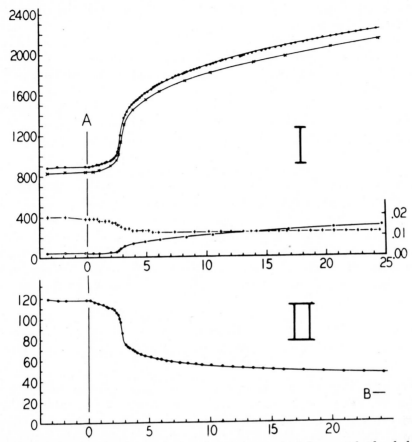

Fig. 1. I, values of resistance (O) and capacitance (+) boxes at bridge balance before and 25 min. after circulatory arrest (at A). Furthermore the real (×), and the imaginary (O) part of the tissue impedance are shown. *Abscissa:* time in minutes: *ordinate* on the left, resistance (and reactance) in ohms; *ordinate* on the right, capacitance of the box in microfarads. II, change in conductance (I/R) of the tissue before and 25 minutes after circulatory arrest. On the abscissa time is plotted in minutes, on the ordinate conductance in mhox × 10^5. B indicates the average level to which conductivity drops in 4–5 hr. (From van Harreveld and Ochs, 1956.)

dendrites. The efflux of potassium ions from the apical dendrites into the extraneuronal space has also been observed (Collewijn and Schadé, 1962).

Cortex treated with the chloride method while the circulation was intact showed a rather uniform distribution of chloride. Only the blood in the vessels and the connective tissue (e.g., pia, vessel wall), in which the chloride concentration was high showed as dark structures. In tissue treated after the rapid anoxial impedance change had taken place, the chloride concentration was quite different. Most evident was the presence of brown, often granular material in the apical dendrites (Van Harreveld and Schadé, 1959). The tissue between these structures had become distinctly lighter, suggesting a transport of chloride from the interneuronal space into the apical dendrites. The perikarya showed these changes to a much less pronounced degree; no

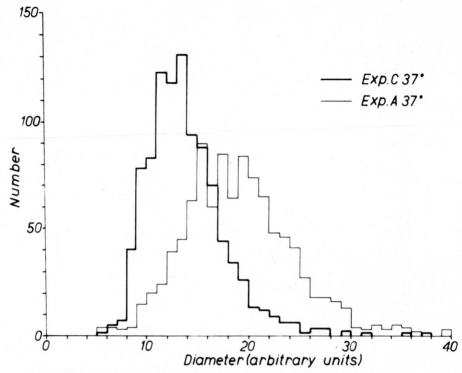

Fig. 2. Histograms of diameters of 2 × 1000 apical dendrites. Normal and anoxic cerebral cortex at 37° C. (Figs. 2–6 from Collewijn and Schadé, 1956.)

chloride transport into the basal dendrites was observed. The histological sections, treated with one of the potassium methods (Collewijn and Schadé, 1962) showed the "negative" picture. In preparations of cortex during anoxia the apical dendrites were revealed as colorless structures, indicating the outflow of potassium ions.

In previous papers the conclusion was drawn (Van Harreveld and Schadé, 1959, 1960) that the large increase in impedance after circulatory arrest must be due to a decrease in the number of extraneuronal ions available for transport of the measuring current. Since extraneuronal ions cannot leave the cortex after circulatory arrest, it was postulated that they move from the extraneuronal spaces into the neuronal elements of the cortex. To maintain osmotic equilibrium such an ionic transport must be accompanied by a movement of water from the extra- into the intraneuronal compartment, resulting in a swelling of neurons. This increase in volume was actually demonstrated by van Harreveld (1957). In rabbits the mean diameter of nerve cells increased more than 11 per cent and that of apical dendrites about 30 per cent. These measurements were recently confirmed for rats and rabbits (Collewijn, 1963). This demonstration of a swelling of neuronal elements supports the explanation of the impedance increase as being caused by a movement of ions accompanied by water from extraneuronal spaces into the neuronal compartment. It has been postulated (van Harreveld and Schadé,

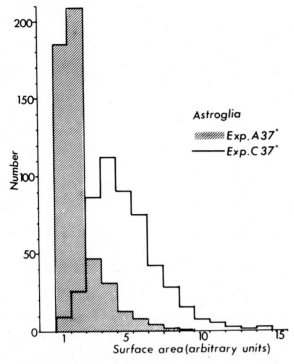

Fig. 3. Histograms of cross sections of 2 × 500 cell bodies of astrocytes. Normal and anoxic cerebral cortex at 37° C.

1959, 1960) that this ionic movement is due to an increase of the sodium permeability of the membrane of perikarya and dendrites. Such a permeability change would cause a Donnan situation in which the membrane is permeable for three ions (sodium, potassium and chloride) but would remain impermeable for the organic intracellular anion. This would result in a transport of sodium and chloride ions, accompanied by water to maintain osmotic equilibrium.

Since electronmicroscopists have demonstrated that almost no extracellular space exists in the brain, it would be of interest to know where the bulk of the water and ions goes after leaving the apical dendrites. The suggestion has been made (Van Harreveld and Schadé, 1960; Schadé, 1963) that the glial compartment, or at least part of it, could act as a functional extraneuronal space.

Size measurements were done on astroglia and oligodendroglia under the same conditions as during impedance changes and ionic movements. The results are shown in Figures 3 and 4. The difference between the histograms of the astroglia (Fig. 3) in well oxygenated and anoxic cortex is evident. The mean cross section (see for details of this method Collewijn and Schadé, 1964) of an astrocyte cell body in control series amounts to 226 (SE = 5) arbitrary units. In anoxic cortex this value amounts to 78 (SE = 3). The difference is highly significant (p < 0.001). Volumes can be calculated from cross sections if the shape of the cell body is known. However, this shape is very different in individual cells. For an approximation the cell body of an astrocyte was considered to be a sphere. Calculation of these volumes then

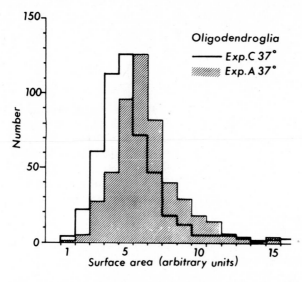

Fig. 4. Histograms of cross sections of 2 × 500 cell bodies of oligodendrocytes. Normal and anoxic cerebral cortex at 37° C.

gives a value of 358 μ^3 for control cortex and a value of 83 μ^3 for anoxic cortex. The latter value if only 23 per cent of the former.

The results of the measurements on oligodendrocytes are presented in figure 4. The mean cross section of the cell body of an oligodendrocyte in control cortex was 100 arbitrary units (SE = 2). In anoxic cortex a value of 123 (SE = 2) was found. Treating the cell bodies again as spheres, values of 105 and 140 μ^3 were found respectively. In view of the above presented data it seems safe to assume that after circulatory arrest a major transport of ions takes place between apical dendrites and astroglia.

2. *Changes in size of neuroglia during hypothermia*

The EEG pattern of the rabbit sensorimotor cortex shows a number of characteristic changes when the body temperature is lowered from 37° C. to 20° C. This condition was selected as an example of reversible EEG changes in a controlled state of decreased cerebral metabolism. Hypothermia has also been shown to be accompanied by changes in impedance of the cerebral cortex (Collewijn, 1963).

The changes in the size of astroglia and oligodendroglia are illustrated in Figures 5 and 6. Astrocytes decreased considerably in size when the brain temperature reached 20° C (Fig. 5). The mean value for the cross sections amounts to 162 arbitrary units (SE = 4). This difference is highly significant (p < 0.001) when compared with the mean value of the cell bodies at normal body temperature. The cell bodies decreased to 64 per cent of their original volume.

The reversal is seen in the volumetric changes of the cell bodies of the oligodendrocytes. The mean cross section amounted to 115 arbitrary units (SE = 2) at 20° C, which corresponds to a volume increase of 18 per cent.

Recently it was found (Collewijn, 1963) that in lowering the body temperature from 37 to 20° C a 32 per cent increase in the diameter of the apical

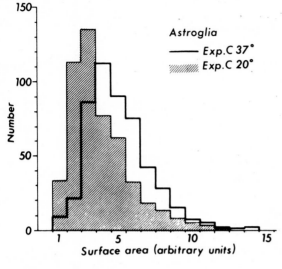

Fig. 5. Histograms of cross sections of 2 × 500 cell bodies of astrocytes. Normal cerebral cortex at 37° and 20° C.

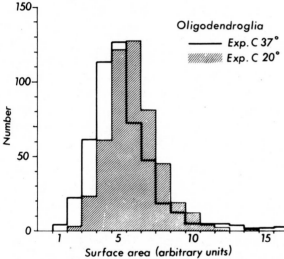

Fig. 6. Histograms of cross sections of 2 × 500 cell bodies of oligodendrocytes. Normal cerebral cortex at 37° and 20° C.

dendrites occurred. This series of experiments then also indicates that ionic and water shifts occur between the apical dendrites and the astroglia. The role of the oligodendroglia is not clear in this respect.

3. *Changes in size of cellular constituents during spreading depression*

Spreading depression (Fig. 8) can be elicited consistently in rabbits by stimulating the cortex with direct current. This phenomenon is characterized by a depression of the spontaneous cortical activity which spreads concentrically from the stimulated area with a velocity of 2 to 5 mm per minute. It is accompanied by a drop in cortical conductivity which in most of the experiments is of the order of 10 per cent (Van Harreveld and Schadé, 1959). Another concomitant is a slowly developing cortical negativity of a

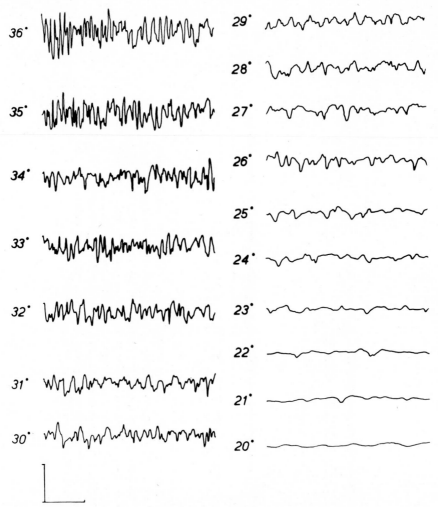

Fig. 7. Electrocorticograms of rabbit at temperatures from 36°–20° C. Calibration lines indicate 1 mV and 1 sec.

magnitude of 5 to 10 mV which is usually followed by surface positivity. The impedance and slow potential changes which accompany spreading depression resemble the corresponding asphyxial changes, and there is experimental evidence that these phenomena are closely related (Van Harreveld and Ochs, 1956; Van Harreveld and Schadé, 1959). Ionic and water movements similar to those observed after anoxia were also found in the cerebral cortex during spreading depression (Van Harreveld and Schadé, 1959).

The apical dendrites during spreading depression (Fig. 9) were an average of 17 per cent greater in diameter than on the contralateral control side (Van Harreveld, 1958). Figure 9 shows an experiment in which the diameter of the apical dendrites had been determined in cortical strips of a hemisphere in which a spreading depression was in progress and also in

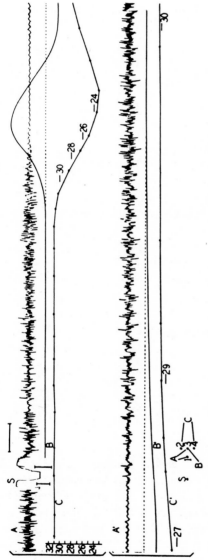

Fig. 8. Electrocorticogram (AA'), slow potential change (BB') and conductivity changes (CC') (in mhos × 10⁵) during spreading depression. (Stimulation 4 V d.c. is applied at S.) In the insertion are shown the positions of the stimulating electrodes (S) the electrodes leading off the electrocorticogram (1 and 3) and the slow potential change (2, 3), and of the electrodes for the impedance measurement (2 and 4). The first vertical calibration line indicates 1 mV for the electrocorticogram, the second 5 mV for the slow potential record, the horizontal line indicates a 10 sec. time interval. (From van Harreveld and Schadé, 1959.)

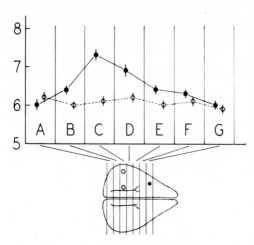

Fig. 9. Volume changes of apical dendrites during spreading depression. The insert shows the stimulation (G) and resistance electrodes (C). The *vertical lines* indicate the slices cut from the experimental and control cortices. In the graph is plotted on the *ordinate* the mean diameter (in an arbitrary unit) of the apical dendrites in each of the slices of the control side *(open circle)* and of the experimental cortex *(points)*. The *small vertical line* through the *circles* and *points* indicates the standard error of each determination. (From van Harreveld, 1958.)

strips of the control hemisphere. The cortices were frozen when the impedance rise in strip C reached a maximum. The diameters of the apical dendrites in the control strips do not differ greatly. On the experimental side, however, the diameter of the apical dendrites is the greatest in strip C in which the impedance rise had reached its maximum, and decreases from there regularly in consecutive strips. These observations demonstrate the swelling of neuronal elements which can be expected to accompany the transport of sodium chloride into apical dendrites during the spreading depression.

In Figure 10 the sizes of cell bodies of astroglia and oligodendroglia are

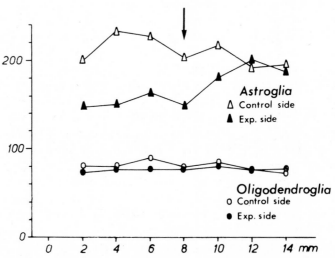

Fig. 10. Changes in the size of glial cell bodies during spreading depression, elicited by application of glutamic acid under frontal pole of the left cortex. Surface areas of cell bodies of astrocytes and oligodendrocytes are presented for the experimental and control cortex. Measurements were made at various distances in caudal direction from the point of origin (zero in the graph) of spreading depression. The arrow indicates the cortical zone where the depression was maximal as judged from the ECoG extinction and impedance rise.

presented during the course of a spreading depression. Every point in the graph represents the average value of 50 cells. The spreading depression was elicited in the left frontal cortex indicated in the figure as point O on the abscissa. As is shown in the figure spreading depression is accompanied by a decrease in size of the cell bodies of the astrocytes. The shrinkage of the astrocytes was estimated as being about half the value as during anoxia. As the oligodendrocytes are concerned, no difference in size was found.

On the basis of these experiments it seemed logical to extend the studies to the early postnatal period of development in the rabbit cerebral cortex, since it was shown that this period is characterized by the appearance of many bioelectrical activities (Schadé, 1959).

4. Impedance changes, ionic shifts and cellular mechanisms during postnatal development

The spontaneous electrical activity of the rabbit cerebral cortex becomes mature in type between 10 and 15 days after birth. In young rabbits the earliest reaction to a stimulus which in adults tends to produce spreading depression was often a spreading convulsion rather than a spreading depression (Fig. 11). In animals of 30 and 35 days spreading depression and slow potential changes can be elicited as regularly as in adult animals.

The period between the maturation of the EEG and the occurrence of spreading depression is also characterized by the ability of the cerebral cortex to show a rise in impedance during anoxia (Tables 1 and 2). The latency period of the impedance rise is still rather long (7.1–6.5 min) as compared with the value found in adult animals. This same period is also marked by the onset of electrolyte shifts during anoxia and the volume changes in apical dendrites and astroglia. It is tempting to speculate that the maturation of the various electrical parameters of the cerebral cortex is not only based on the development of synaptic fields and dendritic patterns, but perhaps on the constitution of the glial-dendritic entity as well.

Discussion

The reciprocal changes in volume of apical dendrites and astroglia indicating ionic and water movements were established in physiological conditions such as hypothermia and spreading depression, as well as during anoxia. All these states are characterized by marked changes in the spontaneous electrical patterns and the impedance. The value of impedance measurements has recently been stressed by Van Harreveld and Schadé (1962) and Adey et al. (1962). When properly used it might not only indicate the shifts of ions between the various compartments in the cerebral cortex or other brain structures but also might indicate the activity-level of small neuron-aggregates.

Several authors have considered glial cells to be of special importance for the transport of water, ions, nutrients, etc., in the central nervous system. Our experiments suggest that the astroglia, or at least a part of the astroglia-pool, may play an essential role in the transport of electrolytes, which are of primary importance for the maintenance of neuronal activity. The astroglia

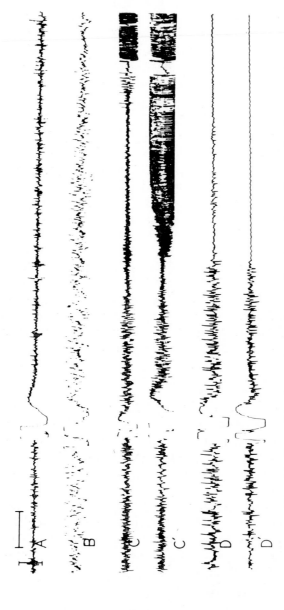

Fig. 11. Spreading depression and spreading convulsion during development. A: Cortical stimulation, intensity 10 V. dc, duration 3 sec. in 15-day-old rabbit. C and C' Cortical stimulation, intensity 10 V. dc, duration 3 sec. in 24-day-old rabbit. C', recording from electrodes closest to stimulus; C, recording from more caudal electrode pair. D and D': Cortical stimulation, intensity 6 V. dc, duration 3 sec. in adult rabbit. D', recording from electrodes closest to stimulus. All preparations lightly anesthetized with urethane. Stimuli are recognizable by stimulus artifact. Calibration: Horizontal line, 10 sec.; vertical line, 1 mV.

Table 1

Age (days)	Number	Rise in impedance during anoxia	Latency period (min.)	Shift of electrolytes
0	10	0	–	–
5	10	0	–	–
10	10	0	–	–
15	10	1	–	–
20	10	3	7.1	3
25	10	8	7.0	9
30	10	9	6.5	9
45	10	10	4.7	10
adult	5	5	3.5	5

Table 2

Age	Number	Mature EEG	Spreading depression and convulsion	Volume change apical dendrites	Volume change astrocytes
0	10	0	0	0	0
5	10	0	0	0	0
10	10	4	0	0	0
15	10	8	1	1	1
20	10	9	1	2	2
25	10	10	2	2	2
30	10	10	8	9	9
45	10	10	10	10	10
adult	5	5	5	5	5

may thus play a role in modulating activity of the apical dendrites or the whole neuron. The close parallelism between the development of the electrical phenomena in the cerebral cortex and the glial-dendritic entity suggests that the latter may be partly responsible for the genesis of the slow components in the electrical activity.

Summary

A report is given of studies of shifts in electrolytes and water and volumetric changes in cellular constituents of the cerebral cortex during anoxia, hypothermia and spreading depression. In all conditions a reciprocal change in the volume of apical dendrites and astroglia was observed.

A glial-dendritic entity was defined, consisting of apical dendrites and (part of) the astroglia-pool.

This glial-dendritic entity begins functioning in the cerebral cortex between 15 and 30 days postnatally, a period which is also characterized by the development of a number of electrical parameters. It is postulated that this glial-dendritic entity may play a role in the genesis of the slow components in the electrical activity of the cerebral cortex.

REFERENCES

ADEY, W. R., KADO, R. T. and DIDIO, J. Impedance measurements in brain tissue of animals using microvolt signals. *Exp. Neurol.*, 1962, 5:47–66.

ALADJALOVA, N. A. Slow electrical processes in the brain. *Progress in Brain Research.* 1964, vol. VII, Elsevier, Amsterdam, New York.

ALADJALOVA, N. A. Metod odnovremennogo izemereniar omicheskos i emkostnoi sostavlavushemikn impedantsa vo vremar bistrogo nestationarnogo protessa. *Tr. Ir-ta. Biophiziki*, 1955, 1:298–305.

COLLEWIJN, H. *Ionic movements in the cerebral cortex*. Thesis, Amsterdam, 1963.

COLLEWIJN, H. and SCHADÉ, J. P. Changes in the size of astrocytes and oligodendrocytes during anoxia, hypothermia and spreading depression. *Progress in Brain Research*. In press.

COLLEWIJN, H. and SCHADÉ, J. P. Potassium movements in the cerebral cortex during asphyxia. *Acta Morphol. Neerl. Scand.*, 1962, 5:11–20.

EFRON, R. Alterations in the electrical impedance of the cerebral cortex during induced seizures. *Trans. Fifth V. A. Conf. Chemother. in Psychiatry.*, 1961, pp. 11–11A.

FREYGANG, W. H. and LANDAU, W. M. Some relations between resistivity and electrical activity in the cerebral cortex of the cat. *J. Cell. Comp. Physiol.*, 1955, 45:377–392.

GALAMBOS, R. A glial-neural theory of brain function. *Proc. Natl. Acad. Sci. U. S.*, 1961, 47:129–136.

GERSCHENFELD, H. M., WALD, F., ZADUNAISKY, J. A. and DE ROBERTIS, E. D. Function of astroglia in the water-ion metabolism of the central nervous system. *Neurol.*, 1959, 9:412–425.

HAMBERGER, A. Oxidation of tricarboxylic acid cycle intermediates by nerve cell bodies and glial cells. *J. Neurochem.*, 1961, 8:31–35.

HAMBERGER, A. Difference between isolated neuronal and vascular glia with respect to respiratory activity. *Acta Physiol Scand.*, 1963, 58: (suppl. 203).

HAMBERGER, A., and HYDÉN, H. Inverse enzymatic changes in neurons and glia during increased function and hypoxia. *J. Cell Biol.*, 1963, 16 (suppl. 3): 521–525.

HARREVELD, A. VAN. Changes in volume of cortical neuronal elements during asphyxiation. *Amer. J. Physiol.*, 1957, 191:233–242.

HARREVELD, A. VAN. Changes in the diameter of apical dendrites during spreading depression. *Amer. J. Physiol.*, 1958, 192:457–463.

HARREVELD, A. VAN. Water and electrolyte distribution in central nervous tissue. *Fed. Proc.*, 1962, 21:659–664.

HARREVELD, A. VAN and OCHS, S. Cerebral impedance changes after circulatory arrest. *Amer. J. Physiol.*, 1956, 187:180–192.

HARREVELD, A. VAN and SCHADÉ, J. P. Chloride movements in cerebral cortex after circulatory arrest and during spreading depression. *J. Cell. Comp. Physiol.*, 1959, 54:65–84.

HARREVELD, A. VAN and SCHADÉ, J. P. On the distribution and movements of water and electrolytes in the cerebral cortex. In: D. B. TOWER and J. P. SCHADÉ (editors), *Structure and function of the cerebral cortex*, Elsevier, Amsterdam, 1959.

HARREVELD, A. VAN and SCHADÉ, J. P. Changes in the electrical conductivity of cerebral cortex during seizure activity. *Exper. Neurol.*, 1962, 5:383–400.

HILD, W., CHANG, J. J. and TASAKI, I. Electrical responses of astrocytic glia from the mammalian central nervous system cultivated *in vitro*. *Experientia*, 1959, 14:220–221.

HILD, W. and TASAKI, I. Morphological and physiological properties of neurons and glial cells in tissue culture. *J. Neurophysiol.*, 1962, 25:277–304.

HYDÉN, H. and EGYHAZI, E. Nuclear RNA changes of nerve cells during a learning experiment in rats. *Proc. Nat. Acad. Sci.*, 1962, 48:1366–1373.

HYDÉN, H. and LANGE, P. A kinetic study of the neuron-glia relationship. *J. Cell. Biol.*, 1962, 13:233–237.

HYDÉN, H., LOVTRUP, S. and PIGON, A. Cytochrome oxidase and succinoxidase activities in spinal ganglion cells and in glial capsule cells. *J. Neurochem.*, 1958, 2:304–311.

HYDÉN, H., and PIGON, A. A cytophysiological study of the functional relationship between oligodendroglial cells and nerve cells of Deiters' nucleus. *J. Neurochem.*, 1960, 6:57–72.

KATZMAN, R. Electrolyte distribution in mammalian central nervous system. Are glia high sodium cells? *Neurol.*, 1961, 11:27–36.

Koch, A., Ranch, J. B., Jr. and Newman, B. L. Ionic content of neuroglia. *Exper. Neurol.*, 1962, 6:186–200.

Lofgren, B. The electrical impedance of a complex tissue and its relation to changes in volume and fluid distribution. *Acta Physiol. Scand.*, 1951, 23: (suppl. 81) 1–51.

Lumsden, Ch. E. Histological and histochemical aspects of normal neuroglia cells. In: W. F. Windle (editor), *Biology of Neuroglia*, Charles C Thomas, Springfield, Ill., 1958.

Robertis, E. de and Gerschenfeld, H. M. Submicroscopic morphology and function of glial cells. In: C. C. Pfeiffer and J. R. Smythies (editors), *International review of Neurobiology*, 3, Academic Press, New York, 1961.

Schadé, J. P. Maturational aspects of EEG and of spreading depression in rabbit. *J. Neurophysiol.*, 1959, 22:245–257.

Schadé, J. P. Functional correlates of ionic movements in the certebral cortex. In: J. P. Schadé and W. H. McMenemey (editors), *Selective Vulnerability of the Brain in Hypoxaemia*, Blackwell, Oxford, 1963, pp. 89–99.

Svaetichin, G., Laufer, M., Mitarai, G., Fatechand, R., Vallecalle, E., and Villegas, J. Glial control of neuronal networks and receptors. In: *The Visual System:* Neurophysiol. and Psychophysics. Symp. Freiburg, 1961, pp. 445–456.

POSTNATAL DEVELOPMENT OF THE CORPUS CALLOSUM IN THE CAT
Myelination of a Fibre Tract in the Central Nervous System*

BERNICE GRAFSTEIN

Department of Physiology, McGill University, Montreal, Canada
and The Rockefeller Institute, New York, N. Y.

The cerebrum of the cat at birth is almost completely devoid of myelin (Vogt, 1900; Tilney and Casamajor, 1924). This makes it possible to follow in the postnatal period the complete sequence of events leading to myelination of a number of important tracts of nerve fibres running through the brain. Of the many pathways involved, the corpus callosum which connects the two cerebral hemispheres is one of the most convenient for this kind of study because it comprises a well-delineated bundle of fibres, easily accessible for examination of its functional and structural properties. When activated, it gives rise to a well-defined electrical response in the cortex. In the study here described, this response was examined at various times during the postnatal period, and it was found to undergo changes in configuration that were diagnostic of the process of myelin formation in the callosal fibres. Certain characteristic features of this process could thus be analysed, and it seems reasonable to suppose that since the corpus callosum appears to be a typical central tract, these features of callosal myelination would also be characteristic of myelination anywhere in the central nervous system.

Although there is evidence from light microscopy that even the well-myelinated tracts of the central nervous system contain a large proportion of unmyelinated fibres (Lassek, 1948; Tomasch, 1954), the normal functioning of these pathways undoubtedly depends on their ability to transmit nervous impulses at the high velocity characteristic of myelinated fibres. Therefore, the question of whether they can carry out their function at all before becoming myelinated has received some consideration in the past (Langworthy, 1932; Tilney and Casamajor, 1924; Ulett *et al.*, 1944; Windle *et al.*, 1934). This problem has been re-evaluated in the light of the present study of the corpus callosum, a distinction being possible for the first time between fibres that had not yet become myelinated, and those that would never do so.

The myelin sheaths of the central fibres do not appear to differ in any

---

*The research on which this paper is based was supported by grants from the United Cerebral Palsy Research and Educational Foundation, Inc. and the Medical Research Council of Canada.

essential way from those of peripheral nerves (Hess and Young, 1952; Maturana, 1960; Peters, 1960; Metuzals, 1963). The layers of myelin form a spiral around the axon, this spiral being continuous with the cytoplasmic membrane of the "supporting cell" within which the myelin is formed (Geren, 1954). In the central nervous system, the "supporting" cells involved have been identified as oligodendroglia (Luse, 1956; de Robertis *et al.*, 1958). The relationship of these cells to the axons they surround appears to differ only slightly from that of Schwann cells to peripheral nerve fibres. Whereas there is only one Schwann cell per myelin segment, several glial cells may participate in the formation of a single segment, and any one of them may form part of the sheath around a number of different fibres (Luse, 1956; Maturana, 1960; Ross *et al.*, 1962). It is evident from the structural relationship of the elements involved that myelin sheath formation depends on an intimate interrelation between the nerve cell and its surrounding glia, but the precise mechanisms that give the myelin its characteristic spiral form, and the stimulus necessary for the initiation of the process are unknown. Earlier workers have considered a number of conditions that might possibly have provided the necessary stimulus for the onset of myelination, including the onset of function in the nerve fibres involved (Tilney and Casamajor, 1924; Langworthy, 1932; Speidel, 1933; Gyllensten and Malmfors, 1963), and their attainment of a critical size (Duncan, 1934).

The anatomical disposition of the callosal fibre system has been clarified by histological studies and by electrophysiological investigations of the responses produced in the cerebral cortex of the cat by callosal activity. It has been established that the most profuse distribution of callosal fibres from any one cortical point is to the corresponding point in the opposite hemisphere (Poljak, 1927). The fibres apparently originate from neurones throughout the depth of the cortex (Grafstein, 1959) and run without synapsing through the corpus callosum to end in the cortex of the opposite side, where their terminations are distributed to all the cortical cell layers (Nauta and Bucher, 1954; Hayhow, W. R., personal communication, 1957).

Activation of the callosal fibre system is readily produced by stimulating a point on the surface of the cortex, and the resulting sequence of changes in cortical activity, termed the transcallosal evoked response, may be recorded from the surface of the symmetrical point. The evoked activity consists of an initial focal response, confined to an area of cortex about 6-8 mm. in diameter and lasting about 30 msec., usually followed by some irregular oscillations (Curtis, 1940; Chang, 1953). In adult cats in which spontaneous cortical activity has been reduced by light anaesthesia or by cutting the cortical radiations to abolish afferent inflow (Grafstein, 1959), the activity following the focal response takes the form of a long-lasting, surface-positive burst which spreads through the cortex without attenuation for distances of at least several cm., presumably by means of self- re-exciting multisynaptic pathways (Burns, 1951). In the suprasylvian gyrus, the focal response has been found to consist of a surface-positive phase lasting about 15 msec., followed by a surface-negative phase having about the same duration (Fig. 1), and

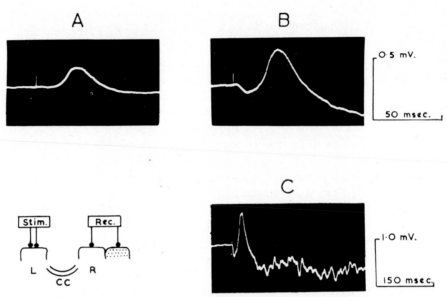

Fig. 1. Transcallosal evoked response in suprasylvian gyrus of adult cat. (Unanaesthetized cerveau isolé with cortical radiations cut). A. Response to weak stimulus (4 V., 1 msec.) applied to surface of contralateral point. Only negative phase of focal response is elicited. B. Stronger stimulus than in A (5 V.) produces both positive and negative phases of focal response followed by burst activity of which only the initial positive deflection is seen. C. Stronger stimulus than in B (6.5 V.), response recorded on slow sweep to show a portion of burst activity. Monopolar recording with Ag-AgCl-saline wick electrodes from surface of cortex, reference electrode on dead cortex. Negativity of focal electrode appears as upward deflection. Inset diagram shows electrode arrangement (L, R: left and right suprasylvian gyri; CC: corpus callosum). (Grafstein, 1959; Figs. 1–4 courtesy *Journal of Neurophysiology*.)

it has been shown (Grafstein, 1959) that each of the two phases arises as a consequence of activity in a different group of callosal fibres. The callosal connections are organized so that the fibres responsible for the production of the negative phase originate in cell bodies lying in the superficial cell layers of the cortex on one side and end near the surface of the cortex on the opposite side, whereas the fibres reponsible for the positive phase originate in deep-lying cell bodies and have deep-lying terminations. It has, moreover, been possible to show that the two groups of fibres involved have different conduction velocities (Grafstein, 1963). The fibres that give rise to the positive phase of the response have a maximum conduction velocity of about 15 M/sec., and an average conduction velocity of about 5 M/sec., while the fibres that give rise to the negative phase have an average conduction velocity of about 2 M/sec. It is readily apparent, therefore, that the fibres of the corpus callosum in the adult cat do not constitute a single homogeneous population, but may be divided into functional groups on the basis of their sites of origin and termination, as well as on the basis of their conduction velocities, and

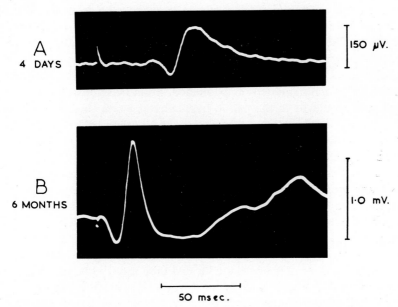

Fig. 2. **Transcallosal evoked response in suprasylvian gyrus of kittens.** A. 4 days old: only focal response is elicited. B. 6 months old: focal response is followed by burst activity of which only the beginning is shown (Grafstein, 1963).

furthermore that these functional differences may be correlated with different components of the evoked response.

When we come now to examine the evoked response in the young kitten, we find that it bears a clearly recognizable similarity to that in the adult (Fig. 2). Even in the very early postnatal period, the focal portion of the response consists of a positive followed by a negative phase, although these are much smaller in amplitude than in the adult, have a considerably longer duration, and a much longer latency. On the other hand, the spreading activity which in the adult follows the focal response is completely absent in animals younger than about 12 days of age. Of the changes which the focal response undergoes as the animal matures, the one that is of most interest is the change in latency, since this is a function of the rate of conduction in the callosal axons and hence may be expected to provide an indication of the state of their myelin development.

Some predictions can be made about when the changes due to myelination might occur on the basis of when myelin actually appears in the corpus callosum. Histological studies indicate that this occurs after most of the cortical radiations are already well-myelinated (Vogt, 1900, Tilney and Casamajor, 1924; Watson, 1903, Jacobson, 1963). It has been reported that a few myelinated callosal fibres are already detectable in the 14-day-old cat (Tilney and Casamajor, 1924), but even toward the end of the fourth week, the myelinated fibres are quite sparse (Grafstein, 1963). However, there is a significantly greater amount of myelin seen in the callosum of a 32-day-old animal than in an animal 27 days of age, reflecting an increase both in the number of individual myelinated fibres and in their maximum sheath thickness. During these early stages, the myelinated fibres seem to be distributed quite uniformly through the thickness of the callosum, and the only obvious regional variation is a slight gradation in the anteroposterior direction, with the anterior portion more densely populated. From these observations, it seems likely that it would be in the period beginning at about the end of the fourth postnatal week that functional evidence of the beginning of myelination would appear, and a decrease in the latency of the transcallosal response at that time would be expected.

When the transcallosal response in the suprasylvian gyrus was examined, its latency was found to decrease from the time of birth onward (Fig. 3). The decrease was a gradual one during the first four weeks and affected equally both the positive and negative phases of the focal response. At the end of the fourth week, however, there was an abrupt discontinuity in the latency curve, with the latency of the initial deflection of the response decreasing from 28 msec. to 16 msec. between the 27th and 28th days, although there was no corresponding shift in the peaks of the positive and negative phases. Examination of the individual responses recorded from animals of different ages (Fig. 4) revealed that the sudden change in latency was due to the emergence of a small, early, positive deflection in the response, appearing at first as a step on the initial limb of the positive phase (Fig. 4C) and then growing in amplitude until in the response recorded at 40–45 days there appeared to be two positive peaks (Fig. 4E). The second of these peaks (corresponding to the original positive peak of the response) subsequently decreased in amplitude (Fig. 4F), leaving a response whose configuration, apart from latency, was hardly distinguishable from that seen in the first four weeks (Fig. 4G).

It has been possible to demonstrate that the change in latency occurring at the end of the fourth postnatal week is the consequence of the onset of activity in a rapidly-conducting group of callosal fibres. By measuring the conduction velocity of the callosal fibres, using the technique of stimulating at two points along their intracallosal course, it was found that in an animal 27 days of age the maximum conduction velocity was 1.5 M/sec., whereas in an animal 43 days of age, when the double-peak configuration of the positive phase was well-developed, the most rapidly-conducting fibres had a velocity of 10 M/sec. It can be calculated that a difference in conduction velocity of this magnitude would adequately account for the demonstrated latency difference if it were assumed that in each case the callosal fibres were conducting at the observed rate along the whole of their extracortical length. These observations, taken together with the histological evidence of the rapid progress of myelination in the same period, suggest that it is the myelination of the callosal fibres that is the basis of the described changes in the configuration of the transcallosal response. One piece of evidence that tends to confirm this is that the beginning of myelination of the pyramidal tract fibres, which occurs between the third and fourth postnatal weeks,

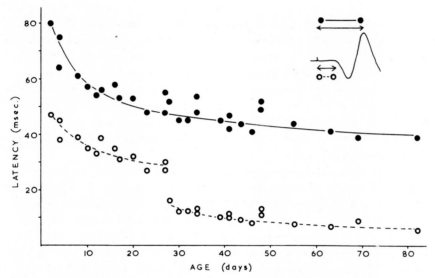

Fig. 3. Latency of transcallosal evoked response during postnatal period. Latencies of the initial deflection (○ - - ○) and of the negative peak (● — ●) are shown (Grafstein, 1963).

produces an increase in conduction velocity of similar magnitude, i.e. about 7-fold (Housepian *et al.*, 1961).

There appears to be a slight discrepancy in the fact that there was already evidence of some myelin in the callosal fibres prior to the critical changes in the response. However, the precise timing of the latency change described above for the suprasylvian gyrus was not duplicated in other cortical regions. In the neighboring mid-ectosylvian gyrus, for example, it was found that the new component in the response appeared slightly earlier, being already clearly evident at 27 days, and that the shift in latency thus produced was less abrupt, occurring over a period of several days. It is evident, therefore, that callosal fibres in all cortical regions do not undergo myelination at exactly the same time, so the small discrepancy between the histological and physiological observations does not weaken the myelination hypothesis.

If the beginning of callosal myelination is identified with the latency change seen at the end of the fourth postnatal week, some other explanation must be found for the change in latency observed before this time—a continuous decrease that affects both the positive and negative phases of the evoked response. In this case, it can again be demonstrated that the basis of the change is an increase in callosal conduction velocity. The explanation that comes most readily to mind is that during this initial period of their development, the callosal fibres are increasing in diameter. However, this explanation appears to be an unlikely one for the following reason. It was found that the conduction velocity of the most rapidly-conducting fibres increased from 0.85 M/sec. at 12 days to 1.5 M/sec. at 27 days, and that even the more slowly-conducting fibres giving rise to the negative phase of the response

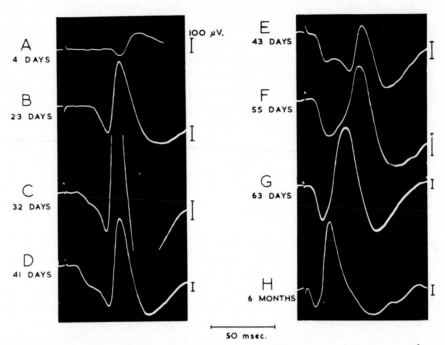

Fig. 4. **Focal transcallosal responses in cats of different ages.** Responses shown were obtained with stimuli of 2X threshold strength in each case. Time scale is the same for all records; amplification differs, as indicated by 100μV. calibration marks for each (Grafstein, 1963).

showed an increase from 0.7 M/sec. to 1.0 M/sec. during the same period. On the assumption that the conduction velocity of the unmyelinated fibres is proportional to their diameter (Gasser, 1950; Hodes, 1953), it would be predicted that the diameter of the fibres involved would have to increase by something between 40 per cent and 80 per cent, but in histological sections of the corpus callosum there is no evidence of any appreciable increase in its overall thickness during this period. Therefore, in order to account for the observed changes in conduction velocity, it seems necessary to postulate that before any of the callosal fibres become myelinated they undergo a change in membrane properties. This might be the consequence of either a change in the axonal membrane itself, or, since the electrical resistance of the medium surrounding the nerve fibre is important in determining the rate of impulse conduction, changes in the properties of the extraneuronal tissue. In the latter case, it is possible that the electrical characteristics of the glial cells or their proximity to the axon might be important determining factors.

The question arises of whether these fibres which undergo some maturational changes before the beginning of myelination are in fact the same ones that eventually become myelinated, or whether the myelinated fibres constitute a completely separate group, making no contribution to the evoked response prior to myelination, either because they are incapable of conducting impulses before their myelin sheaths are formed, or because they do not establish effective synaptic connections until that time. Bearing on this question is the observation that when the short-latency component of the evoked response appeared, indicating that myelinated fibre activity had begun, there was no increase in the maximum amplitude of the positive phase of the response. Such an increase would have been expected at that time if a new set of synaptic connections had come into operation and the activity of the myelinated fibres were summing with that which had previously been produced by the unmyelinated group alone. Instead, examination of the changes in the configuration of the positive phase revealed that as the short-latency component due to myelinated fibre activity grew in amplitude, the later component dwindled and eventually disappeared. This suggests that both components were produced by the same set of fibres, which became myelinated after they had already established functional connections with the cortical cells.

There are two important points here that must be emphasized about the condition of the fibres before they begin to myelinate: One is that they have already reached their terminal destinations, and the other is that they are capable of impulse transmission. Ulett *et al.* (1944) came to the same conclusion when they observed that transcallosal responses could be evoked in the newborn rabbit before myelination had begun, although they were not able to establish wth certainty, as it is here possible to do, that the activity they recorded was produced by fibres that would eventually acquire myelin sheaths. The same uncertainty applies to the work of earlier investigators (Langworthy, 1932; Tilney and Casamajor, 1924; Windle *et al.*, 1934), but a very convincing demonstration has recently been made by Änggård and Ottoson (1963) who showed that stimulation of the sciatic nerve in foetal sheep, before it revealed any electron microscopic evidence of myelin, elicited muscle action potentials and muscular contraction which are normally produced in the adult animal only upon the stimulation of the large, well-myelinated $A\alpha$ motor fibres.

When myelination occurred, the callosal fibres giving rise to the initial deflection of the evoked response underwent an approximately 7-fold increase in conduction velocity, i.e., from 1.5 M/sec. to 10 M/sec. As has been mentioned, a change of this magnitude could account for the concomitant increase in latency only if it were assumed that the increase in conduction velocity had been effective along nearly the whole of the extracortical length of the fibres. Regardless of whether one chooses to consider that the change in conduction rate occurred when myelin formation first began or when the myelin sheath had reached a certain critical thickness, the rapidity with which the change occurred, as indicated by the abruptness with which the latency changed at the critical time, indicates a very rapid rate of growth of myelin along the length of the axon, probably in excess of 1 mm./hr. It does not seem likely, therefore, that this process occurs by the addition of segments of myelin one after the other, as has been observed to occur in amphibian peripheral nerve fibres during their initial outgrowth (Speidel, 1932). Instead, the conditions of myelin formation in the corpus callosum appear to be like those in explanted central nervous system fragments in tissue culture, where myelination occurs simultaneously over long stretches of axon, with many segments of the myelin sheath formed synchronously (Bornstein and Murray, 1961). This latter condition apparently arises when the glial cells are already aligned in series on the nerve fibres before the actual myelin formation begins, so that the progress of myelination is not limited, as it is in peripheral nerve, by the rate of outgrowth of the supporting elements. For the same reason, it is unlikely that myelination of the callosal fibres proceeds, as it does in peripheral nerve, distalward from the cell body, although this cannot be determined with certainty.

It appears, however, that although the glial cells may determine the rate and direction of myelin formation, the stimulus for the initiation of the process does not come from the glial cells alone, but depends on an interaction between the glia and the neurones involved. This emerges from the fact that the callosal fibres showed very marked individual differences in their ability to undergo myelination. For example, in the case of the fibres involved in the positive phase, there was a period of several weeks required for all of them to become myelinated. This was apparently not due to just a random variation within the fibre population since the earliest fibres to become myelinated were found to arise from cells lying at a depth of about 1 mm. from the surface, i.e., in layer V which contains the largest pyramidal cells, while the fibres originating in more deep-lying cells did not undergo myelination till later (Grafstein, 1963).

More striking even than this, however, was the difference between the fibres giving rise to the positive phase of the evoked response and those giving rise to the negative phase. The latter were found not to participate in any of the changes beginning at the end of the fourth postnatal week that have been described above. The latency of the negative phase did not show any abrupt decrease, the fibres giving rise to it retaining their conduction velocity of 1.0 M/sec. throughout the period between 27 and 43 days, and the threshold for electrical excitation of these fibres was found to be higher than that of the myelinated fibres giving rise to the positive phase. Even in animals up to 3 months of age there was no indication of any shift in the latency of the negative phase that might be attributed to myelination. Indeed, since the conduction velocity of the fibres mediating the negative phase in the adult cat was found to be only 2 M/sec., there might be some doubt about whether they became myelinated at all if it were not for the observation of G. H. Bishop (personal communication, 1960; cf. also Shultz et al., 1957, Figs. 7 and 8) that even the smallest callosal fibres in the adult cat show some degree of myelination. One must suppose, therefore, that eventually the fibres giving rise to the negative phase also became involved in myelin formation. Nevertheless, the possibility remains that these fibres may be so thinly myelinated even in their most mature condition that the insulation provided by their sheaths is inadequate to establish saltatory transmission. Alternatively, it is possible that the fibres giving rise to the negative phase finally do acquire myelin sheaths of the ordinary kind but remain, as a group, smaller in diameter than those that myelinate earlier. There is some evidence that the latter is also true in myelination of spinal fibre tracts (Hess, 1954).

Since it has already been established (Grafstein, 1959) that the two different fibre groups giving rise to the positive and negative phases of the evoked response differ sharply with respect to the anatomical arrangement of their sites of origin and termination, it is perhaps not surprising that they should also show such a marked difference in the time at which they become susceptible to myelin formation. However, the basis for the latter difference, even if it is only a quantitative and not a qualitative one, is by no means clear. It is apparently not a simple matter of a generally slower rate of maturation of the elements that produce the negative phase, since both phases showed identical rates of increase in amplitude during the first 3 postnatal weeks (Grafstein, 1963), and, as mentioned above, the maturational changes causing an increase in conduction velocity prior to myelination affected both phases equally. Another possibility, that the fibres must attain a critical size before they can become myelinated (Duncan, 1944) and that they do so at different times, seems unlikely since just before myelination began, i.e., at 27 days of age, the conduction velocities of the fibres involved in the positive and negative phases were found to be the same, i.e., 1 M/sec., so it would be expected that the average diameters of the fibres were the same, unless they had very different membrane properties even then. There do not, therefore, seem to be any obvious differences between the two groups of neurones that might determine when they would become engaged in the process of myelin formation.

General Conclusions

Since there is as yet no clue to why the two neuronal populations should be so different in their susceptibility to myelination, one can do little more than speculate on some of the factors that might be involved, attempting to relate some of the observations reported in the present paper to other known evidence.

1. *Regional Development of the Cortex*

It was shown above that myelination of callosal axons occurred earlier in the ectosylvian gyrus than in the suprasylvian. The same sequence has been observed in the development of other properties, including the appearance of subcortical myelin (Vogt, 1900) and the susceptibility to epileptiform afterdischarge elicited by direct electrical stimualtion (Grossman, 1955). It seems probable, therefore, that the deposition of myelin on the callosal fibres is but one of a number of features of cortical development showing a characteristic regional distribution determined by factors that evidently influence the overall maturation of the cortical neurones. It is not obvious, however, how the operation of such factors could give rise to the observed difference in neuronal properties within any one region of cortex.

An additional possibility to consider is that the regional pattern might be superimposed on a wave of developmental change invading the cortex in a radial direction. The justification for introducing this qualification is that the two groups of callosal fibres on whose differences we have focused arise from nerve cell bodies having different distributions within the cortex. For example, the fibres that are more resistant to myelination, those giving rise to the negative phase of the evoked response, arise from cell bodies confined to the more superficial cell layers of the cortex. It does not seem possible, however, to explain all the observations on the basis of a single radial gradient of development since, as has been shown above, the more deep-lying neurones that give rise to the more readily-myelinating fibres do not become myelinated in order from the deepest-lying ones upward. One could take this into account and yet adhere to the same line of argument by postulating the presence of a more complicated radial profile of developmental change, such as the one that has been described by Conel (1952) in his study of the histologic development of human cortex. Nevertheless, any such hypothesis would be weakened by the fact that developmental differences between the two groups of callosal neurones were not detectable before myelination.

2. Glial Cell Characteristics

It has been shown above that the rapid rate at which the callosal fibres become myelinated is probably determined by the arrangement of the glial cells. Another fact that emphasizes the controlling role of these cells in myelin formation is that it is their arrangement and not the polarity of the neurone that determines the direction in which myelination proceeds. Thus in both peripheral nerve and optic nerve we have instances in which myelination progresses distalward from the central nervous system, but in the former case the advancing myelin is moving away from the cell body of the neurone (Speidel, 1932), whereas in the latter case it is moving toward the cell body of the ganglion cell (Westphal, 1897; Sattler, 1915). In each case, the direction in which myelination proceeds seems to depend on the outgrowth of the appropriate supporting cells. It seems reasonable to suppose, therefore, that differences in the properties of glial cells might be important in establishing different rates of myelination, particularly in different parts of the nervous system. It might be debated whether this kind of mechanism could give rise to the differences observed in the present study, but at least we do seem to have here an adequate explanation of the fact that in a single neurone there may be two axonal branches originating from a common stalk that undergo myelination at different times, as occurs, for example, in rat cortical neurones that give rise to both projection fibres and callosal fibres (Jacobson, 1963). In this case, postulating that there are differences in the properties of glial cells in different regions of the brain seems a more satisfactory alternative than assuming that multiple axons arising from the same nerve cell are fundamentally different from one another.

3. Functional Activity of Neurones

The idea that myelin formation might be related to neuronal activity is one that earlier workers have examined repeatedly, attempting to find some justification for it by correlating the appearance of myelin in a given fibre tract with the appearance of behavioural signs of its function (Flechsig, 1876; Westphal, 1897; Tilney and Casamajor, 1924; Langworthy, 1932; Windle *et al.*, 1934). Some of these workers concluded, and this conclusion has been substantiated in the present study, that nerve fibres may be capable of conducting impulses before they become myelinated, but this is not really relevant to the problem of whether their subsequent myelination is brought about, or even just accelerated to some extent, as a consequence of their activity.

The most convincing demonstration till now of the importance of functional neuronal activity for myelin development is the recent work by Gyllensten and Malmfors (1963) showing that myelination of optic nerve fibres is defective in animals reared in darkness from birth. The results of this study suggest that myelination in these fibres is retarded, but not completely abolished, as a consequence of their inactivity. This might conceivably also describe what happens to those callosal fibres that have been found in the present study to undergo myelination only belatedly. The implication would be that these fibres, which are involved in the negative phase of the evoked response, are less frequently active than those involved in the postive phase, at least in the immature brain. Since the physiological roles of these two fibre groups are still obscure, there is no basis even for speculation about whether such a difference in functional activity might exist.

4. *Idiosyncrasies of Cortical Neurones*

A final possibility that must be considered is that the observed differences in neuronal susceptibility to myelination are the consequence of inherent differences in the individual neurones. Examples abound of phenomena in the embryonic development of nerve cells that can, at present, be explained only by assuming that specific differences among nerve cells exist (Weiss, 1955; Hamburger, 1962), and there is even some evidence that such differences may manifest themselves during myelination in that one nerve fibre may be more receptive than another for the attachment of glial cells (Speidel, 1932). One may still ask why, if such specific differences existed among callosal neurones, they were not also evident in other aspects of the development of these cells prior to myelination. It is possible, of course, that a sufficiently penetrating examination would have revealed them. Alternatively, it is possible that the differences that determine myelination behaviour are latent ones, achieving expression only when an external stimulus for the initiation of myelination is received by the neurones. Such a stimulus might arise from the operation of any of the other factors discussed above.

Summary

Myelination of the corpus callosum in the cat takes place entirely in the postnatal period. Histological examination of the callosal fibres and electrophysiological investigation of the transcallosal evoked response in cats of various ages have been used to determine some of the features of the myelination process.

In the suprasylvian gyrus of the young animals, the positive-negative focal response that was evoked by callosal activity was similar in configuration to that seen in the adult, although it was smaller in amplitude and had a longer latency and a longer duration. The latency of the response was found to decrease continuously from the time of birth onward, but showed a large, abrupt decrease at the end of the fourth postnatal week, caused by the appearance of a new, short-latency component in the positive phase of the response. Concomitantly, there occurred a 7-fold increase in the maximum conduction velocity of the callosal fibres. These changes coincided with a marked increase in the amount of histologically demonstrable myelin in the corpus callosum, which leads to the conclusion that the changes in the evoked response resulted from the onset of myelination in some of the callosal fibres, i.e., those giving rise to the positive phase of the response. Since there was no increase in the maximum amplitude of the positive phase of the response at the same time, it appeared that these fibres had previously established functional connections with the cortical neurones, and that they had been capable of conducting impulses before they became myelinated. The rapidity with which myelin formation progressed suggested that alignment of glial cells along the fibres had taken place before myelination had begun.

Inhomogeneities in the callosal fibre population with respect to myelination were apparent from the fact that the earliest fibres to become myelinated were those that originated in cells in cortical layer V. An even more striking difference among the fibres was inferred from the fact that none of the observed changes in the evoked response affected the negative phase, which indicates that the fibres involved in this phase of the response did not participate at all in the wave of myelination that began at the end of the fourth postnatal week. There was no evidence, however, that prior to the beginning of myelination these fibres were different in their diameter or rate of maturation from those involved in the positive phase of the response.

The reason why different groups of callosal fibres should vary in their susceptibility to myelination remains obscure. Among the factors that may determine some of the characteristics features of the myelination process are: (1) regional differences in the development of the cortex, (2) glial cell characteristics, (3) functional activity of the cortical neurones, and (4) idiosyncratic properties of individual neurones.

REFERENCES

ÄNGGARD, L. and OTTOSON, D. Observations on the functional development of the neuromuscular apparatus in fetal sheep. *Exp. Neurol.*, 1963, 7:294–304.

BURNS, B. D. Some properties of isolated cerebral cortex in the unanaesthetized cat. *J. Physiol. (Lond.)*, 1951, 112:156–175.

CHANG, H.-T. Cortical response to activity of callosal neurones. *J. Neurophysiol.*, 1953, 16:117–131.

CONEL, J. L. Histologic development of the cerebral cortex. In *The Biology of Mental Health and Disease*, Hoeber, New York, 1952, pp. 1–8.

CURTIS, H. J. Intercortical connections of corpus callosum as indicated by evoked potentials. *J. Neurophysiol.*, 1940, 3:407–413.

DUNCAN, D. A relation between axon diameter and myelination determined by measurement of myelinated spinal root fibers. *J. Comp. Neurol.*, 1934, 60: 437–471.

FLECHSIG, P. *Die Leitungsbahnen im Gehirn und Rückenmark des Menschen auf Grund entwicklungsgeschichtlichen Untersuchungen.* W. Engelmann, Leipzig, *1876* (quoted in LANGWORTHY, *1932*).

GASSER, H. S. Unmedullated fibers originating in dorsal root ganglia. *J. Gen. Physiol.,* *1950,* 33:651–690.

GEREN, B. B. The formation from the Schwann cell surface of myelin in the peripheral nerves of chick embryos. *Exp. Cell. Res.,* *1954,* 7:558–562.

GRAFSTEIN, B. Organization of callosal connections in suprasylvian gyrus of cat. *J. Neurophysiol.,* *1959,* 22:504–515.

GRAFSTEIN, B. Postnatal development of the transcallosal evoked response in the cerebral cortex of the cat. *J. Neurophysiol.,* *1963,* 26:79–99.

GROSSMAN, C. Electro-ontogenesis of cerebral activity. *Arch. Neurol. Psychiat. (Chic.),* *1955,* 74:186–202.

GYLLENSTEN, L. and MALMFORS, T. Myelinization of the optic nerve and its dependence on visual function—a quantitative investigation in mice. *J. Embryol. Exp. Morph.,* *1963,* 11:255–266.

HAMBURGER, V. Specificity in neurogenesis. *J. Cell Comp. Physiol.,* *1962, Suppl. 1,* 60:81–92.

HESS, A. Post-natal development and maturation of the nerve fibers of the central nervous system. *J. Comp. Neurol.,* *1954,* 100:461–480.

HESS, A. and YOUNG, J. Z. The nodes of Ranvier. *Proc. Roy. Soc. B,* *1952,* 140:301–320.

HODES, R. Linear relationship between fiber diameter and velocity of conduction in giant axon of squid. *J. Neurophysiol.,* *1953,* 16:145–154.

HOUSEPIAN, E. M., NOBACK, C. R. and PURPURA, D. P. Ontogenetic changes in evoked activity in pyramidal and "extrapyramidal" pathways (cat). *Fed. Proc.,* *1961,* 20:325.

JACOBSON, S. Sequence of myelinization in the brain of the albino rat. A. Cerebral cortex, thalamus and related structures. *J. Comp. Neurol.,* *1963,* 121:5–29.

LANGWORTHY, O. R. Development of behaviour patterns and myelinization of tracts in the nervous system. *Arch. Neurol. Psychiat. (Chic.),* *1932,* 28:1365–1382.

LASSEK, A. M. The pyramidal tract; basic considerations of corticospinal neurons. *A. Res. Nerv. Ment. Dis. Proc.,* *1948,* 27:106–128.

LUSE, S. A. Formation of myelin in the central nervous system of mice and rats, as studied with the electron microscope. *J. Biophys. Biochem. Cytol.,* *1956,* 2:777–784.

MATURANA, H. R. The fine anatomy of the optic nerve of anurans—an electron microscope study. *J. Biophys. Biochem. Cytol.,* *1960,* 7:107–120.

METUZALS, J. Ultrastructure of myelinated nerve fibres in the central nervous system of the frog. *J. Ultrastruct. Res.,* *1963,* 8:30–47.

NAUTA, W. J. H. and BUCHER, V. M. Efferent connections of the striate cortex in the albino rat. *J. Comp. Neurol.,* *1954,* 100:257–285.

PETERS, A. The structure of myelin sheaths in the central nervous system of Xenopus laevis (Daudin). *J. Biophys. Biochem. Cytol.,* *1960,* 7:121–126.

POLJAK, S. An experimental study of the association, callosal and projection fibers of the cerebral cortex of the cat. *J. Comp. Neurol.,* *1927,* 44:197–258.

DEROBERTIS, E., GERSCHENFELD, H. M. and WALD, F. Cellular mechanism of myelination in the central nervous system. *J. Biophys. Biochem. Cytol.,* *1958,* 4:651–656.

ROSS, L. L., BORNSTEIN, M. B. and LEHRER, G. M. Electron microscopic observations of rat and mouse cerebellum in tissue culture. *J. Cell. Biol.,* *1962,* 14:19–30.

SATTLER, C. H. Ueber die Markscheidenentwicklung in Tractus opticus, Chiasma und Nervus opticus. *Albrecht v. Graefes Arch. f. Ophthal. (Leipz.),* *1915,* 90:271–298 (cited in GYLLENSTEN and MALMFORS, *1963*).

SHULTZ, R. L., MAYNARD, E. M. and PEASE, W. C. Electron microscopy of neurons and neuroglia of cerebral cortex and corpus callosum. *Amer. J. Anat.,* *1957,* 100:369–388.

SPEIDEL, C. C. Studies of living nerves; movements of individual sheath cells and nerve sprouts correlated with the process of myelin sheath formation in amphibian larvae. *J. Exp. Zool.,* *1932,* 61:279–331.

SPEIDEL, C. C. Studies of living nerves. II. Activities of amoeboid growth cones, sheath cells and myelin segments as revealed by prolonged observation of individual nerve fibres in frog tadpoles. *Amer. J. Anat.*, *1933*, 52:1–79.

Tilney, F. and Casamajor, L. Myelinogeny as applied to the study of behaviour. *Arch. Neurol. Psychiat. (Chic.)*, *1924*, 12:1–66.

Tomasch, J. Size, distribution, and number of fibres in the human corpus callosum. *Anat. Rec.*, *1954*, 119:119–135.

Ulett, G., Dow, R. S. and Larsell, O. The inception of conductivity in the corpus callosum and the cortico- ponto-cerebellar pathway of young rabbits with reference to myelinization. *J. Comp. Neurol.*, *1944*, 80:1–10.

Vogt, C. *Étude sur la myélinisation des hémisphères cérébraux*. Steinheil, Paris, *1900*, 72 pp.

Watson, J. B. Animal education—an experimental study on the physical development of the white rat, correlated with the growth of its nervous system. *Contrib. Phil.*, *1903*, 4:5–122.

Weiss, P. Nervous system (neurogenesis). *In:* B. H. Willier, P. A. Weiss and V. Hamburger (Editors), *Analysis of Development*. Saunders Co., Philadelphia and London, *1955*, pp. 346–401.

Westphal, A. Ueber die Markscheidenbildung der Gehirnnerven des Menschen. *Arch. Psychiat. (Berlin)*, *1897*, 29:474–527.

Windle, W. F., Fish, M. W. and O'Donnell, J. E. Myelogeny of the cat as related to development of fiber tracts and prenatal behaviour patterns. *J. Comp. Neurol.*, *1934*, 59:139–157.

DISCUSSION

DR. PAMPIGLIONE: I wonder if you have any data on topographical differences in the evolution of the recorded responses; for example, do you have similar steps and similar evolutions at about the same time in the parasagittal regions as the sylvian regions, or are there regional differences?

DR. GRAFSTEIN: I made a detailed comparison of the development of the transcallosal response in the suprasylvian gyrus and in the ectosylvian gyrus at the same anteroposterior level, and found that before the response from the suprasylvian gyrus had changed, there was already an early component due to myelinated fiber activity detectable in the response from the ectosylvian gyrus, indicating that the callosal neurons in the latter region were more precocious in their acquisition of myelin. This leads me to believe that there are indeed significant topographical differences, and I think that myelination of the callosal fibers is only one of the features of neuronal development for which such differences exist, as I have indicated in my paper. I do not, however, know what the basis for these topographical differences may be.

DR. SCHADÉ: I might add to this that in human material you find that the earliest myelination is in the middle portion close to the precentral and postcentral gyrus, then occipital, and later on the frontal. This is always concomitant with the development of basilar dendritic plexus and the further maturation of the whole neuropil of the particular area. Do you, Dr. Grafstein, consider all of your responses a result of callosal fiber activity or do you see them in the split brain animal?

DR. GRAFSTEIN: I don't see any of these responses at all. I think certainly as far as the focal response is concerned that's undoubtedly callosal. However, there's one point I'm not sure about and that is the question of whether the callosal fibers really go directly from one side to the other or whether they synapse somewhere along the way. They don't synapse in the callosum, we know, but it's just conceivable that they have a synapse somewhere along their pathway. I don't think that this would influence our measurements of conduction velocity though because these were always taken by comparing the two points simulated within the corpus callosum itself so we were measuring the conduction velocity of callosal fibers.

MATURATION OF EVOKED CORTICAL RESPONSES IN ANIMAL AND MAN*

S. GOLDRING, E. SUGAYA AND J. L. O'LEARY

*Divisions of Neurosurgery and Neurology and the
Beaumont-May Institute of Neurology,
Washington University School of Medicine, St. Louis, Mo.*

In 1951, Hunt and Goldring provided a detailed description of the evoked visual response in the postnatal rabbit. Changes in the response which developed with increasing age were described and are briefly summarized here.

At birth, an electrical stimulus applied to the optic nerve produces either a single or double surface-negative wave. A low voltage surface-positive deflection may follow either the single or double humped negativity. Not until the eleventh day does a surface-positive component come to initiate the response. Thereafter, the negative phase diminishes in size, the initial positive deflection increasing in amplitude until the adult form is achieved at 21 to 28 days (Fig. 1). Additional features of the immature response are its long latency and duration, and marked fatigability during repetitive stimulation. The response to a light stimulus is essentially the same with the exception that it cannot be evoked until the seventh postnatal day.

Similar findings have been reported for primary sensory responses in the newborn kitten by Scherrer and Oeconomos (1954), Grossman (1955), Ellingson and Wilcott (1960) and Purpura (1961b). The auditory postnatal response has somewhat different features. Rose et al. (1957) observed that a very small positive deflection precedes the negative wave in the newborn kitten. With maturation, the positive wave increases in size at the expense of the negative one.

More recently, the direct cortical response (DCR) has been studied in the newborn rabbit by DoCarmo (1960) and in the kitten by Purpura (1960). In both studies, the postnatal response had a long duration but otherwise was not too dissimilar from responses recorded in mature cortex. Purpura (1960) also described a short-duration response of negative polarity, which lasts no longer than 20 msec. Such a response could only be recorded with a small (.1 mm. tip) electrode placed immediately adjacent to the stimulus site. He concluded that the long-duration potential recorded with the large electrode was due to a temporal summation of 20 msec. postsynaptic potentials, of which the response recorded with the small electrode was the prototype.

Another important feature of the postnatal DCR is observed during repeti-

*Aided by grants from the U. S. Public Health Service (NB-04513-1) and the Allen P. and Josephine B. Green Foundation.

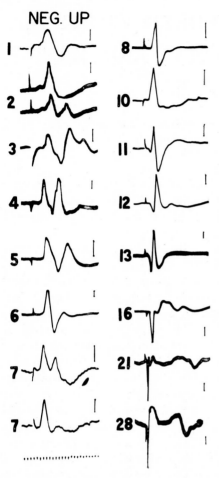

NEG. UP

Fig. 1. Responses of the visual cortex to electrical stimulation of contralateral optic nerve. Numbers indicate age in days. Note two examples each of the responses at 2 and 6 days. The rapid downward (positive) deflections at 16, 21 and 28 days correspond to the less prominent initial positive components seen from 11 to 13 days. To facilitate comparison, all records illustrated have been recorded on the same time line (see 60 c/sec. below 7). Vertical lines at right of figures represent 100 μV for 1 and 2 days, 200 μV from 3 through the first 7-day illustration, and 500 μV thereafter. The shock artifacts and the 21- and 28-day responses have been slightly retouched (from Hunt and Goldring, 1951).

tive stimulation. A 20/sec. stimulus delivered for one second does not produce a summation of slow negativity corresponding to that seen in the adult. In the latter, slow negativity summates to produce a negative steady potential shift which *builds up* during the stimulus period and subsides slowly after the stimulus is terminated. By contrast, in the postnatal animal a repetitive stimulus produces an immediate rise in potential amplitude followed by a *decay* rather than growth of potential. DoCarmo (1960) has observed this in the rabbit and we (Goldring et al., 1961) have made similar observations in the human infant (Fig. 2).

DoCarmo (1960) also studied recruiting responses. At birth, a repetitive stimulus to the midline thalamus yields a large response (negative polarity) to the first stimulus with rapid fall-off in response amplitude with successive shocks. The progressive amplitude augmentation which is characteristic of the adult recruiting response does not occur.

In recent years, we have carried out detailed studies of evoked cortical potentials in patients undergoing neurosurgical procedures. Concurrently, related phenomena have been examined in the laboratory animal. During the

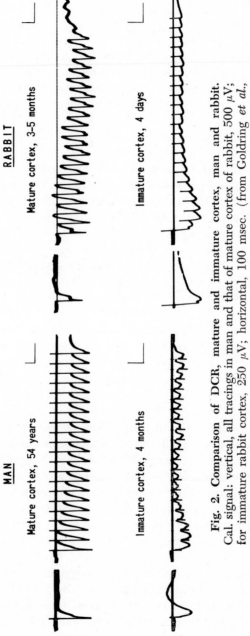

Fig. 2. Comparison of DCR, mature and immature cortex, man and rabbit. Cal. signal: vertical, all tracings in man and that of mature cortex of rabbit, 500 µV; for immature rabbit cortex, 250 µV; horizontal, 100 msec. (from Goldring *et al.*, 1961).

course of these studies, we examined responses in infants as well as adults and the results derived therefrom are relevant to the discussion of cortical onto-genesis. The cortical potentials were evoked by stimulation of the immediate subcortical white matter and responses from the cat were compared to those of man.

Method

The cortex of lateral and of suprasylvian gyri in the cat were studied. In man, those cortical areas made accessible during the surgical procedure were examined. The subjects were those undergoing craniotomy for evacuation of a subdural hematoma or hydrocephalus. Light Nembutal anesthesia was used in the animals; a combination of N_2O, Flaxedil and Pentothal in man.

Stimulating electrodes were tripolar, each pole being insulated to near its tip which was ground to a fine point. The wires were arranged in the form of a triangle, points being equidistant and separated from each other by a distance of 1 mm. in the cat and 2 mm. in man. Electrode tips were placed in the subcortical white matter just beneath the cortical mantle. Recording electrodes made contact with the cortical surface either through a saline-soaked cotton wick or silver ball. The critical electrode was placed on cortical surface in the center of the area delimited by the three poles of the stimu-lating electrode; the reference electrode was situated on the bone. For fur-ther details of recording, see Goldring et al. (1960).

Results

In postnatal kitten, the response of primary visual cortex to subcortical white matter stimulation is a diphasic one showing initial positivity. Thus it differs from primary sensory responses evoked by stimulation of a peripheral receptor, nerve or thalamus. In those situations, as mentioned earlier, a nega-tive wave initiates the response. Purpura (1961b) has reported similar find-ings. The postnatal response to white matter stimulation has a longer dura-tion than the one elicited from mature cortex. In addition, it does not show the positive spikes which are superimposed upon the initial positivity of the mature response (Fig. 3). The newborn response from suprasylvian gyrus also shows an initial positivity, without superimposed positive spikes. Since such brief deflections are absent in the mature syprasylvian response, the latter differs from the postnatal form only in duration.

Human cortical responses of the very young infant differ from those of the kitten in that many cortical areas yield responses which lack initial positivity. Responses in young infants, which do show initial positivity and are presumed to come from somatosensory cortex, do not exhibit positive spikes. In this respect, they are similar to the potentials recorded in the cat (Fig. 4). In older infants, such positive spikes appear upon the initial positive deflection (Fig. 5). In Fig. 5, which is from a 12-month-old infant, the response labeled "1" shows positive spikes superimposed on the initial positivity and is ob-tained from an area presumed to be somatosensory. The response labeled "2," derived from an area anterior to the one yielding the response just described,

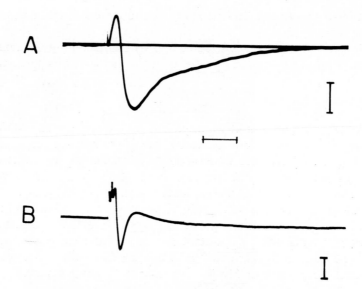

Fig. 3. Cortical response to white matter stimulation in cat. A: 2-day-old kitten. B: Adult cat. Vertical cal. = 500 μV; horizontal cal. = 20 msec. Pos. is up.

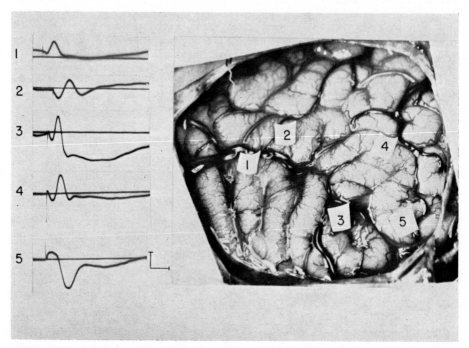

Fig. 4. Cortical responses to subcortical white matter stimulation in man (4-month-old female infant). Records obtained following evacuation of a subdural hematoma. Numbers to left of responses correspond to those on the brain and indicate areas from which responses were obtained. Photograph is of the right hemisphere. Temporal area is at the top; anterior is to the left. Vertical line of cal. = 500 μV; horizontal line = 20 msec. Pos. is up.

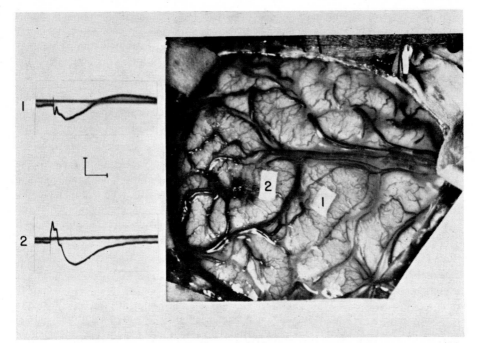

Fig. 5. **Cortical response to subcortical white matter stimulation in man (12-month-old male infant). Records obtained following evacuation of a subdural hematoma.** Numbers to left of responses correspond to those on the brain and indicate areas from which responses were obtained. Photograph is of the left hemisphere. Vessels coursing horizontally are the sylvian group and anterior is to the right. Area labeled 1 is presumed to be motor cortex; 2, somatosensory. Vertical line of cal. = 500 μV; horizontal line = 20 msec. Pos. is up.

has no initial positivity. It shows a short duration negative deflection followed by a slower one of the same polarity. In all likelihood this represents a still immature form since potentials from comparable areas in both animal and man are initiated by a positive deflection. Such an explanation would imply a differential maturation of cortical areas, since the response from area 1 already exhibits an adult configuration. Grossman's studies (1955) support such an interpretation. He showed that the primary somatosensory response appears before the acoustic or visual responses in the postnatal kitten.

Comment

The studies of Bishop (1959) and Clare and Bishop (1956) provide a basis for discussion of our results. Their evidence indicates that the positive spikes of responses from primary sensory cortex are postsynaptic discharges activated from axosomatic synapses. They believe that axosomatic synapses are the terminals of large thalamocortical fibers, while axons making connections with dendritic shafts are principally small, unmyelinated ones. Drawing from their own observations as well as those of Herrick, they have suggested that the large thalamocortical fibers are a late phylogenetic development. Delayed appearance of the spikes in the postnatal responses which we describe suggests a late ontogenetic development of these large fibers as well. Graf-stein (1963) has presented similar evidence for differential maturation of callosal fibers. In the newborn kitten, the cortical response to callosal stimulation consists of a slow positivity followed by a negative wave. Between 27 and 29 days an early positive deflection appears. Appearance of the positive deflection is attributed to the maturation of a fast conducting fiber system. Of special interest is that a large increase of myelin occurs when the early positive deflection first becomes noticeable. Purpura's studies (1960, 1961a, 1961b) have special relevance to the discussion just elaborated. He and his co-workers have presented abundant morphophysiological evidence for early maturation of axodendritic connections. It is not surprising, then, that surface negative responses characterize many evoked potentials of the newborn. In DCR and recruiting responses, the adult forms show a predominantly negative polarity and, since these potentials are attributed to axodentritic excitation, similar forms are present in the early perinatal period. By contrast, the initial positivity of the adult primary response is axosomatic in origin and delayed maturation of axosomatic connections could account for appearance of only the negative phase in the newborn response. Implicit in such an interpretation is that the negativity recorded in the newborn arises from axodendritic excitation. If such is the case, then the negative phase of the adult response may be similarly explained, and the possibility of two projections to primary sensory cortex must be considered—one to cell bodies in the cortical depth, the other to the superficial dendritic arborization. Such a view, which is similar to one entertained by von Euler and Ricci (1958), does not exclude the possibility that other excitations also contribute to the negative phase of primary sensory responses. Either antidromic conduction upwards along apical dendrites or dendritic depolarization resulting from excitation transmitted by recurrent axon collaterals is usually invoked to explain the negative phase (Bremer, 1958). In both schemes, the corticopetal fibers which derive from thalamic relay nuclei are viewed as projecting only to the cell body, dendrites being depolarized secondarily to the soma excitation.

REFERENCES

BISHOP, G. H. The place of cortex in a reticular system. In: *Reticular Formation of the Brain.* Little, Brown Co., Boston, 1958, pp. 413–421.

BREMER, F. Cerebral and cerebellar potentials. *Physiol. Rev.,* 1958, 38:357–388.

CLARE, M. H. and BISHOP, G. H. Potential wave mechanisms in cat cortex. *Electroenceph. clin. Neurophysiol.,* 1956, 8:583–602.

DoCARMO, R. J. Direct cortical and recruiting responses in postnatal rabbit. *J. Neurophysiol.,* 1960, 23:496–504.

ELLINGSON, R. J. and WILCOTT, R. C. Development of evoked responses in visual and auditory cortices of kittens. *J. Neurophysiol.,* 1960, 23:363–375.

VON EULER, C. and RICCI, F. G. Cortical evoked responses in auditory area and significance of apical dendrites. *J. Neurophysiol.,* 1958, 21:231–246.

GOLDRING, S., JERVA, M. J., HOLMES, T. G., O'LEARY, J. L. and SHIELDS, J. R. Direct response of human cerebral cortex. *Arch. Neurol. (Chicago),* 1961, 4:590–598.

GRAFSTEIN, B. Postnatal development of the transcallosal evoked response in the cerebral cortex of the cat. *J. Neurophysiol.,* 1963, 26:79–99.

GROSSMAN, C. Electro-ontogenesis of cerebral activity. *Arch. Neurol. Psychiat. (Chic.)*, 1955, 74:186–202.

HUNT, W. E. and GOLDRING, S. Maturation of evoked response of the visual cortex in the postnatal rabbit. *Electroenceph. clin. Neurophysiol.*, 1951, 3:465–471.

PURPURA, D. P. Ontogenetic analysis of some evoked synaptic activities in superficial neocortical neuropil. *Proc. Intern. Symposium on Nervous Inhibition,* 1961a.

PURPURA, D. P. Analysis of axodendritic synaptic organizations in immature cerebral cortex. *Ann. N. Y. Acad. Sci.,* 1961, b, 94:604–654

PURPURA, D. P., CARMICHAEL, M. W. and HOUSEPIAN, E. M. Physiological and anatomical studies of development of superficial axodendritic synaptic pathways in neocortex. *Exp. Neurol., 1960,* 2:324–347.

ROSE, J. E., ADRIAN, H. and SANTIBANEZ, G. Electrical signs of maturation in the auditory system of the kitten. *Acta. Neurol. Latinoamer.*, 1957, 3:133–143.

SCHERRER, J. and OECONOMOS, D. Réponses corticales somesthésiques du mammifère nouveau-né comparées a celles de l'animal adulte. *Et. Neonat. 1954*, 3:199–216.

DISCUSSION

DR. KELLAWAY: Do you think that in nitrous oxide anesthesia there is any cerebral hypoxia?

DR. GOLDRING: No. Several years ago we studied the direct cortical response under different types of anesthesia as well as during anoxia. As you are probably aware, one can evoke all components of the responses that I have just described—the positive spikes, the negative wave, and the aftermaths that follow the earlier components—by surface stimulation. In the study mentioned above we had the opportunity of recording the direct cortical response in man under local anesthesia. The response recorded under that condition and the one elicited under nitrous oxide, oxygen, neuromuscular paralysis and artificial ventilation are identical. If anesthesia is administered so as to produce anoxia, response changes reflect the anoxic influence.

DR. PURPURA: I want to see if I understand you correctly about the origin of the spikes themselves. You are referring to those spikes on the positive waves or postsynaptic discharges of cells and the failure to see these in a young animal suggests that the weakness of the drive on the cells generates p. s. p.'s which don't fire the cells. They are not strong enough or they don't reach firing level for any significant number of cells to produce an externally recorded synchronous discharge.

DR. GOLDRING: Yes. Now, of course, the thing that we don't know is whether it is the presynaptic fibers that are slow in developing, or is the postsynaptic membrane less capable of discharging such activity.

DR. PURPURA: We will have to get into the cells to find out though.

DR. SCHADÉ: I am still puzzled about the contribution of axosomatic synapses of pyramidal cells and the whole synaptic field of the stellate cells. In our thinking regarding the contribution of various dendritic systems to the direct or superficial cortical responses we should not disregard the stellate cells, because they make out in some areas 25 per cent of the total cell population and they show a very specific pattern of development. Let us assume, for the time being, that the whole receptive surface of a neuron (cell body and dendrites) is equally occupied by synapses. Then the number of axosomatic synapses is very small as compared to the number of axodendritic synapses, since the contribution of the cell body to the receptive surface is less than 5 per cent.

In our rabbits, treated with methionine sulfoximine, a considerable retardation is seen in the development of the dendritic plexus. Various components of the superficial cortical response are delayed in their development. The initial positivity comes about 2–3 days later and the long duration of the negative component persists for 4–5 days.

As far as we could see there was no specific change in the axosomatic synaptic field.

DR. GOLDRING: Could you elaborate on the changes that appear in your potentials?

DR. SCHADÉ: Let me put it this way: in normal animals we find that from day zero to about eighteen days after birth we see a mature superficial cortical response developing, and the positivity starts to develop at about the fourth or fifth day and then the duration of the negativity shortens very considerably.

DR. GOLDRING: What kind of stimulation?

DR. SCHADÉ: Surface cortex stimulation.

DR. GOLDRING: A strong surface stimulus does not produce any initial positivity in the first few days in life, and, then, several days later, initial positivity appears?

DR. SCHADÉ: Yes. The appearance of this initial positivity is delayed in animals treated with methionine sulfoximine at birth.

DR. GOLDRING: Are there positive spikes superimposed upon the initial positivity?

DR. SCHADÉ: We did not look specifically for positive spikes but, in some instances, we did see them.

DR. PURPURA: Dr. Schadé, how are you measuring the synaptic field? What criteria do you use?

DR. SCHADÉ: About four or five months ago we started using the Rasmussen stain which would work very well in neonatal and other brains.

DR. KELLAWAY: To make a digression for just a moment, in the animals treated with methionine sulfoximine, and which showed this delayed development of cortical elements, is the dose used sufficient to produce seizures, and, if, so, do the seizures differ from those normally seen in more mature animals?

DR. SCHADÉ: No. The point is, a single dose of methionine sulfoximine at birth, never produces seizures in the cerebral cortex of rabbits. The immature cortex is still unable to respond with sustained spike activity.

DR. KELLAWAY: So it takes more methionine sulfoximine to produce seizures?

DR. SCHADÉ: Well, in the neocortex it's difficult to produce seizures at all.

DR. WINDLE: Do these rabbits grow up to be "mentally retarded"?

DR. SCHADÉ: They show a considerable deviation from the normal behavior patterns.

DR. GOLDRING: I think that species differences might be important. We studied methionine sulfoximine from a different point of view. We gave it to adult rabbits and studied the electrical events that followed. Following administration of this agent there is a latency of three-quarters to one and one-half hours before electrical alterations appear. Prior to the appearance of any paroxysmal activity a series of large DC changes occur. They are similar in time course and amplitude to the negative voltage change that one sees in spreading depression. There may be two or three such shifts preceding the development of paroxysmal activity. We were unable to reproduce such DC changes in the cat and dog. Of course, if the slow shifts are akin to the ones of spreading depression the observations would be compatible with the fact that the rabbit is the easiest animal in which to produce spreading depression.

DR. PURPURA: But all animals develop seizures.

DR. GOLDRING: Yes.

DR. KELLAWAY: Dr. Proler has done some work in which he has shown that removal of the entire cortex in the methionine sulfoximine treated animals does not produce any change in the seizures except to reduce or abolish the clonic phase of the attack. The decorticate cat shows all the peculiar behavioral manifestations which have been attributed by Gastaut to seizure activity in pararhinal structures.

DR. PURPURA: Is this in the adult cat?

DR. KELLAWAY: Yes.

CEREBRAL ELECTRICAL RESPONSES TO AUDITORY AND VISUAL STIMULI IN THE INFANT (HUMAN AND SUBHUMAN STUDIES)*

ROBERT J. ELLINGSON

Nebraska Psychiatric Institute, University of Nebraska College of Medicine, Omaha, Neb.

Cerebral electrical responses to sensory stimulation can be divided into two broad categories: (1) non-specific responses, or those which tend to occur regardless of the sensory modality stimulated, and (2) specific responses, or those which tend to occur to stimulation in only one modality.

The aspect of the brain electrical response to stimulation which is usually observed and recorded is the change in electrical potential occurring between pairs of points in or over the brain or between points in or over the brain and a more distant point somewhere on the body. Over the years such responses have been used by brain research scientists for various purposes, such as plotting the topography of sensory projection systems in man and animals, judging the intactness of sensory input systems, studying the influence of the reticular formation on the forebrain, and so forth. A relatively recent application has been in the investigation of the physiological development of the nervous system. It is with this application that we will be concerned.

An extensive discussion of methods of recording and analyzing brain electrical responses is not necessary. The techniques of standard electroencephalography, which are used in observing non-specific brain electrical responses, are well-known as are neurophysiological techniques for recording responses directly from the surface or the depths of the brain in animals. Recording specific evoked responses in humans presents some special problems, associated with the inaccessability of much of the brain when electrodes can only be placed on the surface of the scalp, and the consequent low voltage of evoked responses thus detected relative to the voltage of masking background activity. Methods for dealing with these problems will therefore be discussed in some detail in the appropriate places.

Non-Specific Responses

Intense stimulation in any modality may elicit one or more of the following non-specific responses: (1) generalized flattening of background brain

*The original work reported in this paper, and its preparation, were supported by Public Health Service grants NB-01558 and MH-05075 from the National Institute of Neurological Diseases and Blindness and the National Institute of Mental Health, respectively.

wave activity (Fig. 1 and 2A and B), (2) diffuse bursts of polymorphic slow waves (Fig. 1B), and (3) transient negative waves at the vertex (Fig. 2B and C).

These phenomena are most easily elicted by sharp auditory stimuli such as hand claps or loud clicks. About 50 per cent of babies so stimulated will exhibit flattening responses on one or more stimuli. These responses would seem to be classical arousal or activation responses, and are often associated with behavioral signs of arousal. The flattening response is also readily elicited by external or internal somesthetic stimulation, and tends to be most pronounced when preceded by a body movement (Fig. 1C and D). Visual stimuli are less effective in eliciting these responses than are auditory or somesthetic stimuli.

A negative wave at the vertex can be elicited by loud auditory clicks in ¼ of full term newborns in the early neonatal period. The latency of this response to the beginning of the negative vertex wave is about 110 msec, agreeing with latencies reported for adult subjects. This response together with the diffuse polymorphic slow wave response is probably identifiable with the K complex of Davis et al, (1939), subsequently studied by other workers.

Since systematic studies of the development of non-specific responses have not been conducted, and since time is limited, I will devote the remainder of this paper to a discussion of the development of specific responses evoked in the brain by visual and auditory stimulation in the human and subhuman infant. I will not discuss studies involving direct electrical stimulation of nervous tissue, except where such results may be immediately pertinent to interpretation of the effects of sensory stimulation. Dr. Goldring will discuss such studies in more detail.

Reports dealing with the development of evoked responses in infants are widely scattered through the domestic and foreign literature. I will therefore attempt to summarize the published studies of which I am aware, dealing first with subhuman species and then with man.[*]

Visual Evoked Responses

CAT

Time of first appearance. At birth, cortical evoked responses cannot be detected in the cat following illumination of the eyes by bright flashes of light. Marty (1962) reported that a long-latency negative response, which he designated as "component A," can be recorded from the 2nd postnatal day and a shorter-latency response, which he designated "Component B," from the 5th postnatal day. Both components can be seen from birth upon direct electrical stimulation of the optic nerve. Ellingson and Wilcott (1960) failed to record responses in 2 of 10 kittens at ages 7 and 8 days.

---

[*]Many writers fail to present all of their data quantitatively. The reader should be warned that some of the latencies and amplitudes of responses which I will report are estimates based upon examination of the limited numbers of responses to be found illustrating the original papers, and are therefore only approximate values.

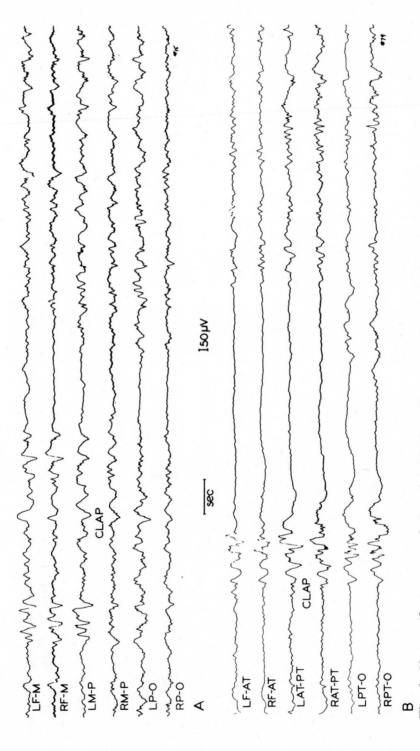

Fig. 1. Non-specific responses during sleep in immediate stimulus. B. Diffuse polymorphic burst and then flattening postnatal EEGs in man. A. Flattening following an auditory following auditory stimulus.

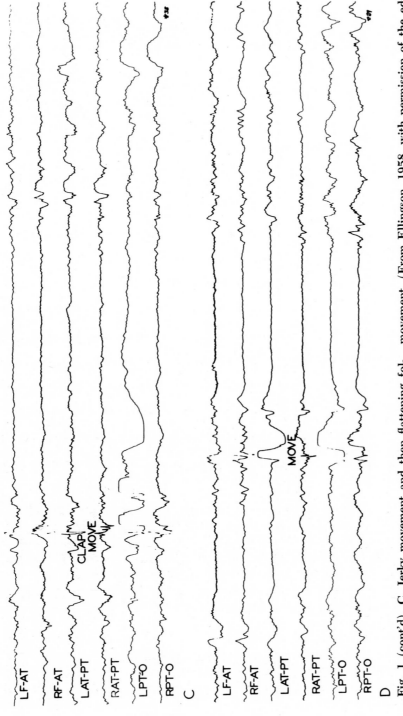

Fig. 1 (cont'd). C. Jerky movement and then flattening following auditory stimulus. D. Flattening following spontaneous movement. (From Ellingson, 1958, with permission of the editors and publishers of *Electroenceph. clin. Neurophysiol.*)

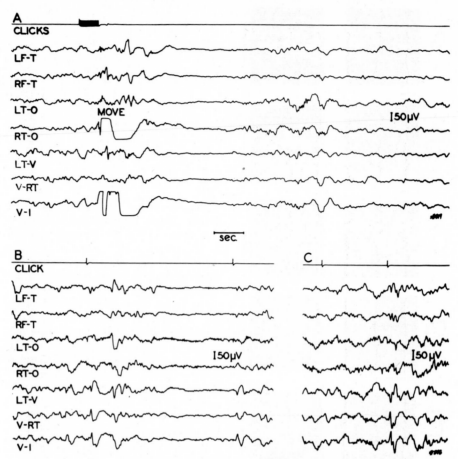

Fig. 2. Responses to auditory stimuli in immediate post-natal EEGs in man. A. Flattening responses to a "burst" of clicks. B. Vertex negative and flattening responses to single clicks. Note phase reversals on the vertex lead (V). C. Vertex negative response to single clicks.

Waveform. The earliest responses observed by Ellingson and Wilcott were usually initially negative, monophasic or biphasic waves (Figure 3), but a few responses showed a small initially positive phase. A second, delayed, negative response was seen in a number of instances. Marty's "Components A and B" were likewise initially surface-negative (Figures 4A and B) at their first appearance. Marty's "Component A" is smaller than the negative phase of "Component B" and tends to become elided with it as the evoked response comes to maturity.

At 2 weeks of age in both Ellingson and Wilcott's series, and Marty's series, most kittens were showing an initial positive phase. Both positive and negative phases of the response increase in amplitude with increasing age, but the rate of increase for the positive phase is greater than that for the negative. When the adult wave form is attained at about 5 weeks of age, the positive phase is usually of greater amplitude than the negative.

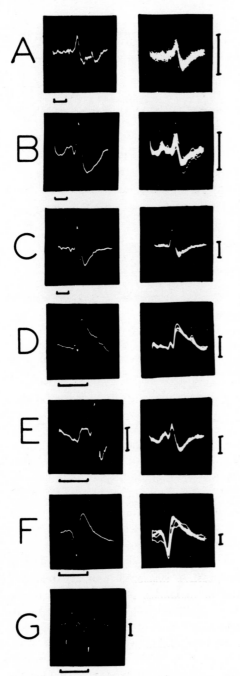

Fig. 3. Visual evoked responses in kittens. Single responses on left, superimpositions of 5 or 20 responses on right. A: 8-days old. B: 8-days old. C: 15-days old. D: 15-days old. E: 22-days old. Stimulus flash to single response on left was at·intensity "2", those to superimposed responses on right were at intensity "8", showing effect on latency. Note also difference in gain. F: 35-days old. Typical adult waveform, but long latency. G: 13-weeks old. Typical adult response, with second delayed response to same stimulus at 100 msec. Horizontal calibration lines indicate 100 msec.; vertical calibration lines indicate 100 μV. (From Ellingson and Wilcott, 1960, with permission of the editors and publishers of *J. Neurophysiol.*)

Marty, in his comprehensive monograph, emphasized the duplexity of the early visual evoked response. He considers that "Component B" is the primary response, and "Component A" reflects a more primitive and extensive projection system (see Topographical distribution, below).

Amplitude. The amplitude of the initially negative waves at their first ap-

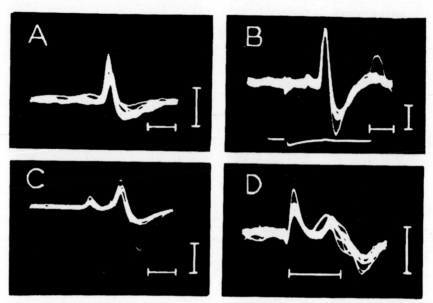

Fig. 4. Visual evoked responses in the kitten. A. 48 hours. B. 5 days. C. 9 days. D. 15 days. Recorded from the posterior part of the lateral gyrus. The short latency component of Marty's double response ("Component B"), develops progressively (B and C) to become the "primary" potential (D). Horizontal calibration lines indicate 100 msec. Vertical calibration lines indicate 200 μV. (From Marty, 1962, with permission of the author and publishers).

pearance may be from less than 50 to over 100 μv according to Ellingson and Wilcott's data, and some of the delayed responses may be as high as 300 μv. Marty's "Component A" often attains 300–400 μv in amplitude, whereas "Component B" at its first appearance may be of considerably lower voltage. By the time the adult waveform is attained the initial positive phase may be up to 300 μv in amplitude, and the negative phase nearly that. This of course refers to responses recorded directly from the surface of the cortex. Marty points out that the amplitude of the negative phase of "Component B" may vary with conditions of anesthesia, etc.

Latency. Latency is approximately 150 msec to the beginning of the surface-negative response at its first appearance at one week and 190 msec to its peak (Figure 5). Latency to the delayed negative response may be as long as 500 msec. At 35 days, latency to the peak of the initial positive phase of the response is approximately 40 msec, which further decreases to 16–24 msec in the adult. Latency to the peak of the first negative phase is 65 msec at 35 days and 28–35 msec in the adult. Marty reports latencies of 300–350 msec to the summit of his "Component A" at its first appearance, decreasing to 200 msec at 7 days. Latency to the summit of the negative phase of "Component B" at its first appearance was about 200 msec, decreasing to 100 msec at 7 days. Latency to the peak of the positive phase of "Component B" was 150 msec at its first appearance, descreasing to less than 100 msec at 7 days. By 30 days of age latency to the peak of "Component B" had de-

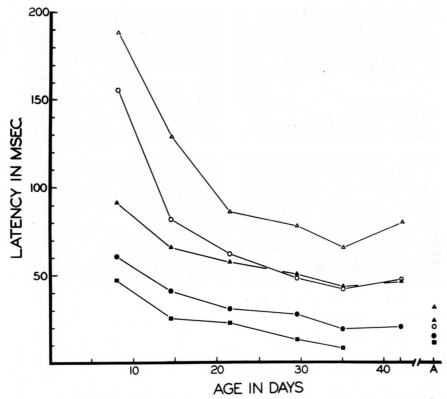

Fig. 5. Relationship of age to response latency in the cat. Latencies measured to small initial negative wave (squares), peak of positive wave (circles), peak of following negative wave (triangles), for auditory (closed) and visual (open) responses. Control (adolescent and adult) group is shown at far right over "A" (From Ellingson and Wilcott, 1960, with permission of the editors and publishers of J. Neurophysiol.)

creased to about 40 msec, to the summit of the negative phase of "Component B" to approximately 50 msec, and to the summit of the negative phase of "Component A" to about 100 msec; these figures corresponding closely to those cited by Ellingson and Wilcott for the kitten at 35 days of age.

Topographical distribution. The responses which have been described can be recorded from the lateral gyrus, but Marty's "Component A" can also be recorded from the suprasylvian and even the superior portion of the middle ectosylvian gyrus, where it appears not to interact with responses simultaneously evoked by auditory stimuli in those regions. He refers to these responses as *"extra-primary."*

Repetitive responses. Ellingson and Wilcott noted that responsiveness to repeated stimuli was poor in the young kitten. This phenomenon of unresponsiveness to stimulation following a previous stimulus has been called "fatigability." The highest frequency at which responses could regularly be elicited by each stimulus was 1 flash per 4 seconds at 9 days of age. This in-

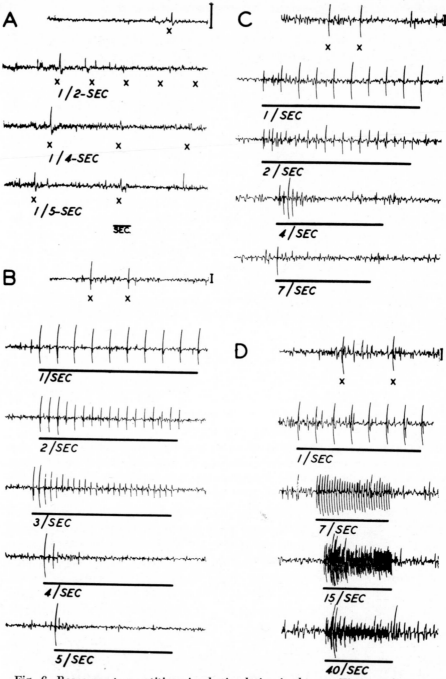

Fig. 6. Responses to repetitive visual stimulation in the cat. First tracing in each group shows responses to randomly presented flashes (Xs), and the remainder to repetitive stimulation. A: 8-days old. Weak negative responses at rates of 0.25/sec. and 0.20/sec. At faster rates response occurred only to the first flash. B: 22-days old. Clear repetitive responses at 3/sec., questionable at 4/sec., none at 5/sec. C: 35-days old. Some repetitive responses at 4/sec., none at faster frequencies. D: 12-weeks old. Responses up to 40/sec. Vertical calibration lines indicate 100 μV. (From Ellingson and Wilcott, 1960, with permission of the editors and publishers of *J. Neurophysiol.*)

crease to 1 flash per second (f/s) at 2 weeks, 3–5 f/s at 3–5 weeks, and 40–60 f/s in the adult cat (Figure 6). Fatigability was also reported by Marty, who observed it both in association with flash stimuli and direct shocks to the optic nerve.

Summary. In spite of differences in details, there appears to be agreement upon the following observations: (1) No responses can be evoked in the visual cortex of the kitten by presenting flashes of light to the eyes at birth. Responses can in most cases be observed by the end of the first week. (2) The first responses to appear are initially surface-negative, and tend to be double, having early and late components. (3) Later an initial surface-positive phase appears. (4) With increase in age the amplitude of the positive phases increases more rapidly than that of the negative phase, becoming the principal feature of the primary cortical evoked response. (5) Latencies of the earliest cortical evoked responses are up to 10 times greater than those observed in the mature animal, and decrease at first rapidly and then more slowly, attaining the adult level 8–12 weeks after birth. (6) Marked "fatigability" of cortical responsiveness if observed in the youngest animal showing evoked responses. Responsiveness to rapidly repeated stimuli increases with age.

Rabbit

Time of first appearance. Hunt and Goldring (1951) and Marty (1962) failed to elicit cortical evoked responses by flash stimulation before the age of 7 days in the rabbit. In both studies evoked responses were elicited from birth by direct electrical stmiulation of the optic nerve.

Waveforms. The earliest responses elicited by Hunt and Goldring were "minimal" surface-negative waves, sometimes followed by larger, initially surface-negative diphasic waves or surface-positive monophasic waves at 250 msec. The earliest responses observed by Marty were often double, surface-negative waves of great lability. In both studies the first surface-positive waves were observed on the 11th day. Subsequently the surface-positive phase increased in amplitude rapidly relative to the surface-negative phase, eventually becoming the most prominent feature of the cortical evoked response.

Amplitude. The earliest negative responses observed by Hunt and Goldring were approximately 200 μV in amplitude. By 28 days the amplitude of the positive phase of the response was 1 mV or greater, and the amplitude of the negative phase was 0.5–1 mV.

Latency. The latency of the first-observed responses to flash stimuli was approximately 100 msec in Hunt and Goldring's series, decreasing rapidly to 20 msec at 28 days. Latency of the cortical response to direct shocks to the optic nerve was 50 msec on day 1, decreasing to 30–40 msec on day 7, and 4 msec on day 21. In Marty's series the earliest responses to flash stimuli showed latencies of 150–180 msec. They were later observed to "decrease rapidly." Latency to direct shock to the optic nerve on day 1 was 50 msec, remaining relatively constant until days 5–7 and then decreasing to 10–15 msec by days 15–17.

Topographical distribution. Marty observed that visual evoked responses in the rabbit were confined from birth to a large primary cortical area.

Repetitive responses. Hunt and Goldring reported marked fatigability of visual evoked responses in the rabbit at 7 days, as much as 3–5 minutes delay being required between stimuli. This fatigability decreased rapidly, and at 16 days full amplitude responses were obtained at a rate of 1 f/s.

THE HUMAN INFANT—METHODS

Placement of electrodes. In our experience the optimal electrode placement for obtaining visual evoked responses is just superior to the inion, but responses can frequently be recorded over most of the occipital region (Ellingson, 1960; Engel, 1961; Engel and Butler, 1963). The reference lead is placed more anteriorly on the head. We use an ear lobe lead. The vicinity of the vertex is not a good location for the reference lead, because non-specific responses occurring in that area can easily be confounded with the occipital response.

It is best to arrange to connect the lead from the area where the evoked response is expected to the Grid 1 input of the push-pull amplifier and the "reference" lead to the Grid 2 input, to preserve the conventional polarity relationships used in most neurophysiological reasearch (a downward deflection indicates increasing relative positivity and an upward deflection indicates increasing relative negativity at the "active" electrode).

Cobb and Dawson used bipolar electrodes spaced 3 to 6 cm apart. Such a technique is of course necessary to determine the precise focus of potential variations by the phase reversal method. Cobb and Dawson showed that the initial, small, positive phase of the occipital evoked response in adults occurs over the midline between the inion and a point 6 cm superior to it.

Recording from "active" leads placed anterior to the occipital region is also desirable, to plot the topographic distributions of components of the evoked response.

Stimulation. The better, commercially available, stroboscopic photic stimulators are satisfactory for eliciting visual evoked responses. It is desirable, but not entirely necessary, to encase the stroboscope unit in a soundproof box to eliminate the clicking sound which the stroboscope makes when it flashes. These clicking sounds are of low intensity, but are certainly capable of producing auditory evoked responses (Ellingson and Wilcott, 1960).

Unless the stimulus intensity variable is being studied specifically, it is advisable to use only one stimulus intensity and to maintain a constant distance of the stroboscope unit from the subject's eyes, because response latency tends to vary inversely with the logarithm of stimulus intensity, and response amplitude tends to vary as an inverted U function of the logarithm of stimulus intensity. It is obvious in this connection that whether the subject's eyes are open or closed is important. Most work with infants must be done with eyes closed during sleep, because the baby tends to move, producing artifact, when bright lights are flashed at him during wakefulness. However, it is often possible to obtain good recordings during wakefulness.

Recording. Traditionally, evoked responses are recorded by means of a high-gain, resistance-capacity coupled, push-pull amplifier, employing a cathode-ray oscilloscope and camera to obtain a permanent record of the responses. As little attenuation, as possible, of high-frequency components should be employed, otherwise some phases of the evoked response may be distorted. A time constant of 0.3 seconds or greater is desirable, since some of the later phases of some responses can have periods of up to several hundred msec.

Despite the cathode-ray oscilloscope's obvious superiority in the reproduction of electrical signals, we have been able to demonstrate accurate recording of the waveforms and latencies of occipital evoked responses in human infants using conventional EEG equipment with ink-writer write-out (Fig. 7). The advantages of using EEG equipment are immediate accessibility of the recording, low cost of the recording material (paper), and availability of several recording channels making it possible to compare simultaneous results from several brain areas. For accurate measurement of latencies of evoked potentials, a paper speed of 60 mm/sec is preferred to the standard 30 mm/sec. For measuring latencies the stimulus artifact should be of course superimposed upon the same tracing in which the evoked response occurs.

Averaging the latencies of 10 responses gives an accurate mean value. We obtained a reliability coefficient of .95 between 2 sets of 10 responses each, recorded during the same session (N = 45, P < .001). Correlating mean latencies based on sets of 30 responses did not improve reliability. We also obtained a reliability coefficient of .99 between latencies measured from ink-writer tracings and latencies of the same responses measured from blown-up cathode-ray photographs (N = 20, P < .001).

A disadvantage of the method of direct recording of evoked potentials by CRO or EEG equipment is that responses are frequently masked by higher voltage background brain wave activity. This is less of a problem during the neonatal period, when the responses are apparently of higher voltage than they are later, and when background activity, even during sleep, is of lower voltage than it is later. Even during the neonatal period, however, we have failed to observe definitely identifiable responses in 40–50 per cent of our recording sessions. Engel and Butler (1963) report a lower, but still significant, percentage of failures to record responses. This is not due to absence of responses in these subjects, because they may have shown responses at earlier recording sessions, and responses may be seen to appear or disappear during the course of a single recording session.

To overcome this difficulty, various techniques of averaging series of short strips of recording, representing successive stimulus-response events, have been applied (Dawson, 1947; 1954; Brazier and Barlow, 1956, Barlow, 1957; Dawson and Cobb, 1960, Goldstein, 1960, Shipton 1960a and b).

An early technique developed by Dawson (1947) and still widely used, involves recording a number of stimulus-response events upon a single frame of photographic film by superimposing successive sweeps of the cathode-ray beam. This method brings out some of the more prominent features of

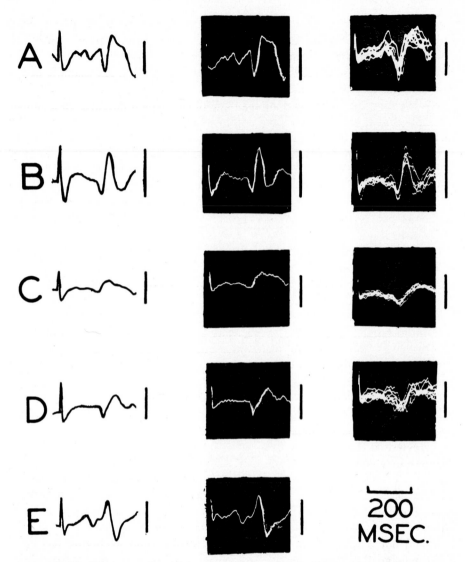

Fig. 7. Simultaneous ink-writer and oscilloscope recordings of the same occipital evoked responses in 5 infants (left and middle columns), and superimpositions of 10 responses in the same subjects (right-hand column). A. Full-term, 6 h. postpartum. B. Full-term, 12 h. postpartum. C. Full-term, 1 h. postpartum. D. Premature, 1930 gm. at birth; estimated gestation 36 weeks: recorded at 22 days postpartum. B. Full-term, 12 h. postpartum. C. Full-term, 51 h. postpartum. D. Premaphase. Vertical calibration lines indicate 50 μV.. (From Ellingson, 1960, with permission of the editors and publishers of *Electroenceph. clin. Neurophysiol.*)

masked responses, but cannot be depended upon to show the finer details. Paper and pencil measurement and averaging of numbers of tracings of stimulus-response events have also been done with some success, but the method is laborious.

Several workers have used photographic averaging techniques, in which voltage changes detected at the scalp are made to modulate the intensity of a sweeping cathode-ray beam, and successive sweeps of the beam are recorded on a piece of photographic film one below the other (Shipton, 1960b). A photoelectric averaging device then reads and averages the responses, and the average response is then written out on an X-Y plotter. An example of the results of this technique is shown in Fig. 8.

We have recently employed an analogue device which operates on a similar principle, but in which successive stimulus-response events are stored on the face of a storage tube, after which they are scanned and averaged. This instrument, called an Average Response Indicator, was devised by Buller and Styles (1960). The American version was designed by Mr. Harold W. Shipton of the State University of Iowa, who generously provided us with his circuit diagrams. The principal advantage of this device is that it provides an immediate write-out of the averaged response. Its principal disadvantage is that it has no memory.

Large digital computers have also been employed for response averaging (Cobb and Dawson, 1960, Williams et. al., 1963). The intermediate step of analogue-digital conversion is necessary, and this together with the fact that it is expensive to use large computers on-line, usually results in a delay in obtaining the results. However, such an arrangement employed in conjunction with multichannel magnetic tape-recording of activity from several brain areas is a versatile and powerful technique. Smaller, on-line, digital computers designed specifically for response averaging are also in use and becoming increasingly popular (Clynes and Kohn, 1961).

Certain cautions should be kept in mind when employing averaging devices: (1) Since the resulting recording is an average, intrasubject variations in response latency, amplitude, and waveform, if they occur, will not be detected. In fact, if there are variations in response latency, the average response may actually be not representative of the individual responses, and if the latency variations are great enough, the responses may not be detected at all. The latter does not seem to be the case, however, in recording cortical evoked responses to sensory stimulation. (2) Background brain wave activity, artifacts, and other phenomena regarded as "noise" may not be effectively averaged out if they are of relatively high voltage and averaging has been done over an insufficient number of events. (3) In extracting signals from noise, noise decreases as $1\sqrt{n}$, and signal/noise decreases as the $\sqrt{n}$. Therefore, increasing the number of to-be-averaged events eventually costs more than it is worth. (4) If regularly recurring components of background "noise," such as the alpha rhythm, lock to a regularly repeated stimulus, they will be included rather than excluded from the averaged result, and may be mistaken for components of evoked responses (Fig. 10G). This may be avoided by presenting stimuli at random time intervals.

In using averaging devices for recording visual evoked responses in the human neonate, we suggest that the duration of the stimulus-response events averaged should be at least 500 msec. The interstimulus interval should be at least 1 sec. With babies displaying unusually great fatigability, it may be necessary to increase interstimulus interval to as much as 5 sec. or even more. Satisfactory average responses can usually be obtained by averaging

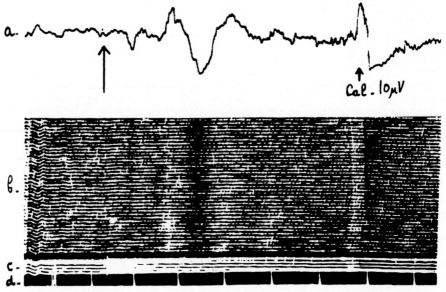

Fig. 8. Comparison of a recording of 40 successive stimulus-response events, one below another, on photographic film (b), and the tracing obtained after "integration" by a photo-multiplier (a). The shock artifact is shown in (c) and by the arrow, above. Time signals at 100 msec. (d). (From Contamin and Cathala, 1961, with permission of the editors and publishers of *Electroenceph. clin. Neurophysiol.*)

50–60 events. At least two types of controls should be employed. First, a series of events should be averaged, during which the stimulus is not presented, or better still, during which stimuli are being presented randomly in time with respect to the events being averaged. Second, some of the average responses recorded should be derived more than once to test the reliability of the technique.

THE HUMAN INFANT—RESULTS[*]

We have subjected well over 600 newborn infants to photic stimulation while recording from all areas of the scalp (Ellingson, 1958, 1960, in press). We have obtained repeat recordings on a large percentage of these infants for periods of 4-8 years. Until recently, recording was done entirely on conventional EEG equipment, and evoked responses were sought in the inkwriter tracings (Fig. 9). Recently we have obtained evoked response recordings from 49 of these subjects employing the Average Response Indicator (ARI) at ages 47–93 months. We have also obtained recordings from a new series of babies starting at birth, which is yet too small to provide definitive results.

In our earlier series we were able to elicit identifiable evoked responses in only 56 per cent of the initial, neonatal recordings. After slow sleep

---

[*]A number of studies of cortical responses evoked by visual, auditory and somesthetic stimulation in adult man have been reported. These are beyond the scope of this paper, but are listed in the bibliography for reference purposes.

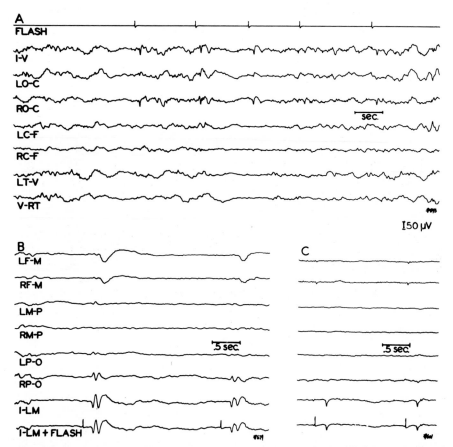

Fig. 9. Evoked responses elicited by single flashes. All full-term babies. A. 16 hours postpartum, asleep. Paper speed = 3 cm./sec. B. 63 hours postpartum, awake. Paper speed = 6 cm./sec. Stimulus artifact superimposed on the bottom channel. Latencies were measured on this type of recording. C. 60 hours postpartum, awake. Same type of recording as in B. (From Ellingson, 1960, with permission of the editors and publishers of *Electroenceph. clin. Neurophysiol.*)

activity became more prominent in the EEG at 1–3 months of age, the percentage of detectable responses dropped to an even lower figure. Among those subjects whose responses we have rcorded by both the EEG ink-writer technique and with the ARI, we have never failed to record evoked responses with the ARI, but our results with the EEG are quite similar to our earlier ones: in the neonatal period responses were detected in 52 per cent of the recordings, and among children 4–8 years of age in 32 per cent.

Reliability. Among subjects yielding responses both by EEG and ARI (not simultaneously) the coefficient of correlation between the 2 types of recordings for latency to the peak of the major positive deflection was .89 (N = 32; P < .001). The reliability coefficient between 2 separately derived average responses for each subject was .97 (N = 36; P < .001).

First appearance of responses. All normal human infants apparently display visual evoked responses at term (conceptual age of 40 weeks). We do

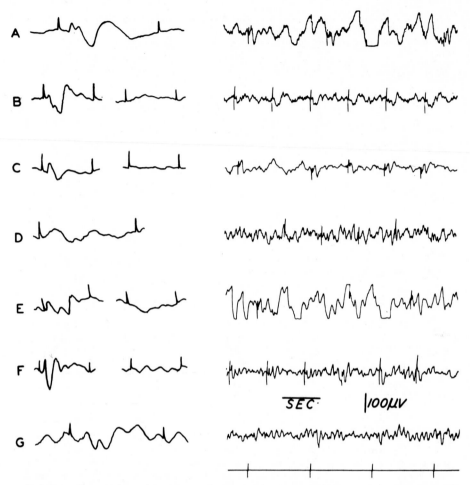

Fig. 10. Occipital (inion-ear) evoked responses to flashes recorded by the Average Response Indicator (left) and the EEG (right) in 7 normal children, ages 54–69 mos. The responses on the left are averages of 60 stimulus-response events. The light flashes appeared at the time of the first spike artifact. The second spike artifact is a time marker, 500 msec. after the first spike. The spike artifacts are superimposed upon the ink-writer tracings, except in G. Average responses A, D, and G were recorded at a paper speed of 100 mm./sec., and the remainder at 50 mm./sec. The second average tracing in B, C, E, and F are controls: averages of 60 counts when no stimulus was presented. A and E. Deep sleep. B and C. Light sleep. D, F, and G. Awake. Note that alpha rhythm appears in the average in G, and also in the control average in F. The calibrations at the right apply only to the EEG tracings.

not know what the average conceptual age at the appearance of these responses is. The earliest responses we have obsrved were in a premature at CA 28 weeks. Engel and Butler (1963) have reported a case at CA 29 weeks.

    Waveforms. As is readily evident from the figures, there is considerable intersubject variability in waveform (Fig. 7, 9, 10-12). More detail is evident in the average responses than in the EEG or CRO tracings. There is

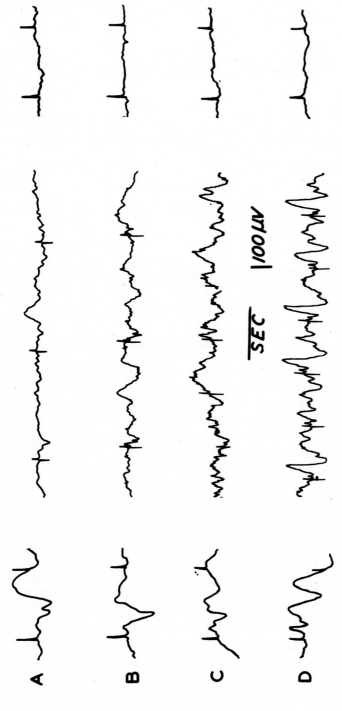

Fig. 11. Occipital (inion-ear) evoked responses to flashes recorded by ARI (left) and EEG (middle) in the same infant at A. 5 days, B. 5 weeks, C. 12 weeks, and D. 25 weeks postpartum. ARI controls are on the right. Note spike-and-wave responses in D. See text for details. The calibrations apply only to the EEG tracings. Interspike interval on ARI tracings was 500 msec.

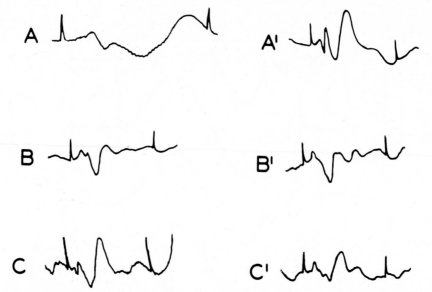

Fig. 12. Occipital (inion-ear) evoked responses to flashes recorded by ARI in three subjects on two separate occasions. A. Age 52 mos. A'. Age 62 mos. B. Age 52 mos. B'. Age 57 mos. C. Age 53 mos. C'. Age 57 mos. Paper speed was 2 times faster for A than for the other 5 tracings. Interspike interval was 500 msec.

definite intrasubject consistency in waveform, but this is less apparent in the average responses (Fig. 12) than in the ink-writer tracings (Fig. 14).

The majority of responses in the neonatal period show an initial, brief positive phase, but 2.3 per cent yield only initially negative responses. Prior to a conceptual age of 32 weeks, we have observed only initially negative responses, and we have never seen an initially negative response at conceptual ages of over 41 weeks. We have presented other evidence suggesting that the initially negative type of response is more primitive than the initially positive response, and we feel that the visual evoked response in the human infant at its first appearance is probably initially negative as it is in cat and rabbit (Ellingson, 1960).

In Fig. 10–12 are shown average responses recorded from subjects of different ages, showing variations in waveform of the visual evoked response. In Fig. 13 is presented a series of "idealized" responses. Whether actual cortical responses show such variations, or whether such variations are due to different positions of the scalp recording electrode with respect to the active cortical field, we do not know. The waveform displayed by the neonate is usually that seen in Fig. 13D.

The small initial positive phase in Fig. 13A and D is probably the primary response (Cobb and Dawson, 1960), and the other phases are secondary responses.* It is now obvious that the components of evoked responses seen

---

*The term "secondary response" may be ill chosen, since it is possible that these voltage variations represent responses of an afferent projection system separate from, and perhaps more primitive, than the so-called "primary" projection system (Bishop, 1961; Marty, 1962).

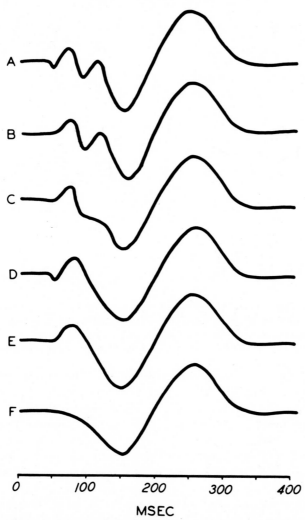

Fig. 13. Variations of occipital evoked responses to flashes most commonly seen in the human infant and young child. The time scale below is that appropriate to the 4–8 year age range. See text for discussion.

in EEG tracings, and which we have previously observed and measured, are not primary responses, but rather late "secondary" components of the response. Like Marty's "Component A" in the cat, such secondary responses may have a wide topographical distribution (Fig. 17–18).

There are no detectable differences in waveform between subjects 4–8 years old given chloral hydrate and those given nothing (no sedation was used with infants). There do however, appear to be some differences in waveform between responses recorded while the subject is awake and while he is asleep. During wakefulness more rhythmic elements are seen in the averages (Fig. 10G), and the components of the responses tend to be of more uniform amplitude than pictured in Fig. 13. The rhythmic elements appear to be alpha waves, since their frequency is identical with that of alpha

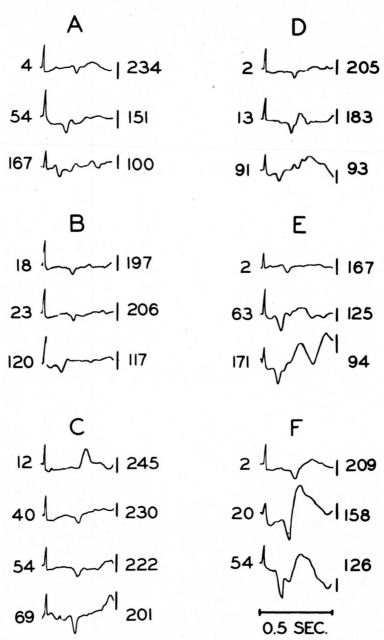

Fig. 14. Typical evoked responses of 3 premature (A–C) and 3 full-term (D–F) infants recorded at different times during the first 6 months of life, showing developmental changes. The number at the left of each tracing is the chronological age of the subject in days at the time of recording; the number at the right is the latency of the response shown in msec. All latencies are to the peak of the positive wave, except for the first (initially negative) response of subject C, which was measured to the beginning of the negative wave. Vertical calibration lines indicate 50 μV. (From Ellingson, 1960, with permission of the editors and publishers of *Electroenceph. clin. Neurophysiol.*)

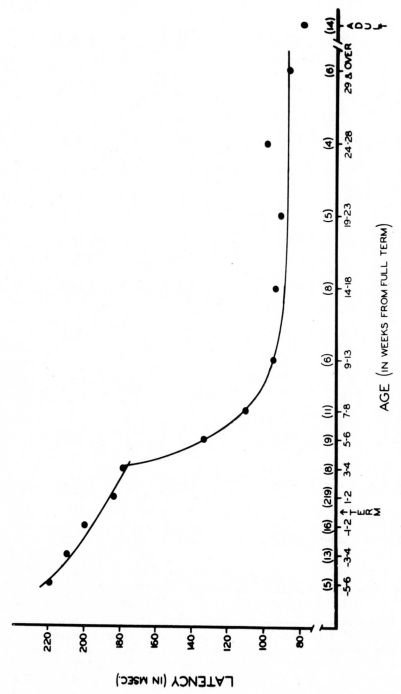

Fig. 15. Plot of mean evoked response latencies against age. The numbers in parentheses just above the abcissa represent the numbers of subjects upon whom the dots above are based. (From Ellingson, 1960, with permission of the editors and publishers of *Electroenceph. clin. Neurophysiol.*)

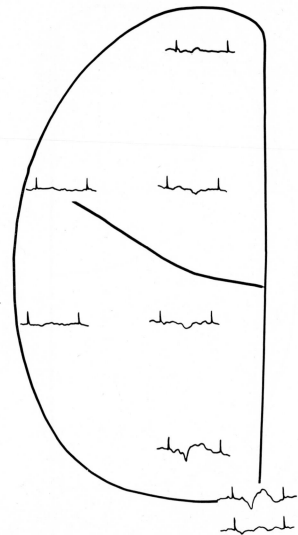

Fig. 16. Topographical distribution of average evoked responses to flashes in a newborn at 5 days. Control at bottom. Interspike time = 500 msec.

waves in the ink-writer tracings. Apparently the alpha rhythm locks with the stimulus even at a presentation rate of 1 f/s.

Several subjects have displayed spike-and-wave complexes in response to randomly presented flashes and/or to sequences of flashes at 1, 2, and 3 f/s (Fig. 11D; Ellingson, in press). It is too early to say whether this is an abnormal response, but one such subject has subsequently displayed spontaneous, diffuse, high-voltage 4–5 sec. spike-and-wave complexes. Thus far, however, no seizures have been reported.

Amplitude. When first observed after birth, the amplitudes of the late "secondary" responses recorded on EEG equpiment are often as high as 50–

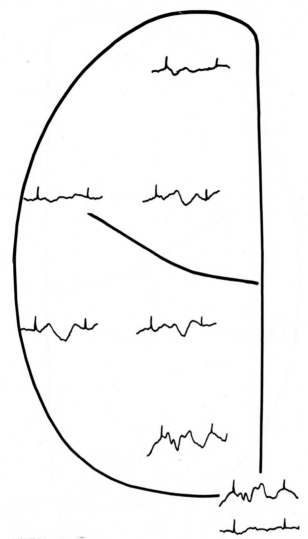

Fig. 17. **Topographical distribution of average evoked responses to flashes in an infant at 12 weeks.** Control at bottom. Interspike time = 500 msec.

100 μV, but may be considerably less. The amplitude of the smaller early components seen in the average response is probably not over a few μV, but we do not at present have satisfactory amplitude calibration for the ARI. These statements of course refer to amplitude at the scalp. The amplitude of responses at the surface of the cortex is not known.

With increasing age the amplitude of the response at the scalp not only does not increase, but appears to decrease. Whether this is due to increasing remoteness of the cortical field of activity from the scalp electrode or to some other factor such as intracortical inhibition of response spread is a moot question.

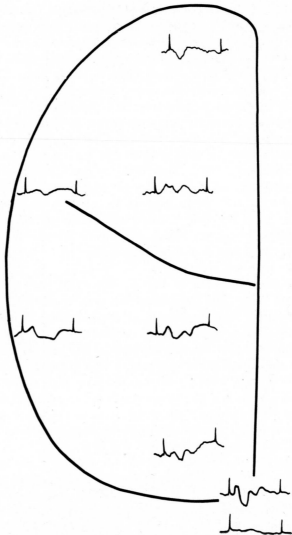

Fig. 18. Topographical distribution of average evoked responses to flashes in a child at 76 months. Response in the frontal area is of extracerebral origin. Control at bottom. Interspike time = 500 msec.

Latency. The mean latency to the peak of the large, "secondary," positive phase of the evoked response as recorded by EEG is 219 msec at a conceptual age of 34–35 weeks, 209 msec. at 36–37 weeks, 200 msec. at 38–39 weeks, and 189 msec. at term (Fig. 14 and 15). There is a further decrease to 180 msec. at 3–4 weeks post-term, after which the latency decreases rapidly to approximately 100 msec. at 12-13 weeks, where it levels off with a very gradual decrease thereafter. Engel (1961) and Engel and Bartlett (1963) reported a mean latency of 153 msec. at birth, measuring to the begining of the first deflection of the response seen in the EEG tracing. Fragmentary returns from our new series of newborns yield a mean latency of 175 msec. to the peak of the large positive wave at 3–5 days post-term. Latency to the peak of the small, early, positive phase seen in the ARI tracings, but not in the EEG tracings, is approximately 115 msec. at 3–5 days post-term.

Among subjects 4–8 years old, there are no latency differences between subjects receiving chloral hydrate and those receiving none. The latency to the peak of the first positive wave recorded during sleep was 6.5 msec. longer than that recorded during wakefulness (not significant).

The developmental curve for latencies shown in Figure 15 is two-legged rather than monotonic. We also obtained a two-legged curve by plotting evoked response latency against body weight for infants 6 months of age and younger (Ellingson, 1960). This might be due either to a growth spurt in the visual system at 5–10 weeks of age, or to different developmental rates in two parts of the visual system, perhaps the photopic and scotopic.

The situation is far from clear. Engel and Butler (1963) obtained a developmental curve for latency which was clearly linear from a conceptual age of 28 weeks to 6 weeks post-term, and their curve has a steeper slope than ours over the same age range.

Furthermore, an examination of Fig. 13 shows that latency of the greatest positive phase of the evoked response at 4–8 years is about 150 msec., which is 50 per cent longer than the latency of the greatest positive phase of responses seen in EEG recordings at 3–6 months of age. This is disturbing. It can only be supposed that the response seen at 3–6 months in EEG tracings is the same as the *second* postitive response seen in the average responses at 4–8 years (latency = 90 msec.), and that the later, higher amplitude positive wave seen at 4–8 years is a phenomenon which has appeared in the interim.

It is evident that additional cross-validation is needed. Fragmentary results from our new series of newborns so far appear to parallel our earlier data for the first 3 months post-term.

We have observed no differences in response latency in the neonatal period between subjects later showing developmental abnormalities and those displaying normal development. This agrees with the observations of Engel and Butler (1963). We further have observed no latency differences between normals and abnormals in the 4–8 year age range.

On the other hand, there is a significant difference between prematures and full-term infants in the age range of 40–60 weeks conceptual age, the prematures displaying longer response latencies. The prematures, however, catch up in the second 6 months post-term. There is no difference at all in mean latency of any component of the evoked response at 4–8 years of age.

Topographical distribution. It will be seen from Fig. 9 that visual evoked responses appear to be confined to the occipital area in the newborn. Average response data tend to bear out this observation, originally based on EEG-type recording. Of 8 children whose visual evoked responses were recorded in the 41st week after conception, none showed any responses outside the occipital area (Fig. 16). The earliest responses outside the occipital area thus far observed were in one of these subjects at 12 weeks of age (Fig. 17). On the other hand, widespread responses outside the occipital area have been observed in 42 of 62 recordings at 4–8 years. It further appears that the later components of the evoked response are those which are more widely distributed over the surface of the head, agreeing with Marty's observations in the cat.

These data suggest that a further characteristic of the development of evoked response activity in the visual system is an increasingly wide topographical distribution, at least of the later components of the response.

Responses to the repetitive stimulation. At term most babies will display responses to most stimuli when they are presented at a rate of 1 f/s, but not more frequently. Some however require intervals of 3–4 or more seconds between stimuli. This is especially true of early prematures. Later in the first year of life many babies will display responses to every stimulus at rates of 2, 3, or even 4 f/s.

Repetitive photic stimulation, regardless of the frequency of repetition, may elicit ON responses which appear to be identical in latency, waveform, and distribution with responses evoked by single flashes, and OFF responses which differ from ON responses in latency and often in waveform (Ellingson, 1958, 1960, in press). A "following" response (sometimes called a "driving" response) may also be elicited at low flash frequencies. In our experience this response is relatively rare in the newborn, but some workers have reported observing it more frequently than we. Eichorn (1951) observed following, primarily in the 1–3 and 4/6 sec. frequency ranges in 33 of 38 subjects, aged 7–81 days, but the percent-time of following was very low in most subjects. Following responses occur in the newborn in the range of 2–5 f/s. The frequency at which the following response may be obtained increases with age in the infant (Eichorn, 1951; Ellingson, 1960) and on into later childhood (Schaper, 1957).

Summary. At present, the following reasonable generalizations can be made concerning the development of visual evoked responses in the human infant. (1) Visual evoked responses first appear during fetal life, probably prior to the third trimester. (2) The first responses to appear are probably initially surface negative. (3) An initial surface positive phase appears later, but still prior to term in most individuals. (4) Postnatally, there is a gradual increase in the complexity of the response, with additional responses or response components appearing at some time after birth. (5) There is a decrease in amplitude of responses with age, at least as recorded from the scalp. (6) The latency of evoked responses when first seen in the newborn is 2–3 times greater than that of the same components of the response seen in older children and adults. There is a rapid decrease in latency to 13 weeks, and then a much more gradual decrease. (7) Topographical distribution of the response is limited to the occipital area in the newborn, but later at least the "secondary" components of the response become more widespread, starting probably during the first 3 months post-term. (8) Fatigability is a notable characteristic of evoked responses in the newborn, and this decreases with age as shown by increased responsiveness to repetitive stimulation.

In general, the characteristics of the visual evoked response in the human newborn are similar to those observed in cats and rabbits with the following exceptions: (1) The first appearance of the response in the lower animals occurs after term birth rather than before; (2) the waveform in the human eventually attains greater complexity than in the lower animals; (3) response amplitude increases with age in the lower animals, but this statement is based upon observations of responses recorded directly from the surface of the cortex, which have not been obtained in the human infant.

Auditory Evoked Responses
CAT

Time of first appearance. The earliest auditory evoked responses observed by Rose et al, (1957) were on the 5th postnatal day in the kitten. Stable responses occurred from the 6th day. Ellingson and Wilcott (1960) observed responses in all of their kittens from 6½ days of age. Marty (1962) did not observe auditory evoked responses before the 8th postnatal day. Such differences in age of onset as have been observed could be accounted for on the basis of differences in stimulus intensity.

Waveform. All of the above investigators report that the auditory evoked response consists of a positive phase followed by a negative phase from the first appearance of the response (Fig. 19). Occasionally there is a small negative phase preceding the initial positive phase, which Rose et al attribute to events in the medial geniculate body. With increasing age there is a greater increase in amplitude of the positive phase than of the negative phase, and there is a decrease in the period of the negative phase.

Amplitude. At its first appearance Rose et al measured the initial positive phase at 20 μV and the following negative phase at 100 μV. Respective figures for Marty were 20 μV and 50–100 μV, and for Ellingson and Wilcott, 40 μV and 200 μV. By the 32 day Rose et al observed amplitudes of 400 μV for the positive phase and 200 μV for the negative, while Ellingson and Wilcott observed respective values of 400 μV and 500 μV. Marty observed amplitudes of the initial positive phase of over 600 μV by the 4th week.

Although no one has done precise threshold studies, sensitivity to sound stimuli apparently increases rapidly so that by 12–14 days the soft click produced by the stroboscope unit used in visual stimulation can elicit auditory evoked responses (Ellingson and Wilcott, Marty).

Latency. Rose et al observed latencies of approximately 54, 61, and 83 msec. for the small negative phase, the initial positive phase, and the larger negative phase of the auditory evoked response, respectively, at their first appearance (N = 6). The respective latencies reported by Ellingson and Wilcott were 47, 61, and 92 msec. (N = 8). Marty reported latencies of 50–60 msec. for the initial positive phase at 8 days.

Response latencies decrease rapidly during the 2nd week and then more slowly for the succeeding 4–5 weeks. Ellingson and Wilcott reported latencies for the 3 components of the response of 17, 19, and 43 msec., respectively, at 5 weeks of age (N = 6), and 11, 16, and 31 msec., respectively, for

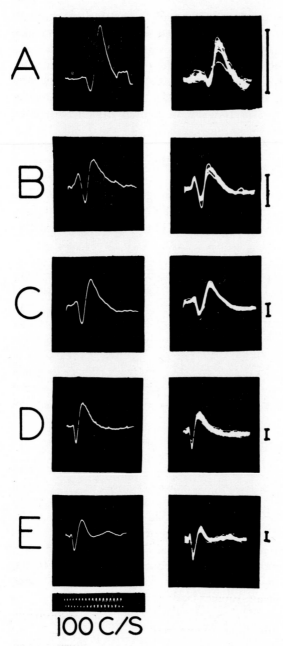

Fig. 19. Auditory evoked responses in kittens. A: 9-days old. B: 15-days old. C: 22-days old. D: 35-days old. Typical of adult responses. E: 13-weeks old. Typical adult response. Vertical calibration lines indicate 200 μV. (From Ellingson and Wilcott, 1960, with permission of the editors and publishers of *J. Neurophysiol.*)

100 C/S

adults ($N = 13$). Rose *et al* reported latencies of 15, 25, and 43 msec. for the 3 components at 5 weeks. The developmental curves published by Rose *et al* and by Ellingson and Wilcott (Fig. 5) are virtually superimposable.

Topographical distribution. Only Marty discusses the matter of the extra-primary distribution of auditory evoked responses. He reported responses occurring over the middle suprasylvian gyrus of higher threshold and longer latency than those seen over the ectosylvian gyrus at 8 days. He speculates that this area may constitute an auditory association area.

Repetitive stimulation. The same phenomenon of fatigability observed in the visual system of the infant animal is observed in the auditory system. Grossman reported a maximum frequency of response of 1.5/sec at 13 days, Ellingson and Wilcott of 1.5/sec at 9 days, and Marty of 1/sec at 15 days. Grossman reported a maximal frequency of response of 3/sec at 3 weeks and Ellingson and Wilcott of 10/sec at 3, 4, and 5 weeks. Differences in intensity of stimuli may be a factor in such differences in responsivity as have been reported.

Summary. Like visual responses in the kitten, auditory responses evoked by natural end-organ stimulation appear postnatally, their latency is greater than in the adult animal and approaches adult latency with decelerating rapidity, their amplitude increases with age, and fatigability is notable. They differ from visual responses in that they are initially surface-positive from their first appearance, and adult latencies and amplitudes are attained earlier.

RABBIT

I am aware only of Marty's report (1962) on the development of auditory evoked responses in the rabbit. Responses appear first on the 9th postnatal day, and as in the cat, are positive-negative from the beginning. A small initial negative phase occurs rarely. A phenomenon similar to Marty's "Component A" in the visual system is likewise seen rarely. Amplitude of the re- sponse at first appearance is 300–400 μV. Latency at first appearance is 20 msec., decreasing to 12 to 15 msec. by the 4th week. There is some convergence of auditory and somesthetic evoked responses in the anterior part of the auditory area. Marty does not discuss the effects of repetitive stimulation in the rabbit.

THE HUMAN INFANT*

Method. In attempting to record auditory evoked potentials, one or more "active" electrodes should be placed over the sylvian region. We have been using a midtemporal lead in the T_3 or T_4 international 10–20 position with anterior- and posterior-temporal leads on either side of it, but closer to T_3 (or T_4) than the F_7 (F_8) and T_5 ((T_6) electrodes of the 10–20 system. The reference lead for these active leads should be at a distance. Ear lobe leads may be a poor choice for reference leads because of the proximity to the temporal lobe. An "active" vertex lead (C_0) is also desirable to detect vertex negative responses, should they occur. Bipolar leads may also be used.

For initial work, a broad-spectrum noise stimulus, a click, is probably best. Later, pure-tones or other stimuli may be desired.

As far as I can determine, no one has recorded primary auditory evoked responses from the scalp in man using EEG or CRO recording equipment. An averaging device is apparently necessary. More events must be averaged usually than in the case of the visual response, often up to several hundred, and even then results are less satisfactory than with the visual system.

---

*A number of studies of cortical responses evoked by visual, auditory and somesthetic stimulation in adult man have been reported. These are beyond the scope of this paper, but are listed in the bibliography for reference purposes.

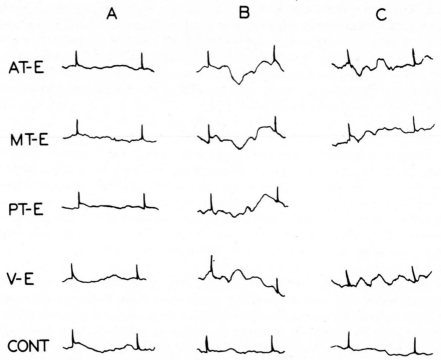

Fig. 20. Average evoked responses to clicks in 3 human subjects in the temporal area (AT-E, MT-E, PT-E) and at the vertex (V-E). Control tracings from temporal area without stimulus presentation (CONT). A. Age 5 days. No responses. B. Age 92 mos. C. Age 76 mos. Interspike time = 500 msec.

Results: We have consistently failed to record any signals identifiable as evoked responses in the sylvian region in over 100 newborns stimulated by electronically generated clicks, using standard EEG recording methods. We have seen possible responses in 2 of 6 newborns and in 10 of 23 children 4–8 years of age using the ARI (Fig. 20). These results are not very impressive, and it would be premature to elaborate on these preliminary data at this time.

Eichorn (1951) failed to demonstrate following to repetitive auditory stimulation.

Somesthetic Evoked Responses

To the best of my knowledge no attempt has been made to study somesthetic evoked responses in the human infant. They have however been studied in the cat (Scherrer and Oeconomos, 1954; Grossman, 1955; Marty, 1962) and the rabbit (Marty, 1962). A brief summary of the results is presented for comparison with vision and audition. The somesthetic evoked response is present at birth and has been observed in prematurely delivered animals. The waveform at first appearance is initially negative, often double, and sometimes followed by a series of waves of diminishing amplitude. After a few days, sometimes as early as the 2nd day, a small initial positive phase appears, which gradually increases in amplitude relative to the negative phase. The latency of the response is approximately 90 msec. in the premature and from 50–80 msec on the first day post-term. The adult level is attained by 30–35 days, in the cat. Latency at birth in the rabbit is 90–65 msec. and adult latency is attained by 3 weeks. Marked fatigability in the neonatal period has been observed in both cat and rabbit.

Discussion

Time of appearance of evoked responses. Among the 3 species studied, the higher the species stands in the phylogenetic scale the earlier cortical evoked responses appear relative to the date of birth. For vision they probably appear before the end of the second trimester in man, by the second or third day after birth in the cat, but not until the end of the first postnatal week in the rabbit. For somesthesis and hearing the interspecies differences are in the same direction, but not so striking. Definite data for man are not yet available.

In the cat and the rabbit, somesthetic evoked responses are the earliest to appear, visual next, and auditory last. In man it is likely that this comparison will be difficult or impossible to make, since it is probable that evoked responses in all 3 modalities are present at, or even before, the conceptual age at which fetus becomes viable in the extra-uterine environment.

It is obvious that the sensory end organ, afferent neurons, and cortical neurons must all be functional in some degree for the evoked response to become manifest. The complex end organs of the visual and auditory systems are apparently the last components of these systems to become operative. Marty (1962) and Hunt and Goldring (1951) have shown that afferent and cortical neurons of the visual system will respond to direct electrical stimulation before evoked responses can be elicited by illumination of the retina. Zetterstrom's studies (1951, 1952, 1955) of the ERG demonstrate the functional immaturity of the human retina throughout the first year of life.

The relatively mature waveform and relatively short latency of the auditory evoked response, in spite of its relatively late appearance, implies that the organ of Corti is the last component of that system to become operative. On the other hand, the relatively simple and primitive free nerve endings of the somesthetic system probably become operative at an early date, perhaps accounting for the early appearance of evoked responses in that system (Marty, 1962).

Waveform. The evoked response as recorded from the surface of the cortex or from the scalp is due largely or entirely to potential changes occurring in neuronal elements of the cortex. The waveform of the evoked response should therefore by and large reflect the functional maturity of the cortex.

It is reasonably clear that the most primitive evoked responses are initially surface-negative, although this is difficult to demonstrate in man, in whom the responses appear relatively early in fetal life. The cortex is capable of positive-negative potential sequences at this time, however, since it has been shown so to respond to direct electrical stimulation of thalamocortical pathways in the kitten at a time when it produces only a negative response to stimulation more peripherally (Purpura, 1961).

Considerable work has been done in the functional neuroanatomy of the cortical evoked response in adult and infant animals. Purpura (1961) has presented evidence to support the proposition that the initial surface negative configuration of evoked responses in the infant animal "may be accountable for by the prominent synaptic activity in superficial dendritic elements which are sufficiently intense to swamp out the relatively weak synaptic activity initiated in the cortical depths." This area of investigation is a complex and extensive one, and I shall not presume to discuss it further.

Latency. The prolonged latencies of cortical evoked responses at their first appearance may be due to slow reactivity in sensory end organs and/or slow transmission over afferent pathways, but is apparently not due to any process in the cortex (Rose *et al*, 1957). Zetterstrom has demonstrated prolonged latency of the ERG at its first appearance. Marty has shown that latency of responses to direct electrical stimulation of the optic nerve in both the neonatal cat and rabbit remains unchanged over a period of several days, during which latency of responses to illumination of the retina is decreasing rapidly. This suggests that the initial decrease in latency is due to functional changes in the retina. and the later more gradual decrease in latency is due both to further functional maturation of the retina and to maturation of the afferent pathways. Several workers have shown increasing rates of transmission over neuronal pathways with increasing age in various species of animals (Del Castillo and Vizoso, 1953; Hursh, 1939a and b; Thomas and Lambert, 1958; and Ulett *et al*, 1944).

Topographical distribution. The evidence we have presented indicates that with increasing age there is an increasingly widespread topographical distribution of visual evoked responses in man, accompanied by increasing complexity of waveform. This is especially evident in the adult (Contamin and Cathala, 1961; Vanzulli *et al*, 1960). Marty's observations suggest, and ours appear to confirm, that it is the later, "secondary" components of the evoked response which are thus widespread. Marty's observations also suggest that these components are more primitive than the primary evoked response. This is reminiscent of Bishop's suggestion (1961) that there may be both more primitive, slowly conducting, afferent systems projecting upon the "association" cortex and phylogenetically more recent, rapidly conducting, afferent systems projecting upon the primary sensory areas of the cortex.

Fatigability. It is tempting to attribute the phenomenon of fatigability entirely to functional immaturity of sensory organs. However, Purpura's observation (1961) that post-activation depression in the somesthetic system of the newborn kitten is demonstrable upon direct electrical stimulation of ventrolateral thalamic nuclei, indicates that this is not the entire explanation. High order afferent relays and possibly the cortex itself are apparently involved in this phenomenon.

Needed studies. Much has been accomplished in the study of the development of cortical evoked potentials, but much more needs to be done. Further cross validational data on visual evoked responses in the human infant, especially with respect to latency, will be needed to clear up present inconsistencies. Systematic investigations of the development of auditory and somesthetic evoked responses in the human infant need to be done. More species could be studied—I would suggest not only an animal much lower in the phylogenetic scale than the cat or the rabbit, but also a primate. More extensive and systematic study of the development of non-specific brain electrical responses to sensory stimulation should be undertaken. Finally, parallel neurophysiological, neuroanatomical, and behavioral studies of development are most desirable. I would point out especially the work of the Scheibels (1962) as an example.

Potential applications. The presence or absence of cortical evoked potentials, or abnormalities of latency, waveform, etc., could be useful in the diagnosis and evaluation of sensory defects in non-communicatiing subjects, especially in the early detection of sensory defects in infants. Derbyshire and his colleagues (1959) have shown that this is feasible, using brain electrical responses other than specific evoked responses. Scherrer and Fourment (in press) and Hubel and Wiesel (in press) have demonstrated changes in evoked responses due to early sensory deprivation.

I would also like to suggest that brain electrical phenomena known to undergo maturational changes in early life should be measurable, and that from such measurements an index or indices of the maturation of brain electrical activity could be derived which should have functional significance. Conventional EEG records could be reliably rated, I believe, on the basis of the presence or absence of various activity and relationships already known to appear and/or disappear or change during late fetal and early postnatal life—for example, large 1–2/sec waves surcharge with fast rhythms in the occipital and temporal areas, the presence and bilateral synchrony of clear-cut sleep spindles, the degree of bilateral synchrony in the frontal, parietal, occipital, and temporal areas, etc. Autocorrelational or power spectra analyses might contribute further to quantifiability and reliability of EEG evaluations. The latencies of evoked responses in the three major sensory modalities are easily measurable, and waveforms could be classified. From these various data a maturational index might be derived which could then be correlated with clinical and behavioral data in both cross-sectional and longitudinal studies. It is conceivable that such an index might be a powerful tool in the evaluation of the early functioning of the nervous system.

Summary

1. The literature dealing with the development of cortical evoked responses in the visual, auditory, and somesthetic systems of the rabbit, the cat, and man has been reviewed.

2. Some previously unpublished original data on averaged evoked responses in the visual system of the human infant and young child have been presented.

3. Some tentative generalizations concerning interspecies and intermodality similarities and differences have been presented. Some functional anatomical correlates have been discussed.

4. Needs for future research and possible future applications of the results of such research have been pointed out.

REFERENCES

BANCAUD, J., BLOCH, V. and PAILLARD, J. Contribution EEG a l'étude des potentiels evoqués chez l'homme au niveau du vertex. *Rev. Neurol.*, *1953*, 89:399–418.

BARLOW, J. S. An electronic method for detecting evoked responses of the brain and for reproducing their average waveforms. *Electroenceph. clin. Neurophysiol. 1957*, 9:340–343.

BISHOP, G. H. The organization of cortex with respect to its afferent supply. *Ann. N. Y. Acad. Sci.*, *1961*, 94:559–659.

BOGACZ, J., VANZULLI, A., HANDLER, P. and GARCIA-AUSTT, E. Evoked responses in man. II. Habituation of visual evoked response. *Acta neurol. latinoamer.*, *1960*, 6:353–362.

BRAZIER, M. A. B. Studies of evoked responses in man and cat. *In:* H. Jasper *et al.*, (editors), *Reticular Formation of the Brain*, Little Brown, Boston, 1958, pp. 151–168.

BRAZIER, M. A. B. and BARLOW, J. S. Some applications of correlation analysis to clinical problems in electroencephalography. *Electroenceph. clin. Neurophysiol.*, *1956*, 8:325–331.

BULLER, A. J. and STYLES, P. R. Improvement in signal/noise ratio with aid of a barrier-grid storage tube. *Proc. third internat. Congr. med. Electronics, 1960*, 63–64.

CALVET, J., CATHALA, H.-P., CONTAMIN, F., HIRSCH, J. ET SCHERRER, J. Potentiels évoqués corticaux chez l'homme. *Rév. neurol.*, *1956*, 95:445–454.

CALVET, J., CATHALA, H.-P., HIRSCH, J. ET SCHERRER, J. La résponse corticale visuelle de l'homme étudiée par une méthode d'intégration. *Comptes rendus* (Paris), *1956*, 150:1348–1351.

CLYNES, M. and KOHN, M. Portable 4 channel online digital average response computer, CAT., *Proc. fourth internat. Congr. med. Electronics, 1961*:23.

COBB, W. A. and DAWSON, G. D. The latency and form in man of the occiptal potentials evoked by bright flashes. *J. Physiol.*, *1960*, 152:108–121.

CONTAMIN, F. ET CATHALA, H.-P., Réponses électro-corticales de l'homme normal éveillé à des éclairs lumineux. *Electroenceph. clin. Neurophysiol.*, *1961*, 13:674–694.

DAVIS, H., DAVIS, P. A., LOOMIS, A. L., HARVEY, E. N. and HOBART, G. A. Electrical reactions of human brain to auditory stimulation during sleep. *J. Neurophysiol.*, *1939*, 2:500–514.

DAWSON, G. D. Cerebral responses to electrical stimulation of peripheral nerve in man. *J. Neurol. Neurosurg. Psychiat.*, *1947*, 10:134–140.

DAWSON, G. D. A comparison of potentials evoked by sensory stimuli in man with those described in animals. *Electroenceph. clin. Neurophysiol.*, *1953*, 5:123.

DAWSON, G. D. A summation technique for the detection of small evoked potentials. *Electroenceph. clin. Neurophysiol.*, *1954*, 6:65–84.

DES CASTILLO, J. and VIZOSO, A. D. The electrical activity of embryonic nerves. *J. Physiol.*, *1953*, 122:33–34.

DERBYSHIRE, A. J. and FARLEY, J. C. Sampling auditory responses at the cortical level. A routine for EER-audiometer testing. *Ann. Oto-rhinolaryngol.*, *1959*, 68:657–697.

EICHORN, D. H. Electrocortical and autonomic response in infants to visual and auditory stimuli. Dissertation, Northwestern University, *1951*.

ELLINGSON, R. J. Electroencephalograms of normal, full-term newborns immediately after birth with observations on arousal and visual evoked responses. *Electroenceph. clin. Neurophysiol.*, *1958*, 10:31–50.

ELLINGSON, R. J. Cortical electrical responses to visual stimulation in the human infant. *Electroenceph. clin. Neuro-*

physiol., 1960, 12:663–677.

ELLINGSON, R. J. Studies of the electrical activity of the developing human brain. In: W. A. Himwich and H. E. Himwich, (editors), Developing Brain. Progress in Brain Research, Vol. 8. Elsevier, Amsterdam, in press.

ELLINGSON, R. J. and WILCOTT, R. C. Development of evoked responses in the visual and auditory cortices of kittens. J. Neurophysiol., 1960, 23:363–375.

ENGEL, R. Evaluation of electroencephalographic tracings of newborns. J. Lancet, 1961, 81:523–532.

ENGEL, R. and BUTLER, B. V. Appraisal of conceptual age of newborn infants by electroencephalographic methods. J. Pediat., 1963, 63:386–393.

GEISLER, C. D., FISHKOPF, L. S. and ROSENBLITH, W. A. Extracranial response to acoustic clicks in man. Science, 1958, 128:1210–1211.

GOLDSTEIN, M. H. Averaging techniques applied to evoked responses. In: M. A. B. Brazier, (editor), Computer techniques in EEG analysis. Electroenceph. clin. Neurophysiol., 1960, (suppl. 20):59–63.

GROSSMAN, C. Electro-ontogenesis of cerebral activity. Forms of neonatal responses and their recurrence in epileptic discharges. Arch. Neurol. Psychiat., (Chic.), 1955, 74:186–202.

HIRSCH, J. F., PERTUISET, B., CALVET, J., BUISSON-FEREY, J., FISCHGOLD, H. ET SCHERRER, J. Etude des réponses électrocorticales obtenues chez l'homme par des stimulations somesthésiques et visuelles. Electroenceph. clin. Neurophysiol., 1961, 13:411–424.

HUBEL, D. and WIESEL, T. N. Receptive field studies in the visual system of newborn and monocularly deprived kittens. Proc. XVIIth internat. Congr. Psychol., 1963, in press.

HUNT, W. E. and GOLDRING, S. Maturation of evoked response of the visual cortex in the postnatal rabbit. Electroenceph. clin. Neurophysiol., 1951, 3:465–471.

HURSH, J. B. Conduction velocity and diameter of nerve fibers. Amer. J. Physiol., 1939a, 127:131–139.

HURSH, J. B. The properties of growing nerve fibers. Amer. J. Physiol., 1939b, 127:140–153.

MARTY, R. Développement postnatal des résponses sensorielles du cortex cérébral chez le chat et le lapin. Thèse, L'Université de Paris. Masson, Paris, 1962.

MARTY, R., CONTAMIN, F. and SCHERRER, J. Cortical response to photic stimulation in a newborn cat. Electroenceph. clin. Neurophysiol., 1958, 10:761.

MONNIER, M. Retinal, cortical and motor responses to photic stimulation in man. Retino-cortical time and opto-motor integration time. J. Neurophysiol., 1952, 15:469–486.

NEKHOROCHEFF, I. La stimulation lumineuse intermittente chez l'enfant normal. Rev. Neurol., (Paris), 1950, 83:601–602.

PURPURA, D. P. Analysis of axodendritic synaptic organizations in immature cerebral cortex. Ann. N. Y. Acad. Sci., 1961, 94:604–654.

ROSE, J. E., ADRIAN, H. and SANTIBANEZ, G. Electrical signs of maturation in the auditory system of the kitten. Acta. neurol. latinoamer., 1957, 3:133–143.

SCHAPER, G. Discussion of Kellaway's "Ontogenetic evolution of the electroencephalogram in human and animals." Proc. IV int. Congr. Electroenceph. clin. Neurophysiol. Acta Med. Belg., 1957, 31–32.

SCHEIBEL, A. B. Neural correlates of psychophysiological developments in the young organism. In: J. Wortis, (editor), Recent Advances in Biological Psychiatry, 1962, 4:313–327.

SCHERRER, J. and FOURMENT, A. Electrocortical effects of sensory deprivation during development. In: W. A. Himwich and H. E. Himwich, (editors), Developing Brain. Progress in Brain Research, Vol. 8. Amsterdam, Elsevier, in press.

SCHERRER, J. and OECONOMOS, D. Réponses corticales somesthésiques du mammifère nouveau-né comparées à celles de l'animal adulte. Et. Neonat., 1954, 3:199–216.

SCHERRER, J. and OECONOMOS, D. Réponses évoquées corticales somesthésiques des mammifères adulte et nouveau-né. Les grandes activites du lobe temporal. Masson, Paris, 1955, 249–268.

SHAGASS, C. and SCHWARTZ, M. Reactivity cycle of somatosensory cortex in humans with and without psychiatric disorder.

Science, 1961, 134:1757–1759.

SHIPTON, H. W. Simplified averaging technique for the detection of evoked cortical responses. *In:* C. N. Smyth, (editor) *Medical Electronics.* Iliffe, London, 1960a, 120–127.

SHIPTON, H. W. Photographic averaging technique for the study of evoked potentials in man. *In:* C. N. Smyth, (editor), *Medical Electronics.* Iliffe, London, 1960b, 186–187.

THOMAS, J. E. and LAMBERT, E. H. Conduction velocity of motor fibers of peripheral nerves in infants and children. *Electroenceph. clin. Neurophysiol., 1958,* 10:577.

ULETT, G., Dow, R. S. and LARSELL, O. The inception of conductivity in the corpus callosum and the cortico-pontocerebellar pathway of young rabbits, with reference to myelination. *J. comp. Neurol., 1944,* 80:1–10.

VANZULLI, A., BOGACZ, J. and GARCIA-

AUSTT, E. Evoked responses in man. III. Auditory response. *Acta Neurol. Latinoamer., 1961,* 7:303–309.

VANZULLI, A., GOBACZ, J., HANDLER, P. and GARCIA-AUSTT, E. Evoked responses in man. I. Photic responses. *Acta Neurol. Latinoamer., 1960,* 6:219–231.

WILLIAMS, H. L., TEPAS, D. I. and MARLOCK, H. C. Evoked responses to clicks and electroencephalographic stages of sleep in man. *Science, 1962,* 138:685–686.

ZETTERSTRÖM, B. The clinical electroretinogram. IV. The electroretinogram in children during the first year of life. *Acta Ophthalmol., 1951,* 29:295–304.

ZETTERSTRÖM, B. The electroretinogram in prematurely (sic) children. *Acta Ophthalmol., 1952,* 30:405–408.

ZETTERSTRÖM, B. Flicker electroretinography in newborn infants. *Acta Ophthalmol., 1955,* 33:157–166.

DISCUSSION

DR. PRICHARD: What do you think about Dr. Bickford's work? He suggested that a lot of the average evoked responses were due to artifact.

DR. ELLINGSON: Dr. Bickford produced what he calls a myotonic type of response from the area of the inion. He produces them best with loud-click stimuli. We did not get such responses if we covered up the stroboscope but still let it click. The click of the stroboscope is fairly soft, but it will produce evoked responses in the cat or kitten if you record directly from the cortex.

DR. SAMSON-DOLLFUS: Dr. Ellingson, were these studies done with light or dark adaptation?

DR. ELLINGSON: The room is not completely darkened, but the ambient illumination is very low.

DR. SAMSON-DOLLFUS: Are the eyes open?

DR. ELLINGSON: Usually not. Most of the infant work is done with the baby asleep. The infants move too much if you flash at them while they are awake. Latencies are the same awake or asleep. We can't be sure, of course, if an infant is awake when his eyes are closed. We have recorded evoked responses in adults with eyes open and closed. In some cases there seems to be some difference in amplitude, but that's about all. There is no difference in the latencies.

DR. TORRES: I'd like to ask Dr. Ellingson where his reference electrodes are placed and also to suggest the possibility that the early response in the frontal tracings might be a part of the electroretinogram.

DR. ELLINGSON: The reference electrodes in the babies have been variously placed: earlobe, anterior temporal, or precentral areas, usually. We stay away from the vertex to avoid confounding our responses with various responses that occur around the vertex. We have considered the possibility that the short-latency responses seen in frontal tracings are electroretinographic. With some of the older children we covered the eye on the side from which we were recording with a light-tight eye patch, and then flashed only the other eye. The short-latency response was still obtained. This is evidence of a sort that this response is due to eyeblink and not ERG.

DR. WILSON: Would you comment on the great variations of the average evoked responses?

DR. ELLINGSON: I do not know if we would see such a variety of evoked response wave forms if we could record directly from the primary visual cortex. Differences in wave form might be due simply to differences in position of the pickup electrodes with respect to the active area of the visual cortex. I suspect that this is the reason for much of the variation we do see, but I don't know this.

DR. ENGEL: We have tested the photic response to repeated single flashes in premature, full-term, and postmature infants, using the same technique as described by Ellingson. In many instances the electroencephalographic testing was done within hours after birth and usually within the first five days. Premature and sick babies, however, were not always permitted to have a test immediately after birth or under adverse conditions.

In determining the latency interval, Ellingson measured the time from the peak of the signal artifact to the peak of the response by visual inspection. I tried to determine the latency as measured from the initial deviation from the baseline caused by the signal to the beginning deviation from the background activity caused by the response sequence. The response over the occipital area or the inion precedes the so-called nonspecific response which is also seen with acoustic or other sensory stimulation.

In 74.9 per cent of 1002 newborn infants, interpretable responses over the occipital area were obtained and latency measurements could be made on visual inspection. The percentage of interpretable responses was the same in the full-term, premature, and postmature group. The latency measurement was inversely proportional to the conceptual age at the time of the EEG (Fig. 1).

In 624 infants the test was carried out within five days of birth. In these the correlation of conceptual age and birth weight was .531, while that for conceptual age and photic latency was .468. When the effect of weight was partialled out, the correlation between conceptual age and photic latency was still .349, indicating that the measurement of photic latency con-

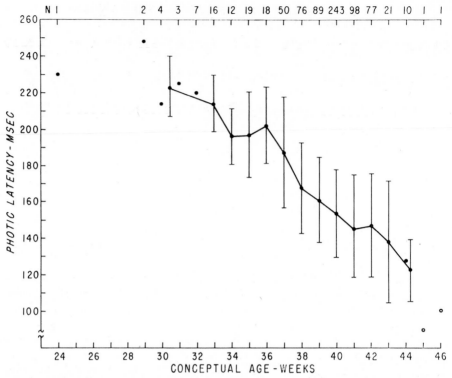

Fig. 1. Relationship and standard deviation of mean latency of photic response and conceptual age at time of EEG pooled from different individuals. Correlation coefficient −.607 (p <.001). N = Number of individuals with interpretable response to photic stimulation on visual inspection.

tributes independently to the estimate of the conceptual age in the newborn. Follow-up of the premature group indicates that their latency period shortens proportionally as they approach the conceptual age of 40–42 weeks.

Psychological testing at the age of eight months showed that full-term infants with relatively short photic latency at birth had a significantly higher mental score at the age of eight months than the group of neonates with relatively long individual latency measurements.

In spite of great individual variations, just as in weight, the latency measurement is an independent and useful tool in the evaluation of the conceptual age.

RELATIONSHIP OF SEIZURE SUSCEPTIBILITY TO MORPHOLOGIC AND PHYSIOLOGIC PROPERTIES OF NORMAL AND ABNORMAL IMMATURE CORTEX*

DOMINICK P. PURPURA†

*Department of Neurological Surgery, Columbia University,
College of Physicians and Surgeons, New York, N. Y.*

Introduction

It has long been recognized that disturbances in the external or internal milieu of the developing nervous system are responsible for a wide variety of neurological and behavioral disorders which may manifest themselves at different times after the initial insult. Control of the factors underlying these disturbances is the primary objective of any comprehensive program of preventive medicine. But the establishment of effective controls and safeguards against metabolic or traumatic insults to the immature brain requires first a more satisfactory understanding of normal ontogenetic patterns and the manner in which disturbances in these patterns are reflected in functional abnormalities. To achieve these objectives, attention to the various mechanisms regulating the differentiation of complex organizations of neurons is a necessary prerequisite. Here the problem is not merely one of defining the sequential stages of morphogenesis of different neuronal organizations but elucidation of the processes linking one stage to the other.

At the outset of such an inquiry, it must be recognized that the differentiation of developing cell systems in the brain is programmed differently with respect to time and rate of maturation in different populations of neurons. Consequently, functional disturbances resulting from an insult to the immature brain at a particular ontogenetic phase may produce effects which are referable to differences in maturational patterns. Functional disturbances resulting from a severe insult to the immature brain are likely to be expressions of activities in organizations which have already attained a relatively advanced stage of differentiation at the time of the insult. This is particularly true in the case of pathophysiological processes which are expressed, in part, in an abnormal increase in the overall activity of a particular neuronal organization. In the exploration of the basis of hyperexcitability or seizure sus-

*This study was supported in part by the National Institute of Neurological Diseases and Blindness, National Institutes of Health, NB 01312-07, the United Cerebral Palsy Research and Educational Foundation, R-135-62C, and the Epilepsy Foundation.

†Supported by Public Health Service Research Career Program Award, NB-K3-5280-03, National Institute of Neurological Diseases and Blindness, National Institutes of Health.

117

ceptibility in immature cortex, differential rate of development is only one element in a constellation of factors to be considered. For example, disturbances of maturational patterns may accelerate as well as retard normal developmental processes. And what is perhaps more important is that acceleration of one developmental process and retardation or another may occur in the same neuronal organization as a result of a cataclysmic disturbance in maturational patterns. The appearance of paroxysmal activity in the immature brain conveys no information regarding mechanism. Consequently, the compilation of detailed descriptions of abnormal electroencephalographic activities is of little more than nosological significance. The particular value of ontogenetic studies lies in the possibility of effecting structure-function correlations that are rarely achieved in studies of mature animals. Although correlative ontogenetic studies have been useful in facilitating an understanding of the origin and nature of several varieties of electrocortical phenomena (Purpura, 1959 a; Purpura, 1961 a; Purpura, et al., 1963), few attempts have been made to extend the analytical approach to a consideration of pathophysiological events.

The present report summarizes investigations which evaluate the contribution of the factors noted above in the development of hyperexcitability in different neuronal organizations. Examples of hyperexcitability resulting from normal differences in maturational patterns, as well as traumatic and/or metabolic insults to the immature brain, are presented to indicate how disturbances in maturational patterns may set into operation fundamentally different pathophysiological processes which are expressed in alterations in excitability.

A. Differences in Morphophysiological Development of Neocortex and Archicortex; The Hyperexcitability of Immature Hippocampus

ANATOMICAL CONSIDERATIONS

The normal postnatal morphogenesis of pyramidal neurons, stellate cells, and Cajal-Retzius cells in the feline neocortex has been described in detail elsewhere (Noback and Purpura, 1961). For present purposes, it is to be recalled that pyramidal neurons in neocortex have well-developed apical dendrites which extend into the molecular layer in newborn kittens. Basilar dendrites of most pyramidal neurons are short and may be absent on many cells. No dendritic spines are obvious and dendritic branching is minimal in the neonatal period. In contrast, stellate cells have their normal complement of dendrites but these, too, lack spines. Cajal-Retzius cells are readily identifiable in Golgi-Cox preparations of neonatal kitten neocortex but are not noted after the first postnatal week. The major developmental changes in neocortical pyramidal neurons in the second and third postnatal weeks are summarized in Fig. 1 Emphasis is to be placed on the elaboration of basilar dendritic systems, which is essentially a postnatal event, and the further growth and development of apical dendrites. Axon-collateral growth, increases in axon diameter, and myelination of corticospinal neurons are relatively late

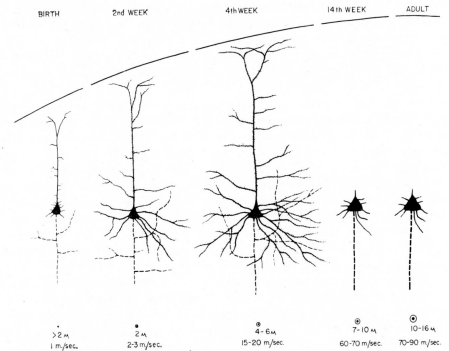

Fig. 1. **General features of morphogenesis of large pyramidal neurons in feline neocortex.** Dendritic ramifications were not added in 14-week and adult animals since there is little change in dendrites after the first month. Below, representation of axon-diameters of largest pyramidal fibers and their conduction velocities at various ages. (From Purpura, *et al.*, 1963).

postnatal maturational events (Purpura, *et al.*, 1963). From examination of the general features of neocortical neurons at various developmental stages, it has been concluded that in the kitten pyramidal and stellate cells acquire mature characteristics by the end of the third postnatal week (Noback and Purpura, 1961).

The differential rate of development of apical and basilar dendritic systems is reflected in a predominance of axodendritic synapses on apical dendrites of pyramidal neurons in the immediate neonatal period (Voeller, Pappas and Purpura, 1963). Electron microscope studies of immature neocortex have also revealed a paucity of fine neuronal and non-neuronal processes between neuron cell bodies and between large dendritic trunks in newborn kittens (Pappas and Purpura, 1963). The homogeneity of dendritic processes in the superficial neuropil in the newborn kitten is illustrated in Fig. 2. At this developmental stage, neuron cell bodies are densely packed and are virtually devoid of axosomatic synaptic contacts. Axosomatic synapses are more readily identified in 5–7-day-old kittens and become more numerous along with the development of basilar dendritic systems and axon-collaterals. It is of interest to note that the cytoplasm of neocortical neuron cell bodies in newborn kittens contains poorly organized cisternae of the endoplasmic

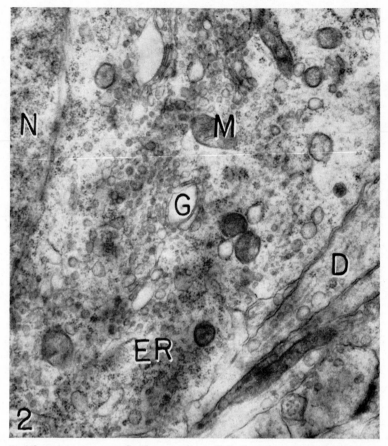

Fig. 2. Electron micrograph of part of a cell body from the superficial neocortex of a kitten 36 hours old. A nucleus (N) is visible. There is a Golgi complex (G) consisting of vacuoles and small vesicles. Numerous mitochondria (M) can be seen. The endoplasmic reticulum (ER) has cisternae lined with RNP particles that are also thickly scattered throughout the cytoplasm. A dendrite (D) lies along the cell membrane. x 24,500. (From Voeller, Pappas and Purpura, 1963).

reticulum (ER) and densely scattered ribosomes which are generally unrelated to membranous components of the ER (Fig. 2). The fine structure of kitten neocortex appears to acquire mature characteristics (Pappas and Purpura, 1961) by the end of the second postnatal week (Voeller, Pappas and Purpura, 1963).

A remarkably different pattern of morphogenesis is noted with respect to the feline hippocampus. As pointed out previously (Purpura, 1960 a), hippocampal pyramidal neurons have extraordinarily well-developed basilar dendrites as well as apical dendrites in the neonatal kitten. These dendrites have numerous spines and branches. The morphological features of "typical" hippocampal pyramidal neurons from a 2-day-old kitten are shown in Fig. 3A. Comparison with the neocortical pyramidal neuron in Fig. 3B indicates that the hippocampal pyramidal neurons in the neonatal kitten have general

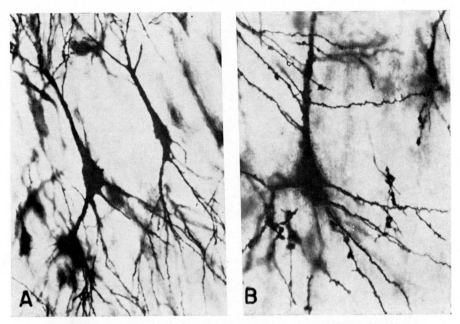

Fig. 3. Golgi-Cox preparations of pyramidal neurons in the hippocampus of a 2-day-old kitten (A) and the neocortex of a 14-day-old kitten (B). Basilar dendritic system of hippocampal neurons in neonatal kittens has developmental characteristics similar to that of neocortical pyramidal neurons at 2 weeks. A, x 520; B, x 660.

morphological characteristics which are not seen in neocortical pyramidal neurons until the end of the second postnatal week (Purpura, 1960 a).

The relatively mature status of hippocampal pyramidal neurons in neonatal kittens has been clearly revealed in recent electron microscope studies (Fig. 4–8). Perhaps the most impressive finding to date with respect to the maturational differences in neocortical and hippocampal neurons bears on the organization of intracytoplasmic organelles in the immediate neonatal period. A striking development of the Golgi-complex and other elements of the endoplasmic reticulum (Fig. 4 and 5) is an outstanding characteristic of hippocampal neurons in the immediate neonatal period. Also in contrast to findings in immature neocortex is the presence of a large number of fine processes in the neuropil. Axodendritic synapses are seen in large numbers in the hippocampus of newborn kittens (Fig. 6) but more important is the finding of axosomatic synapses at this developmental stage (Fig. 7).

In view of the findings that the hippocampus exhibits such advanced maturational features in newborn kittens, considerable difficulty has been encountered in defining additional maturational characteristics that are particularly related to the fine structure of pyramidal neurons or their synaptic relations. As a matter of fact, virtually all of the fine structural characteristics of the hippocampus in adult animals (Green and Maxwell, 1961; Hamlyn, 1963) are detectable in the hippocampus of the newborn kitten. These features include soma-to-soma appositions (Fig. 8), desmosomal relations be-

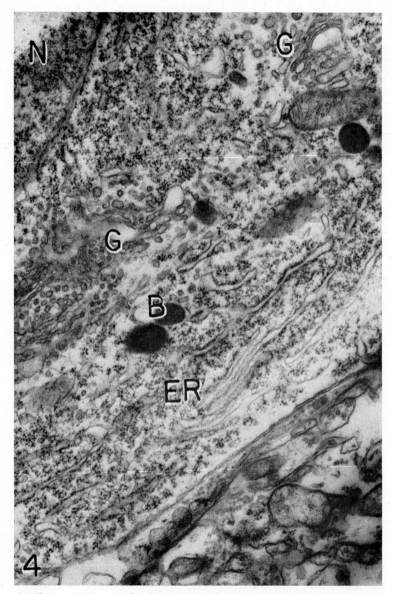

Fig. 4. Electron micrograph of a pyramidal neuron in the hippocampus of a new-born kitten. Peripheral portion of cytoplasm contains well-developed cisternae of the endoplasmic reticulum (ER) with attached ribosomes. A highly differentiated Golgi complex (G) can be seen in a paranuclear position. Nucleus = N, Several granular inclusion bodies (B) are present. x 28,000. (From Pappas and Purpura, in preparation).

tween neuron cell bodies, and the interposition of fine glial processes between neuronal elements.

ELECTROPHYSIOLOGICAL CONSIDERATIONS

The differential development of axodendritic synaptic pathways in the neocortex of the newborn kitten is reflected in the prominence of surface

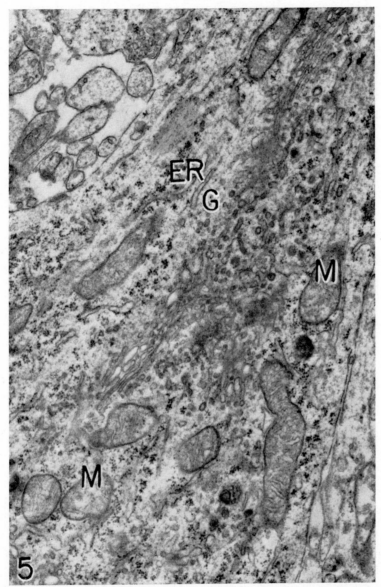

Fig. 5. Electron micrograph of part of a pyramidal neuron cell body in the hippocampus of a newborn kitten. This section clearly shows the marked differentiation of the Golgi complex (G) oriented toward a large dendritic process. Some elements of the endoplasmic reticulum (ER) are present in the cytoplasm. Numerous mitochondria (M) are also evident. x 24,000. (From Pappas and Purpura, in preparation).

negative potentials in response to cortical surface stimulation (Purpura, Carmichael and Housepian, 1960) and stimulation of medial and lateral thalamic nuclei and mesencephalic reticular regions (Fig. 9). In the case of primary evoked responses to sciatic nerve stimulation, surface positive components are not obvious until after the fifth postnatal day, which corresponds to the phase of initial elaboration of the deep neuropil and axosomatic synapses

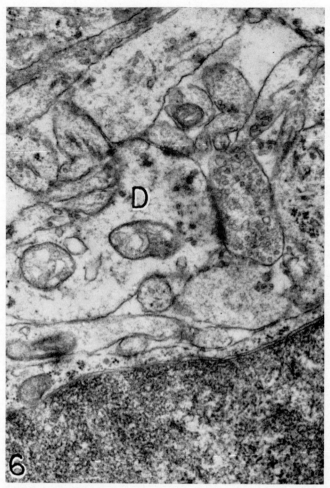

Fig. 6. Axodendritic synapses in the hippocampus of a newborn kitten. The large dendrite (D) is in synaptic relation with two axonal terminals containing numerous vesicles. x 31,500. (From Pappas and Purpura, in preparation).

(Purpura, 1961 a; Purpura, *et al.*, 1963; and elsewhere in this volume).

Attempts have been made in several types of studies of evoked activities in young kittens to elicit convulsant activity in neocortex by stimulation of afferent pathways and superficial elements contributing to the local response to surface stimulation. Repetitive surface stimulation results in rapid attenuation of local negativities and prolonged depression of responsiveness (Fig. 9A-C). Low-frequency (0.5/sec.) stimulation of mesodiencephalic areas in neonatal kittens produces loss of prominent surface negativities (Fig. 9D), although high-frequency stimulation results in marked post-activation facilitation of this variety of activity (Purpura, 1961 a). Similar depression of specific evoked responses in somesthetic projection cortex is noted following repetitive stimulation of lateral thalamic nuclei in neonatal kittens (Fig. 9E-H).

In contrast to the relatively low level of excitability of neuronal organiza-

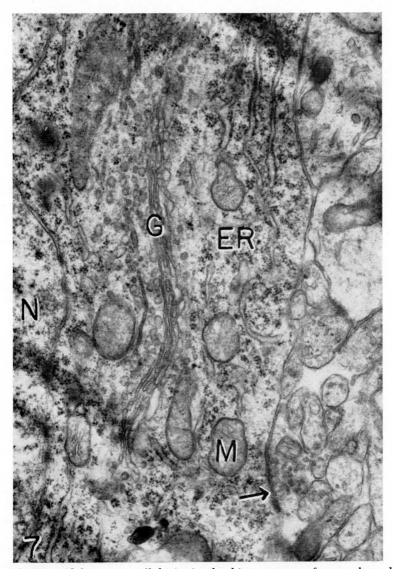

Fig. 7. Pyramidal neuron cell body in the hippocampus of a newborn kitten.
The perikaryon contains a prominent and extensive Golgi complex (G) characteristically located between the nucleus (N) and well-developed elements of the
endoplasmic reticulum (ER). Some mitochondria (M) are dispersed throughout the
cytoplasm. Note, at arrow, axosomatic synapse. These are frequently observed in
the hippocampus of the neonatal kitten. x 29,000. (From Pappas and Purpura, in
preparation).

tions in the neocortex of newborn kittens, hippocampal pathways exhibit
excitability characteristics which are qualitatively similar to those reported
by many investigators in studies of adult animals (cf. Passouant, 1962). Differences in the overall excitability of neocortex and archicortex were noted previously with respect to effects of topically applied convulsant ω-amino acids
and stimulation of the ventricular surface and fimbria (Purpura, 1960 a;

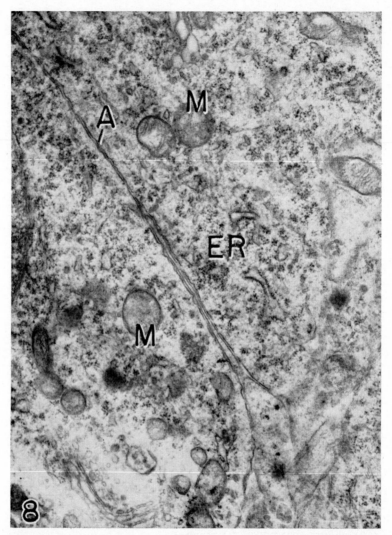

Fig. 8. Portions of two pyramidal neurons in the hippocampus of a newborn kitten. The cell bodies are in close apposition (A). A fine process, probably glial, is interposed up to the region of apposition. ER = endoplasmic reticulum; M = mitochondria. x 25,000. (From Pappas and Purpura, in preparation).

Purpura, 1961 b). Further examination of the functional properties of hippocampal synaptic organizations has revealed additional features of the maturational status of archicortex in newborn kittens. In these studies, the hippocampus was exposed by suction-ablation of overlying neocortex and stimulating electrodes were placed in the region of the dorsal fimbria and the subiculum. Recording electrodes were generally applied to the ventricular surface of the exposed hippocampus at the fimbrial-hippocampal junction (CA_2 region) and at various sites along the longitudinal axis of the hippocampus in areas corresponding to the CA_1 zone (Purpura, 1959 b).

In neonatal kittens (locally anesthetized-succinylcholine paralyzed) fimbrial

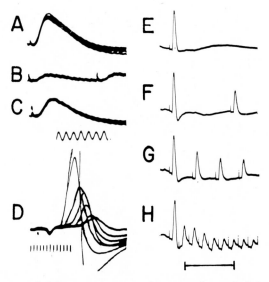

Fig. 9. Composite of different varieties of potentials evoked in the neocortex of neonatal kittens. Negativity upwards in this and all subsequent records. A, superficial cortical responses (SCR) to local surface stimulation consist in long-duration negativity. Stimulus frequency in A, 0.5/sec. B, increase in stimulus frequency (12/sec.) produces marked depression of SCR which persists for many seconds after return to 0.5/sec. stimulus frequency (C). Cal. 100 cycles/sec. D, superimposed responses recorded from the anterior syprasylvian gyrus during 0.5/sec. stimulation in medial mesencephalic reticular regions in a 2-day-old kitten. Early low amplitude surface-positive component is unaltered, whereas late prominent negativity rapidly attenuates at this stimulus frequency, indicating marked "fatigability" of reticulocortical evoked responses. Cal. 100 cycles/sec. E–H, predominantly surface-negative specific responses evoked in posterior sigmoid gyrus following stimulation of ventrolateral thalamic nuclei and their projections in an 8-hour-old kitten. Stimulus frequency as follows: E, 0.5/sec.; F, 2/sec.; G, 5/sec.; H, 10/sec. Depression of response is evident during 2/sec. stimulation and profound during 10/sec. stimulation. Time calibration, 0.5 sec.

stimulation elicited two types of responses from the fimbrial-hippocampal region and the CA_1 zone. A diphasic spike-like component succeeded by a slow negativity was characteristically recorded from the CA_2 zone, whereas a prominent long-latency negativity was evoked from the CA_1 region (Fig. 10A). During low-frequency fimbrial stimulation, augmentation of slow-negative components was observed and, at higher stimulus frequencies, slow negativity was eliminated and the conductile response depressed (Fig. 10B-D). Cessation of high-frequency stimulation resulted in the appearance of sustained rhythmical activity which tended to obscure late negative components of evoked responses (Fig. 10F). The details of the transitions in these evoked potentials and the development of sustained rhythmical 14–22 sec. oscillations with temporal relations similar to the evoked potentials are shown in Fig. 11. Weak-fimbrial stimulation was not always effective in eliciting sustained rhythmical after-discharge in newborn kittens. However, even when such stimulation failed in this respect, it was usually possible to observe post-

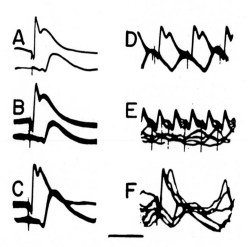

Fig. 10. Responses evoked from ventricular surface of the exposed hippocampus following stimulation of the fimbria in a 3-day-old kitten. Upper channel responses recorded from fimbrial-hippocampal junction; lower channel responses recorded from CA_1 region. Spike component represents conductile response in fimbria. Stimulus frequency as follows: A, 0.5/sec.; B, 5/sec.; C, 10/sec.; D, 25/sec.; E, 50/sec.; F, 0.5/sec. Note augmentation of responses during 10/sec. stimulation and attenuation at higher stimulus frequencies. Post-activation period (F) is characterized by development of convulsant activity. Time calibration, 50 msec.

activation facilitation of responses of the type described previously (Purpura, 1960 a). Variations were also seen in which late negative components exhibited marked prolongation and superimposed 10–12/sec. oscillations (Fig. 12).

The effects of subicular stimulation in newborn kittens are probably more relevant to the central issue of the excitability of hippocampal synaptic organizations inasmuch as these effects are referable to orthodromic activation of pyramidal neurons and elements of the fascia dentata. It is of interest that responses recorded from the ventricular surface of the hippocampus in newborn kittens following subicular stimulation were similar in many respects to those observed in adult animals (Purpura, 1959 b). As in the case of fimbrial stimulation, evoked potentials in newborn kittens initiated by subicular stimulation were frequently succeeded by "spontaneous" discharges with characteristics similar to those of the evoked potentials (Fig. 13A). Low-frequency subicular stimulation in satisfactory preparations was also capable of initiating or augmenting 10–14/sec. sustained rhythmical activity (Fig. 13B-D). In kittens less than one week old, paired conditioning-testing subicular stimulation revealed extraordinary short-latency facilitatory interactions (Fig. 14) with temporal features described previously in adult cats (Purpura, 1959 b). The transition from relatively simple evoked potentials to complex activities and after-discharges is clearly demonstrated in Fig. 15 in records obtained from a 5-day-old kitten. Finally, it should be pointed out that in later developmental states little change was noted in the excitability characteristics of hippocampal synaptic pathways. Quantitative differ-

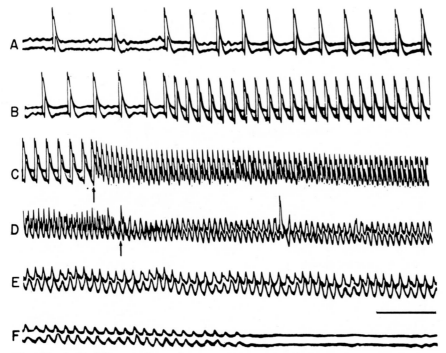

Fig. 11. A–F, different phases from continuous record of build-up and attenuation of responses similar to those shown in Fig. 10 during repetitive fimbrial stimulation. A, transition from 2/sec. to 5/sec. stimulation; B, augmentation during 10/sec. stimulation. Arrows in C and D signal beginning and end of 25/sec. stimulation, respectively. D–F, characteristics of after-discharge resemble those of evoked responses. After-discharge persisted for 90 seconds following fimbrial stimulation. Time bar, 0.5 sec.

ences in the complexity of responses evoked by repetitive subicular (or fimbrial) stimulation as well as marked prolongation of post-tetanic or post-activation facilitatory effects were the major developmental alterations noted in the second postnatal week (Fig. 16). It was not possible to detect further functional changes in hippocampal synaptic organizations after the second week, at least in terms of activities evoked by fimbrial or subicular stimulation.

CORRELATIVE ANALYSIS

Differences in the excitability of neocortex and archicortex have been noted previously in studies of the effects of Metrazol and gross electrical stimulation in newborn kittens (Cadilhac, et al., 1960). The results described above confirm and extend these observations to include the different effects of stimulation of afferent pathways to neocortex and archicortex. It has, of course, long been known that in adult animals the hippocampus has the lowest threshold for eliciting seizure activity of any structure in the mammalian brain. In view of this, it might be expected that similar findings in newborn kittens merely reflect differences in overall excitability between neocortical

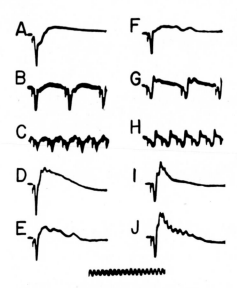

Fig. 12. Atypical responses evoked from exposed hippocampus following fimbrial stimulation at different frequencies in a 1-day-old kitten. Responses elicited by 0.5/sec. stimulation (A) exhibit marked attenuation during 10/sec. (B) and 25/sec. stimulation (C). Immediate post-activation phase is characterized by augmentation of late negativity (D and E). A second series of repetitive stimulation results in polarity changes of initial component of response. During the second post-activation phase (I and J), low-frequency stimulation (0.5/sec.) elicits responses with prominent late negativity and superimposed 10/sec. oscillations. Calibration, 100 cycles/sec.

and hippocampal synaptic organizations. Although the present studies permit a satisfactory explanation of these differences in newborn animals, they do not elucidate the basis for the general hyperexcitability of archicortex (Kandel and Spencer, 1961).

Light and electron microscope studies reveal that in newborn animals the hippocampus has attained a maturational stage which is not reached in the neocortex until the end of the second postnatal week. This is particularly evident with respect to the fine structural characteristics of intracytoplasmic organelles which house the internal metabolic machinery of the neuron. Other factors relating to the development of axosomatic synaptic pathways and the general characteristics of the neuropil in the hippocampus of the newborn kitten may also be cited in support of this conclusion.

The correlation of relatively advanced structural and functional development in the hippocampus of newborn kittens is of interest from the standpoint of the well-known susceptibility of the archicortex to various birth injuries and antenatal and neonatal hypoxemic episodes. In this context, it is to be recalled that hippocampal neurons in the newborn kitten have elaborated a Golgi-complex which appears more highly differentiated than in neurons in other parts of the neonatal kitten brain. Such fine structural characteristics are suggestive of a high metabolic activity critically dependent on a relatively high tissue oxygen tension. It is inferred from this that alterations in oxygenation secondary to disturbances in intracranial hemo-dynamics, pulmonary exchange or minor asphyxial episodes may produce selective damage to hippocampal neurons by virtue of their relatively advanced differentiation and high metabolic activity. The morphophysiological data summarized here would thus appear to provide important clues to the ontogenesis of seizure activities that involve neuronal organizations in the temporal lobe with powerful relations with brain stem reticular regions. These studies also indicate that the differences in the rate of maturation of neocortex and archi-

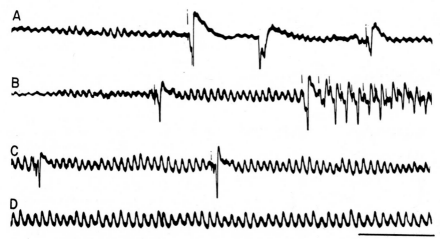

Fig. 13. **Hippocampus responses evoked by subicular stimulation in a 1-day-old kitten.** Recordings from exposed ventricular surface of dorsal CA_1 region. A, initial stimulus elicits a prominent positive-negative sequence succeeded by a spontaneous discharge similar to the evoked potential. B–C, build-up of after-discharge following stimulation at higher frequencies. D, general characteristics of 14/sec. discharge following subicular stimulation. Time bar, 0.5 sec.

cortex adequately account for the dominant role of hippocampal organizations in the electrographic expression of generalized abnormalities involving the immature brain (Cadilhac and Passouant-Fontaine, 1962).

B. Traumatic Lesions of Immature Neocortex and the Development of Focal Discharges

Despite the difficulty of eliciting paroxysmal discharges in the neocortex of newborn kittens following electrical stimulation of afferent pathways or the cortical surface, convulsant activity is clearly demonstrable following topical application of various pharmacological agents (Purpura, 1961 b) and systemic administration of the antimetabolite, methoxypyridoxine (Purpura, 1962). Inasmuch as the present report is concerned with the relationship of seizure activities to the morphological properties of cortex, the problem of the development of "responsiveness" to different types of convulsant agents will not be discussed further. Rather some consideration will be given to the effects observed in immature neocortex following two types of traumatic lesions: one produced by rapid freezing of a small circumscribed area of neocortex, the other resulting from the neuronal isolation of a region of neocortex in the immediate neonatal period.

Focal Paroxysmal Discharges in Freezing Lesions

The production of a 4 mm. cold lesion of neocortex in adult cats is generally followed in 1–2 hours by the development of focal discharges which may attain a remarkable regularity (0.5–1.5/sec.) and overt configuration. The diphasic negative-positive EEG spikes resulting from such lesions in adult cats have been studied in our laboratory with respect to the synaptic organiza-

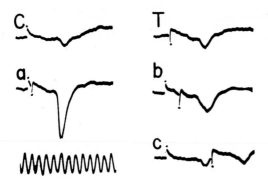

Fig. 14. Short-latency facilitation of hippocampal evoked responses to subicular stimulation in a 5-day-old kitten. C and T, weak conditioning and testing responses, respectively. Marked potentiation of surface-positive response is observed at 4 msec. C–T intervals (a). Facilitatory interaction is reduced at 20 msec. intervals (b) and is absent at 60 msec. interval. Calibration, 100 cycles/sec.

tions underlying their production (Smith and Purpura, 1960), the alterations in amino acid metabolism found in the lesion site (Berl, *et al.*, 1959), and the characteristics of the postsynaptic potentials involved in the focal discharge (Goldensohn and Purpura, 1963). In view of the fact that focal discharges in freezing lesions of neocortex have been useful in the analysis of the permeability of the blood-brain barrier to GABA in newborn (Purpura and Carmichael, 1960) and adult animals (Purpura, *et al.*, 1958) as well as in studies of the "pacemaker" characteristics of traumatized neurons (Musgrave, Sanaman and Purpura, 1962), observations were made on the epileptogenic effects of freezing lesions in the immature brain (Goldensohn, Shofer and Purpura, 1962).

Attempts to elicit focal discharges with characteristics similar to those of adult animals have been unsuccessful in kittens less than 2–3 months old. It must not be inferred from this that the failure to induce focal discharges in freezing lesions was a reflection of the inability of neocortical neuronal organizations to generate such discharges by other means. Actually, sporadic spontaneous focal discharges were frequently observed in the neocortex of newborn and young kittens (Fig. 17A and B). These were probably related to the exquisite fragility of the cortex to experimental manipulations. Paroxysmal activities of a focal nature were also frequently observed in immature neocortex, especially when the cortex was treated with KCl solutions (Fig. 17C) in attempts to activate focal discharges in freezing lesions. Spontaneous focal discharges might be observed in a particular region of cortex prior to the production of the freezing lesion (Fig. 18A). After the lesion, such discharges were eliminated, and treatment of the cortex with Ringer's solution containing 10 times extracellular potassium activated spikes in areas remote from the lesion site but failed to initiate focal discharges at the lesion (Fig. 18B). In relatively few cases was it possible to detect focal discharges of any variety at the site of a freezing lesion of neocortex in kittens less than two months. The possibility that focal spikes of relatively low amplitude and frequency might be obscured by other types of ongoing activity was examined in several suggestive cases. In only one preparation out of twenty under two months of age was it possible to detect focal discharges of very low frequency in the background electrocortical activity. The simple maneuver of mild asphyxia potentiated these discharges and facilitated their further detection in a 16-day-old kitten (Fig. 19).

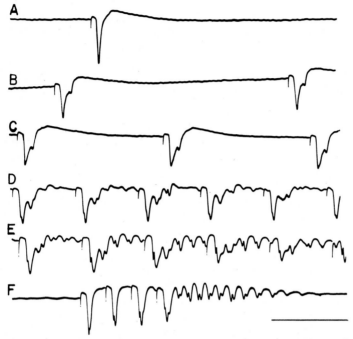

Fig. 15. Changing characteristics of responses recorded from the surface of the hippocampus following subicular stimulation at different frequencies in a 5-day-old kitten. A, positive-negative sequence develops a late positive inflection during 1/sec. stimulation (B). Late positivity increases in amplitude at 2/sec. stimulation (C) and is succeeded by after-discharge in D and E. During a period of post-activation facilitation (F), a train of four stimuli at 8/sec. elicits a 14/sec. after-discharge with characteristics similar to evoked responses. Time bar, 0.5 sec.

The negative effect of freezing lesions of neocortex in kittens less than eight weeks old raises the question as to the nature of the ontogenetic processes most likely to be related to the development of focal epileptogenic discharges. Since focal discharges with similar electrographic characteristics can be elicited in the neocortex of newborn and young kittens by pharmacological agents or strong electrical stimulation, it goes without saying that the capacity for focal spiking is present in the immediate neonatal period. In attempts to explain the delayed ontogenetic appearance of paroxysmal discharges in freezing lesions, it is to be recalled that neuronal elements in neocortex have acquired their complete maturational features by the end of the first month (Noback and Purpura, 1961). Recent studies of the amino acid content of immature neocortex have also shown that adult values of free amino acids are acquired by the fourth week (Berl and Purpura, 1963). At this time, virtually all varieties of electrocortical potentials have electrographic characteristics that are similar to those of adult animals. This is not true, however, with respect to the latency of many evoked potentials, since myelination of most central pathways is not completed until well after the first month (Langworthy, 1929). This has been particularly evident in studies of the relationship of conduction velocity of pyramidal axons to their growth and myelination (Purpura, *et al.*, 1963). If the corticospinal tract may be

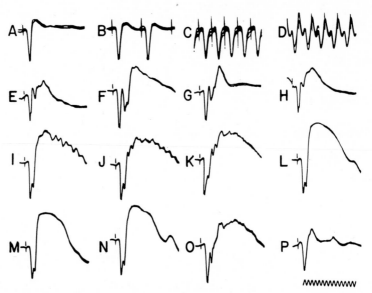

Fig. 16. Post-activation facilitation of hippocampal responses to repetitive subicu-lar stimulation in a 13-day-old kitten. Stimulus frequencies as follows: A, 0.5/sec.; B, 12/sec.; C and D, 25/sec.; E–P, 0.5/sec. Note changes in responses during period of high-frequency (25/sec.) stimulation. Immediate post-activation phase (E–H) is characterized by prominent late positivity and enhancement of late negativity. Late negativity rapidly increases during the succeeding 90 seconds and occasionally exhibits 10–14/sec. oscillations (I–O). P, recovery. Calibration, 100 cycles/sec.

taken as a suitable example for studies of this relationship in neocortex, it is clear that the one ontogenetic event which has a temporal correspondence with the appearance of focal discharges in freezing lesions is activation of glial elements as seen in the rapid phase of myelination of pyramidal neuron axons. Here myelination is considered but one sign of this "glial activation" and not a process required for the development of focal discharges. The question raised, then, is whether the appearance of paroxysmal discharges subsequent to freezing lesions of neocortex is dependent on some maturational change in glia-neuronal relations rather than a developmental process confined to neurons. In seeking further explanations of the delayed onset of focal spikes in freezing lesions, the search for more subtle matura-tional events involving perhaps the development of compartmentation of metabolic processes linked to excitability properties of neurons may provide important clues (Berl and Purpura, 1963).

MECHANISM OF HYPEREXCITABILITY IN ISOLATED IMMATURE NEOCORTEX

Complete or partial isolation of a slab of neocortex in adult animals pro-duces changes in the excitability of the isolated area which are characterized by various types of activities not encountered in intact cortex (Burns, 1958; Echlin, 1959). The resemblance of this phenomenon to that observed in denervated peripheral structures (Cannon, 1939) has lead to the notion that the hyperexcitability of chronic isloated neocortex is referable to the mechan-

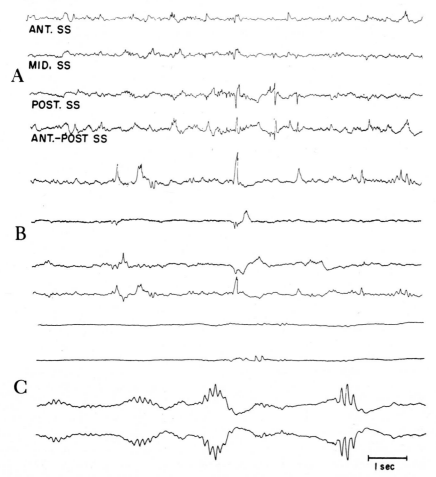

Fig. 17. A, spontaneous electrical activity recorded from the neocortical surface in a 6-day-old locally anesthetized-paralyzed kitten. (SS = syprasylvian gyrus). Sporadic focal discharges are evident in posterior syrpasylvian leads. B, spontaneous electrical activity from neocortex of a 3-day-old kitten. Electrode placements as in A. Intermittent discharges noted from several sites. C, same preparation as in B, several seconds after rinsing cortex with Ringer's solution containing 30 mM KCl. Note activation of 8–10/sec. spindle-like discharges localized to posterior suprasylvian region. (From Goldensohn, Shofer and Purpura, 1963).

ism of "denervation hypersensitivity" (Echlin, 1959). This problem has been explored in ontogenetic studies which have provided an alternative explanation of the hyperexcitability of isolated immature cortex (Purpura and Housepian, 1961).

Acute subpial isolation of a slab of neocortex in young kittens generally results in some depression of evoked activities with gradual recovery in suitable preparations over 1–2 hours. During this period, local negative responses to cortical surface stimulation (superficial cortical responses, SCR) are preserved, but repetitive stimulation introduces no new activities (Fig. 20). Several hours after recovery of SCR's, repetitive stimulation may lead

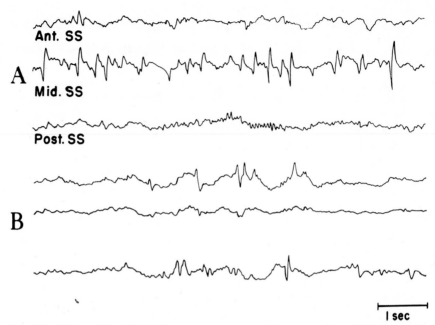

Fig. 18. Effects of KCl—Ringer's solution on spontaneous focal discharges appearing sporadically in a 10-day-old kitten. A, predominantly diphasic positive-negative spikes localized to middle syprasylvian (SS) gyrus. B, after freezing lesion in middle SS, spontaneous spikes are abolished. Treatment of cortex with KCl—Ringer's solution activates hypersynchronous activity in normal areas but not at the lesion site. (From Goldensohn, Shofer and Purpura, 1963).

to the appearance of surface-positive responses indicating activation of subsurface elements by the surface stimulation (Purpura, 1959 a). Evoked responses may exhibit considerable post-activation facilitation during this acute post-isolation period (cf. Goldring, in this volume).

An entirely different situation is encountered several days after cortical isolation carried out in the immediate neonatal period. In preparations exhibiting adequate vascularization in the region of complete isolation, surface stimulation elicits prominent SCR's which are often succeeded by repetitive surface-positive bursts (Fig. 21) not unlike those observed in chronically isolated mature cortex (Burns, 1958). Spontaneous complex discharges are also detectable in different sites in the isolated slab of immature neocortex. One feature which distinguishes "burst-like" responses in immature isolated neocortex from those noted in adult isolated preparations is the stereotyped configuration of the activities in immature animals. This is clearly evident in Fig. 22 in which complex discharges succeeding the SCR were of remarkable regularity.

Attempts to define the elements in isolated cortex giving rise to the surface-positive repetitive discharges have provided satisfactory evidence that the major generators for this activity are located at a depth corresponding to the cell bodies and proximal portions of apical dendrites of the largest pyramidal

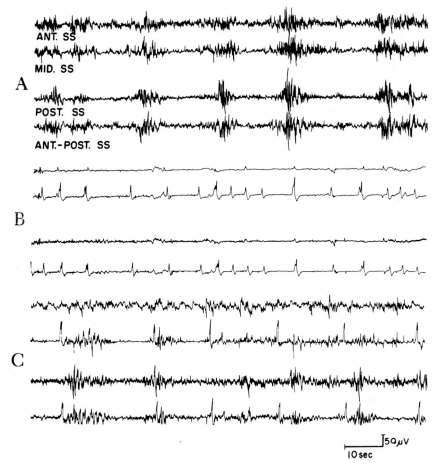

Fig. 19. Activation of focal spiking in a freezing lesion of middle suprasylvian gyrus in a 16-day-old kitten. A, focal spiking is not apparent in normal resting record. B, 45 seconds after onset of asphyxia, spontaneous electrocortical activity is abolished and focal spiking is potentiated. C, recovery from asphyxia; low-frequency spiking persists at the lesion site. (From Goldensohn, Shofer and Purpura, 1963).

neurons. The evidence for this is summarized in Fig. 23 which emphasizes the relationship of surface and sub-surface activities, the latter recorded with a penetrating microelectrode in an area of isolated cortex in a 5-day-old kitten, 3 days post-isolation. Also of importance are findings on the pharmacological effects of topically applied GABA, ε-amino caproic acid and strychnine on repetitive responses of isolated immature neocortex (Purpura and Housepian, 1961). These are indicative of prominent excitatory synaptic events generated in part in proximal apical dendritic regions (Purpura, 1960 b).

Examination of Golgi-Cox preparations from animals utilized in the electro-physiological studies has revealed several findings relevant to the interpreta-tion of the hyperexcitability of isolated immature neocortex. The most impres-sive feature of pyramidal neurons in regions of hyperexcitability is seen in the

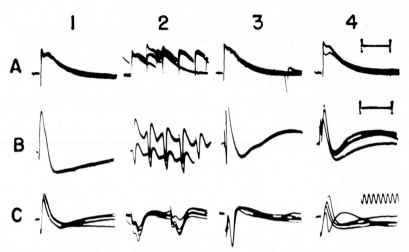

Fig. 20. Characteristics of SCR's evoked by stimulation of an acutely isolated region of neocortex in a 10-day-old kitten. A, responses elicited one hour after preparation of the isolated slab; stimulation at 0.5/sec. in 1, 3 and 4, and 10/sec. in 2. Depression of SCR is produced during 10/sec. stimulation, whereas following repetitive stimulation, the SCR is minimally augmented and a rare surface-positive discharge is observed in 3. B, 3 hours after A. In 1, SCR's are evoked with relatively weaker stimuli; during continued 10/sec. stimulation in 2, development of short latency surface-positivity occurs. The prior surface-positivity persists for several seconds during the post-activation stage in 3, then gradually diminishes in 4. C, 2 hours after B, 6 hours after preparation of the isolated slab; weak stimuli evoke SCR's that are rapidly eliminated during repetitive stimulation in 2. Note prominent surface-positivity in the post-activation period shown in 3. In 4, various stages in the recovery of the SCR are seen. Calibration, 0.2 sec. in A and B, and 100 cycles/sec. in C. (From Purpura and Housepian, 1961).

precocious development of intracortical axon-collaterals of elements whose main stem axons were interrupted in the process of preparing the cortical slab (Fig. 24). These axon-collaterals in 5–7-day-old kittens acquire developmental features several days after damage to the parent axon which are not ordinarily seen in neocortical pyramidal neurons until after the third to fourth week (Noback and Purpura, 1961; Purpura, et al., 1963). The extraordinary development of axon-collaterals of traumatized pyramidal neurons results in conversion of large Type I neurons into Type II cells with axons ramifying completely in cortex (Cajal, 1959 a). The physiological consequences of this alteration in morphogenetic pattern are seen in the development of increased excitatory synaptic drives. These are initiated by recurrent axon-collaterals which effect synaptic relations with adjacent pyramidal neurons via their cell bodies as well as basilar dendrites and proximal portions of apical dendrites (Purpura and Housepian, 1961). These studies, which essentially confirm and extend the original morphological observations of Cajal (1959 a) on the effect of trauma to pyramidal neurons in newborn animals, provide an understanding of the substrate for the development of paroxysmal activities in traumatized immature neocortex. On the basis of the morphological and physiological data obtained in these investigations, it is clear that the major

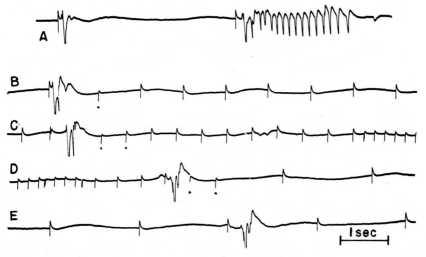

Fig. 21. The SCR's and repetitive activity evoked in an isolated cortical slab in a 5-day-old kitten, 3 days after cortical isolation; recording electrode 1 mm. from the site of stimulation. A, a stimulus to the cortical surface evokes a SCR and a multi-phasic predominantly surface-positive discharge, whereas a second stimulus delivered 3 seconds later elicits a SCR and a repetitive 8–10/sec. train of positive-negative responses. B to E, continuous record in which surface stimulus frequency is increased from 0.5 to 5/sec., then decreased to 0.5/sec. Multiphasic discharges appear randomly, but when stimuli (indicated by black dots under stimulus artifacts) are superimposed on descending phases of surface-negative components of paroxysmal discharges, or 0.5 to 1 sec. thereafter, evoked SCR's are markedly attenuated. (From Purpura and Housepian, 1961).

developmental alterations underlying the hyperexcitability of traumatized immature neocortex are related to reorganization of subsurface synaptic pathways leading to an overall increase in net excitatory synaptic drives on pyramidal neurons.

C. Induced "Hyperexcitability" of Immature Cerebellar Cortex Following Alterations in Maturational Patterns

An instructive example of the functional consequences of some disturbances in maturational patterns is seen in the short-term effects of x-irradiation of cerebellar cortex in newborn kittens. A detailed analysis of these effects as they relate to the normal maturational sequences is beyond the scope of this paper and the reader may consult other reports for further information on this point (Purpura, et al., 1963; Shofer, Pappas and Purpura, 1964). For present purposes, attention may be directed to the most obvious morphogenetic and physiological events in the maturation of cerebellar cortex and the manner in which radiation-induced changes are reflected in the appearance of hyperexcitability in intracortical neuronal organizations.

The postnatal development of the mammalian cerebellar cortex is prolonged in comparison to the cerebral neocortex. To appreciate the reasons for this requires consideration of the two major developmental features in the

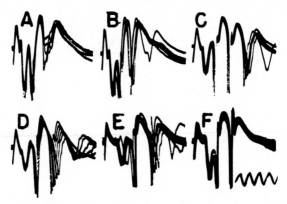

Fig. 22. **Responses elicited during surface stimulation of an isolated cortical slab in a 5-day-old kitten, 3 days after cortical isolation.** Surface responses recorded 1.5 mm. from the site of stimulation. Stimulus frequency 0.5/sec. in A to E (five to eight superposed responses) and 0.25 per second in F (ten superposed responses). The initial stable pattern of paroxysmal activity following the SCR (A) gradually changes in overt characteristics as a consequence of a progressive decrease in excitability. A new pattern of activity appears at 0.25/sec. stimulation. Calibration, 100 cycles/sec.; 0.1 mv. (From Purpura and Housepian, 1961).

morphogenesis of cerebellar cortex: the differentiation of the external granular layer, and the growth and development of Purkinje cells (Cajal, 1911; 1959 b).

The external granular layer (EGL) is approximately 10–12 cell layers thick in the immediate neonatal period. During the first six postnatal weeks, these cells undergo inward migration and differentiation. By the end of the second month, only a small remnant of the EGL is detectable. Cells of the EGL give rise to many elements of the internal granular layer, particularly those which contribute to the development of the parallel fiber system of the molecular layer (Fox and Barnard, 1957). Purkinje cells in the newborn kittens have very small dendrites and many perisomatic processes (Fig. 25A). The tips of the dentrites interdigitate with elements along the lower border of the EGL. During the second week, two types of Purkinje cells have been observed. In one type, primary and secondary rami are prominent and smoothly contoured (Fig. 25C). Most Purkinje cells, however, have well-developed primary, secondary and early tertiary rami. The delicate distal tertiary branches give rise to a few spiny branchlets (Fig. 25B). As in earlier stages, dendritic processes terminate at the lower border of the EGL which appears less densely packed than in neonatal animals. Further elaboration of Purkinje cell dendrites occurs during the third to sixth week. Tertiary branches containing spiny branchlets are seen on all Purkinje cells by the third week (Fig. 25D and E).

In studies of electrophysiological correlates of cerebellar morphogenesis, emphasis has been placed on developmental changes in two varieties of responses: that elicited by weak folial stimulation and stimulation of the contralateral motor cortex (Purpura, *et al.*, 1963).

Weak stimulation of the folial surface in adult animals evokes local graded 10–15 msec. surface-negative potentials (superficial cerebellar responses,

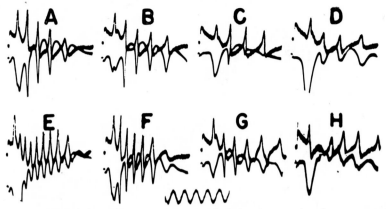

Fig. 23. Evoked repetitive responses recorded from an isolated neocortical slab in a 5-day-old kitten, 3 days post-isolation. Stimulating wire electrodes located at a depth of 0.8 mm. Surface responses (lower channel) recorded 3 mm. from the site of stimulation. Focally evoked responses (upper channel) simultaneously recorded with a microelectrode in the cortical depths (0.5–0.6 mm.); stimulus frequency 0.5/sec. A, control repetitive sequence elicited by single intracortical stimulus. Surface-positive responses are associated with focal-negativity. B, 3 minutes after topical application of ε-amino caproic acid (C_6). Note depression of surface and focally recorded responses with greater depression of the late components of surface activity. C and D, few seconds after addition of GABA during C_6 action. Surface responses augment, but focally recorded activity is decreased. E, phase of post-GABA augmentation after removal of both ω-amino acids. F, control. G, maximum effect produced by topically applied strychnine sulfate (1:1000). H, few seconds after addition of GABA during strychnine action. Calibration, 100 cycles/sec.; 0.1 mv. (From Purpura and Housepian, 1961).

SCbR) (Dow, 1949; Purpura and Grundfest, 1956; Purpura, Girado and Grundfest, 1959). Such SCbR's are not obtainable in young kittens until the end of the third week (Fig. 26). In neonatal preparations, surface folial stimulation elicits low-amplitude spike-like responses that are generally succeeded by slow surface-positive waves. The threshold for evoking cerebellar responses by surface stimulation is relatively high until after the second week. After the fourth week, SCbR's electrographic characteristics and properties are identical to those observed in adult animals.

Relatively strong stimuli to the motor cortex are required to evoke afferent responses in the paramedian lobule of the cerebellum in newborn kittens. These responses are of long latency and are relatively simple in configuration, as in newborn rabbits (Ulett, Dow and Larsell, 1944). They exhibit no significant change in latency with supramaximal stimuli (Fig. 27A). Although stimulus-increment series recorded at later stages reveal additional complexities in paramedian lobule (PML) responses, it is not until the end of the second month that stimuli of different strength evoke different latency responses. The complexity of PML responses increases during the second month, at which time they have all the electrographic characteristics of responses in adult animals (Jansen, 1957; Purpura, Girado and Grundfest, 1959).

In newborn rodents, x-irradiation produces dramatic effects on the cerebel-

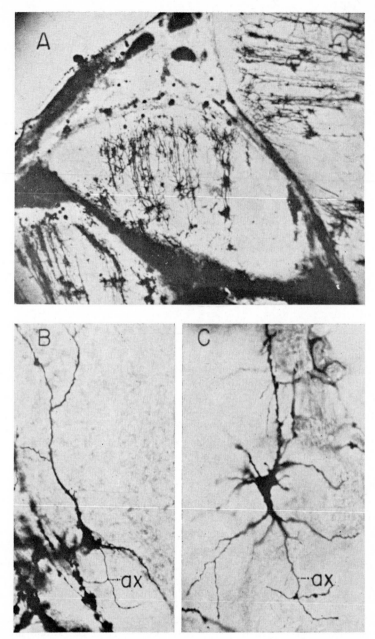

Fig. 24. A, low power photomicrograph of a neuronally isolated cortex in a 10-day-old kitten, 9 days after preparation of the slab. The section is taken through a small corner of the slab to show the completeness of the surgical procedure carried out on the first postnatal day. Golgi-Cox preparation; about x 25. B, large pyramidal neuron near the margin of undercutting (passing from middle left to lower right) from the same preparation as that shown in A, but from another site in the slab. The axon (ax) is shown giving off two recurrent collaterals, but no segment below the collaterals is seen; x 300. C, large pyramidal neuron with axon dividing into three collaterals. The plane of undercutting is about 0.1 mm. below the lower limits of the photomicrograph. This neuron is from an isolated slab of cortex from a 7-day-old kitten, 4 days after cortical isolation; x 300. (From Purpura and Housepian, 1961).

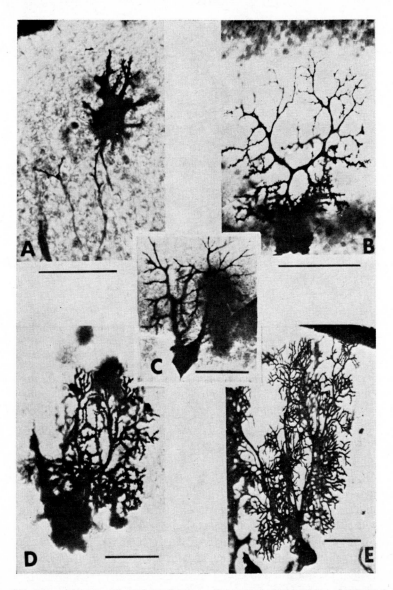

Fig. 25. Microphotographs of Purkinje cells revealed in 200 μ-thick Golgi-Cox sections of cerebellum in kittens of various ages. A, 2-day-old kitten. Main stem dendrites are short, occasionally branched, and have several protuberances. Dendrite-like ramifications are seen emerging from the cell body. B and C, two different stages of Purkinje cell development seen in the same section but from different parts of the cerebellum in an 8-day-old kitten. Note, in B, terminal portions of dendrites do not penetrate into lower border of external granular layer. C, possible "transitional" stage of Purkinje cell with smoothly contoured primary, secondary, and tertiary rami. D, 20-day-old kitten. E, 42-day-old kitten. Note that during the second month, a marked increase in length of dendrites occurs but not in density of tertiary rami and spiny branchlets. Horizontal bar below each microphotograph is 50μ. (From Purpura, *et al.*, 1963).

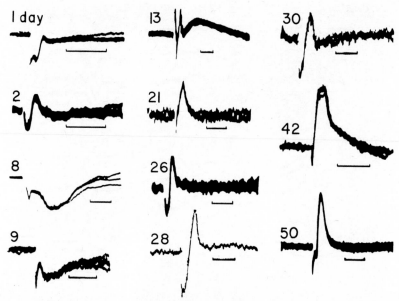

Fig. 26. Electrographic characteristics of local responses of cerebellar cortex to surface folial stimulation in normal kittens of various ages, as shown. Each record formed by 3–10 superimposed traces except that of the 28-day-old animal. First postnatal week (p.n.w.) responses consist of "spike-like" components followed by slow positive waves. During the second p.n.w., slow positivity becomes well developed and early positive-negative spikes are occasionally seen. Early surface negativity of superficial cerebellar cortical responses (SCbR's) of adult animals are seen by the third week. Thereafter, SCbR's with adult characteristics are noted until, at 5–6 weeks, responses are identical to those of mature animals. Calibrations, 20 msec. for all records. (From Shofer, Pappas and Purpura, 1964).

lum which have largely been related to destruction of elements of the external granular layer (Schmidt, 1962). Although similar effects on the EGL have been noted in kittens in the first two post-irradiation weeks, particular interest attaches to the finding of developmental alterations in Purkinje cells. Purkinje cells in the first post-irradiation week may exhibit unusually precocious maturational characteristics (Shofer, Pappas and Purpura, 1964). For the most part, terminal portions of Purkinje cell dendrites are in contact with pial surface elements as a consequence of the destruction of the EGL. Marked maturational differences are also seen in Purkinje cells in the first post-irradiation week. These differences may be noted in the same preparation from one cerebellar cortical area to another. Progressive alterations in the maturation of Purkinje cells are seen in the second and third post-irradiation weeks. Little increase in dendritic branching is noted at twelve days and even less at fifteen days (Fig. 28). At this stage, primary and secondary branches are proportionately thicker and less delicate than in the first week. Some indications of growth of the dendritic trunk are inferred from observations on primary branching of tangentially-oriented dendrites in subpial locations (Fig. 28). In these elements, primary branches are directed in a lateral and inferior

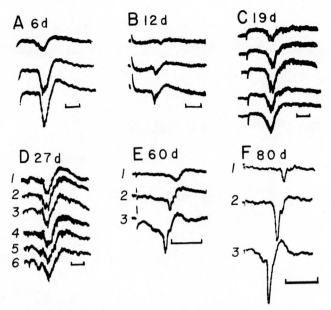

Fig. 27. PML afferent responses evoked by stimuli of progessively increasing strengths in normal kittens whose ages are indicated. A, in a 6-day-old kitten, simple wave form is maintained and no latency shift is observed with strong stimulation. B and C, essentially similar to A. D, weak stimulation (1 and 2) elicits prominent positive-negative sequence, whereas stronger stimulation introduces an early positive component of short duration (3–6). E, weak stimulation (1) elicits long-latency response. Shift in peak latency of positive response is seen with stronger stimulation (2 and 3). F, similar to E, but note prominent slow positivity preceding the major deflection elicited by strong stimulation (3). Calibrations, A–D, 50 msec.; E and F, 20 msec. (From Shofer, Pappas and Purpura, 1964).

direction. Although some atypical spiny processes are seen in smaller branches, more proximal branches have smooth contours. Thick, shorter, primary rami give rise to branches just below the pial surface (Fig. 28B).

Alterations in the morphogenesis of cerebellar cortex induced by irradiation are accompanied by dramatic changes in response to surface folial stimulation. Particularly impressive are findings of complex single and multiple spikes of relatively large amplitude superimposed on various multiphasic components of slow waves (Fig. 29A). In older irradiated kittens, multiple spikes superimposed on slow negative waves were especially prominent (Fig. 28B and C). Reciprocal changes in the magnitude of early and late spike components of responses elicited in the third post-irradiation week are shown in the stimulus increment series of Fig. 28D. These responses, as well as other complex electrographic activities, are indicative of augmented excitability of elements responsive to surface stimulation. The relatively simple early surface-negativity of SCbR's, which appears during the third week in normal kittens, is not observed in responses of irradiated kittens of comparable ages.

Excitability changes are also noted in the immediate post-irradiation period in afferent responses in PML evoked by motor cortex stimulation. Augmented

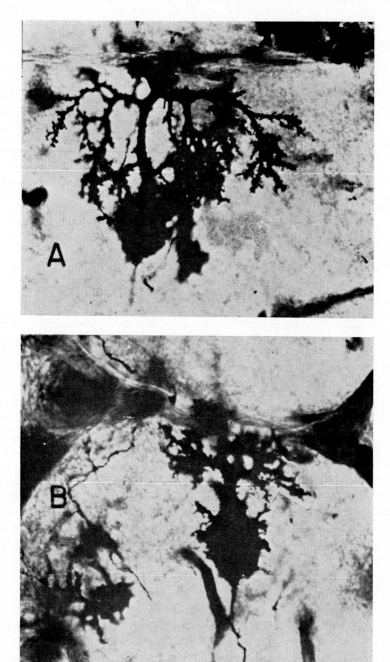

Fig. 28. Characteristics of Purkinje cells in irradiated cerebellum during the second postnatal week. A, 12 days. Large dendrites at surface are deflected laterally and downward during their attempted maturation. This unusual growth pattern is related, in part, to loss of the EGL. x 660. B, 15 days. Marked retardation of dendritic growth is evident. Other features are similar to those noted in A. x 660. (From Shofer, Pappas and Purpura, 1964).

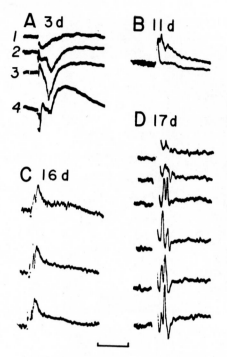

Fig. 29. Characteristics of local responses to surface folial stimulation in irradiated kittens, ages as indicated. A, weak stimulation elicits prominent positivity and barely detectable spike (1), whereas stronger stimulation (2–4) evokes additional complex positive-negative components and large amplitude early multiphasic spike. B and C, examples of spikes superimposed on slow negativities. D, stimulus increment series illustrating reciprocal changes in magnitude of early and late components of multiphasic spikes. Calibration, 20 msec. for all records. (From: Shofer, Pappas and Purpura, 1964).

excitability in synaptic pathways involved in the production of these responses is seen in the overall complexity of PML activities elicited in young kittens and latency shifts of peak-positivities with increasing strengths of stimulation (Fig. 30A). It has been noted above that in normal kittens such characteristics of PML responses are not ordinarily observed until after the second month. Some idea of the complexity of PML responses elicited during the second post-irradiation week is gained from the stimulus increment series shown in Fig. 30C. PML responses in this preparation exhibited cyclic alterations with respect to latency shifts and amplitudes of peak-positivity, as well as relative changes in magnitudes of preceding and succeeding components. It is of interest that irradiation effects on PML responses similar to those seen in 1–2-week-old animals were not obvious after the second post-irradiation week (Fig. 30D-F).

CORRELATIVE ANALYSIS

It has been proposed that the locally-evoked surface-negative responses of cerebellar cortex in adult animals represent activity synaptically generated in superficially located Purkinje cell dendrites by elements of the parallel fiber system (Dow, 1949; Purpura, Girado and Grundfest, 1959; Purpura and Grundfest, 1956). Ontogenetic studies in normal kittens on the relationship of dendritic growth and development and the appearance of typical SCbR's are consistent with this hypothesis. From these investigations, it is clear that the absence of an SCbR in normal young kittens is attributable to the lack of a sufficient number and particular variety of axodendritic synapses related to fine spiny branchlets of tertiary rami of superficially located Purkinje cell

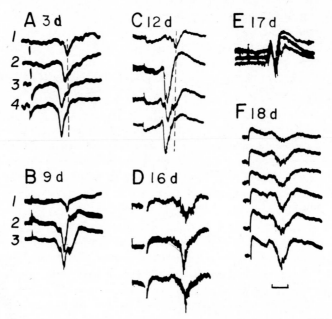

Fig. 30. Changes in characteristics of PML afferent responses evoked in irradiated kittens of various ages, as indicated. A, weak motor cortex stimulation (1) elicits long-latency positivity, whereas stronger stimulation (2–4) evokes responses with major positive deflections of shorter latency. B–C, essentially similar changes in configuration and latency of evoked responses during stimulus increment series. Vertical dashed lines in A and C drawn through peak of positivity elicited by weak stimulation. Note peak latency shift and inflection on responses to strong stimulation that are temporally related to long-latency positivity of responses to weak stimulation. D–F, lack of significant changes in latency and overt configuration of responses in stimulus increment series. Calibrations, 50 msec. for all records.

dendrites. Such a substrate for the SCbR is present by the second to third postnatal week in normal kittens. A few days after irradiation, Purkinje cell dendrites attain the pial surface due to the destruction of the EGL. Spiny branchlets of Purkinje cell dendrites are few in number and atypical in the immediate post-irradiation period, though they appear to increase considerably in the next few days. The eventual loss of typical spiny branchlets in irradiated preparations is undoubtedly related to alterations in the differentiation of cells of the EGL, since these elements eventually give rise to cells whose axons constitute the parallel fiber system (Cajal, 1911; 1959 b). Purkinje cells also appear to acquire mature characteristics within a few days post-irradiation. This finding, taken together with observations on the bizarre and pleomorphic appearance of Purkinje cell dendrites in subpial locations, could account for some of the complex responses elicited by surface stimulation. It is also conceivable that irradiation has caused changes in the membrane properties of dendrites which would permit conductile responses in these elements which, under ordinary conditions, are probably not capable of supporting regenerative activity (Purpura and Grundfest, 1956). Such an explanation may be considered in attempts to explain the high-amplitude spikes elicited by surface stimulation in irradiated kittens. In these preparations, large primary and secondary dendritic trunks of Purkinje cells have been observed in close tangential relationship to the pial surface. Such an arrangement is never found in normal kittens.

Although it is not possible to provide a complete picture of the developmental changes responsible for the appearance of hyperexcitability in cerebellar neuronal organizations involved in afferent PML responses, several of the factors noted in connection with ontogenetic changes in local responses to surface stimulation in normal and irradiated animals are undoubtedly applicable. The chief finding in PML responses in the immediate post-irradiation period is their precocious complexity and low threshold for activation. Here it is necessary to consider that the appearance of both short- and long-latency components in PML responses is probably indicative of the operation of both the mossy fiber and climbing fiber-synaptic systems (Jansen, 1957). Since it is known that the mossy fiber-granule cell multisynaptic system develops later than the climbing-fiber Purkinje cell monosynaptic afferent pathway (Cajal, 1911; 1959 b), it may be argued that irradiation has, in some obscure fashion, induced "maturation acceleration" of the mossy fiber-granule cell synaptic organizations involved in the production of PML complexities. The point of emphasis is that both phenomena, acceleration of development of some elements and destruction of others, must be recognized in attempts to explain the hyperexcitability of synaptic pathways involved in PML responses.

D. General Remarks

Hyperexcitability in any neuronal organization can result from an increase in excitatory synaptic drives, a decrease in inhibitory activity, or various combinations of these two factors. Although the view that the activity of a particular population of neural elements represents the sum of opposing excitatory and inhibitory processes has long been championed, only in the past few years has it been possible to demonstrate the operation of inhibitory as well as excitatory synaptic activities in a wide variety of electrocortical potentials. Suffice it to say that intracellular recordings from thalamic (Purpura and Cohen, 1962; Purpura and Shofer, 1963) and neocortical neurons during different types of evoked cortical responses (Purpura and Shofer, 1964; Purpura, Shofer and Musgrave, 1964) have provided strong support for the hypothesis that spontaneous and evoked potentials are summations of excitatory and inhibitory postsynaptic potentials generated in the soma-dendritic membrane of neurons in different complex organizations (Purpura, 1959 a; Purpura and Grundfest, 1956). Thus, in the analysis of electroencephalographic abnormalities in the immature brain, considerable importance is to be attached to studies which might reveal differences in the functional differentiation of excitatory and inhibitory neurons, increases in overall excitatory activities, or changes in the membrane properties of neurons which could conceivably alter their responsiveness to synaptic bombardment.

The several examples of ontogenetic studies summarized above are illustrative of the wide variety of pathophysiological processes which may be expressed in electroencephalographic abnormalities in the immature brain. Although the factors noted in these studies by no means exhaust the possible mechanisms underlying the development of seizures in immature animals, they do serve to indicate the manner in which specific disturbances in maturational patterns may give rise to hyperexcitability or overt convulsant activity in different neuronal organizations.

The point of departure of the present line of investigation relates to observations on the maturational sequences in different types of cortex and the modifying effects of different pathophysiological processes. The electrographic characteristics of normal and abnormal responses recorded from the neocortex in neonatal animals appear to be determined by the prominence of superficial axodendritic synaptic activities in the overt responses. Activation of these pathways can be expected to produce summated potentials of relatively long duration due, in part, to the packing density of apical dendrites and temporal dispersion in conductile pathways in immature neocortex. Restricted distribution of EEG abnormalities and slowness of propagation are referable to the paucity of axosomatic synaptic pathways in the depths of the cortex and the limited growth of deep neuropil in neonatal animals. Other factors related to the general properties of synapses (transmitter synthesis, release and receptor activation and inactivation) probably combine to limit the overall excitability of neocortical neuronal organizations in the immediate neonatal period.

The effects of trauma to the neocortex in newborn animals depend in large part on the nature of the injury. Thus a stab wound of the cortex which interrupts pyramidal axons in their subcortical trajectory may set into operation changes in patterns of pyramidal neuron development which result in proliferation of axon-collaterals and a net increase in excitatory synaptic activity as noted above. However, there are undoubtedly many types of injuries to immature cortex which may not be reflected in obvious anatomical changes in synaptic pathways, albeit hyperexcitability and seizures may be important consequences. This is the problem raised by effects of "biochemical lesions," broadly defined, which may leave in their wake little in the way of structural changes detectable with currently available light or electron microscope techniques. However, some severe "biochemical lesions" may result in obvious structural alterations in neurons in specific locations. This is amply illustrated in the hippocampal effects observed following sustained generalized seizures induced by the antimetabolite, methoxypyridoxine (Purpura and Gonzalez-Monteagudo, 1960). Such an example of "special pathoclisis" (Vogt and Vogt, 1922) probably has its counterpart in the alterations observed in the hippocampus in many severe metabolic or mechanical disturbances to the immature brain. In this context, it is of interest that the findings summarized above on the differential rate of structural and functional maturation of hippocampal neurons may account for the selective vulnerability of the hippocampus to pathophysiological processes during antenatal and postnatal ontogenesis.

In a number of instances it has been shown that the development of hyperexcitability in the immature brain may be either an expression or the precocious maturation of some component of a neuronal organization or a change in the morphological substrate for a particular variety of electrocortical activity. These factors are evident in the dramatic disturbance in maturational processes observed in immature cerebellar cortex, following x-irradiation. Thus, destruction of elements (external granular cells) which, under ordinary conditions, would eventually participate in several different types of synaptic organizations in the mature cerebellar cortex initiates a sequence of related maturational changes which affect the development of superficial axodendritic pathways and the reorganization of subsurface synaptic organizations involved in afferent evoked activities. Although these changes, in combination with effects of radiation on the growth and differentiation of Purkinje cell dendrites, are reflected in an augmented excitability of immature cerebellar cortex, it is obvious that an "excitability change" is but one sign of altered functional activity. Neglecting any further consideration of the consequences of such maturational changes, it is clear that correlations of structure and function such as those noted in the foregoing sections add a new dimension to studies of electroencephalographic abnormalities in the immature brain. And it is to be expected that further understanding of the pathophysiological processes underlying EEG abnormalities will permit a more rational approach to the control and prevention of neurological and behavior disorders of infancy and childhood.

Summary

Morphological and electrophysiological studies of the comparative postnatal ontogenesis of feline neocortex, archicortex, and cerebellar cortex are summarized from the standpoint of their relevancy to the general problem of the development of hyperexcitability in different neuronal organizations. Differences in the rate of maturation of neocortex and archicortex are described in light and electron microscope observations and studies of neocortical and hippocampal synaptic organizations. The relatively advanced development of hippocampal neurons in the neonatal kitten is viewed as an important factor in the expression of overt effects of generalized disturbances involving the immature brain.

Maturational sequences in neocortex are determinants of the overt effects of trauma produced by interruption of pyramidal axons and freezing lesions. Examples of the consequences of cortical lesions are summarized to indicate the manner in which reorganization of synaptic pathways may contribute to the development of hyperexcitability in isolated cortex.

Developmental changes in immature cerebellar cortex following x-irradiation result in augmented excitability of synaptic pathways involved in responses to folial surface and afferent stimulation. These functional alterations are related to destruction of external granule cells, maturation acceleration of pathways involved in subsurface activities, and changes in growth and differentiation of dendrites and related axodendritic pathways. These and other studies are illustrative of an approach to the study of electroencephalographic abnormalities in the immature brain which permits definition of pathophysiological processes in terms of altered structure- function relations.

ACKNOWLEDGMENTS

The author wishes to thank Dr. M. W. Carmichael, Dr. E. S. Goldensohn, Dr. E. M. Housepian, Dr. C. R. Noback, Dr. G. D. Pappas, Dr. R. J. Shofer and Dr. K. Voeller for their kind permission to reproduce data obtained in collaborative studies during various aspects of the work summarized in this report.

REFERENCES

BERL, S. and PURPURA, D. P. Postnatal changes in amino acid content of kitten cerebral cortex. *J. Neurochem., 1963*, 10: 237–240.

BERL, S., PURPURA, D. P., GIRADO, H. and WAELSCH, H. Amino acid metabolism in epileptogenic and non-epileptogenic lesions of the neocortex (cat.) *J. Neurochem., 1959*, 4:311–317.

BURNS, B. D. *The Mammalian Cerebral Cortex.* Arnold, London, 1958.

CADILHAC, J. et PASSOUANT-FONTAINE, Th. Décharges épileptiques et activité électrique de veille et de sommeil dans l'hippocampe au cours de l'ontogenese. *In:* P. PASSOUNT (Editor), *Physiologie de l'hippocampe.* Centre National de la Recherche Scientifique, Paris, 1962, pp. 429–442.

CADILHAC, J., PASSOUANT-FONTAINE, Th., MIHAILOVIC, L. et PASSOUANT, P. L'épilepsie expérimentale du chaton en fonction de l'age; étude corticale et sous-corticale. *Pathologie-Biologie, 1960*, 8: 1571–1581.

CANNON, W. B. A law of denervation. *Amer. J. Med. Sci., 1939*, 198:737–750.

DOW, R. S. Action potentials of cerebellar cortex in response to local electrical stimulation. *J. Neurophysiol., 1949*, 12:245–256.

ECHLIN, F. A. The supersensitivity of chronically "isolated" cerebral cortex as a mechanism in focal epilepsy. *Electroenceph. clin. Neurophysiol., 1959*, 11: 697–722.

FOX, C. A. and BARNARD, J. W. A quantitative study of the Purkinje cell dendritic branchlets and their relationship to afferent fibers. *J. Anat., 1957*, 91:299–313.

GOLDENSOHN, E. S. and PURPURA, D. P. Intracellular potentials of cortical neurons during focal epileptogenic discharges. *Science, 1963*, 139:840–842.

GOLDENSOHN, E. S., SHOFER, R. J. and PURPURA, D. P. Ontogenesis of focal discharges in epileptogenic lesions of cat neocortex. *Electroenceph. clin. Neurophysiol., 1963*, 15:153–154.

GREEN, J. D. and MAXWELL, D. S. Hippocampal electrical activity. I. Morphological aspects. *Electroenceph. clin. Neurophysiol., 1961*, 13:837–846.

HAMLYN, L. H. An electron microscope study of pyramidal neurons in the Ammon's Horn of the rabbit. *J. Anat., 1963*, 97:189–201.

KANDEL, E. R. and SPENCER, W. A. Electrophysiological properties of an archicortical neuron. *Ann. N. Y. Acad. Sci., 1961*, 94:570–603.

LANGWORTHY, O. R. A correlated study of the development of reflex activity in fetal and young kittens and the myelinization of tracts in the nervous system. *Contr. Embryol. Carneg. Inst., 1929*, 20:127–172.

MUSGRAVE, F. S., SANAMAN, M. and PURPURA, D. P. Factors affecting focal discharges of epileptogenic cortex. *Physiologist, 1962*, 5:187.

NOBACK, C. R. and PURPURA, D. P. Postnatal ontogenesis of cat neocortex. *J. comp. Neurol., 1961*, 117:291–308.

PAPPAS, G. D. and PURPURA, D. P. Fine structure of dendrites in the superficial neocortical neuropil. *Exp. Neurol., 1961*, 4:507–530.

PAPPAS, G. D. and PURPURA, D. P. Electron microscopy of immature human and feline neocortex. *In:* D. P. PURPURA, and J. P. SCHADÉ (Editors), *Growth and Maturation of the Brain.* Elsevier, Amsterdam, 1963, (In Press).

PASSOUANT, P. *Physiologie de l'hippocampe.* Centre National de la Recherche Scientifique, Paris, 1962.

PURPURA, D. P. Nature of electrocortical potentials and synaptic organizations in cerebral and cerebellar cortex. *In:* C. C. PFEIFFER and J. R. SMYTHIES (Editors), *International Review of Neurobiology,* Vol. I, Academic Press, New York, 1959a, pp. 47–163.

PURPURA, D. P. *In:* M. A. B. BRAZIER (Editor), *Central Nervous System and Behavior.* Josiah Macy Jr. Foundation, New York, 1959b.

Purpura, D. P. *In:* M. A. B. Brazier (Editor), *Second Conference on Central Nervous System and Behavior.* Josiah Macy Jr. Foundation, New York, *1960a,* pp. 253–271.

Purpura, D. P. Pharmacological actions of ω-amino acid drugs on different cortical synaptic organizations. *In:* E. Roberts (Editor), *Inhibition in the Nervous System and γ-Aminobutyric Acid.* Pergamon, New York, *1960b,* pp. 495–514.

Purpura, D. P. Analysis of axodendritic synaptic organizations in immature cerebral cortex. *Ann. N. Y. Acad. Sci., 1961a,* 94:604–654.

Purpura, D. P. Ontogenetic analysis of some evoked synaptic activities in superficial neocortical neuropil. *In:* E. Florey (Editor), *International Symposium on Nervous Inhibition.* Pergamon, New York, *1961b,* pb. 424–446.

Purpura, D. P. Synaptic organization of immature cerebral cortex. *World Neurol., 1962,* 3:275–298.

Purpura, D. P. and Carmichael, M. W. Characteristics of the blood-brain barrier to gamma-aminobutyric acid in neonatal cat. *Science, 1960,* 131:410–412.

Purpura, D. P., Carmichael, M. W. and Housepian, E. M. Physiological and anatomical studies of development of superficial axodendritic synaptic pathways in neocortex. *Exp. Neurol., 1960,* 2:324–347.

Purpura, D. P. and Cohen, B. Intracellular recordings from thalamic neurons during recruiting responses. *J. Neurophysiol., 1962,* 25:621–635.

Purpura, D. P. and Gonzalez-Monteagudo, O. Acute effects of methoxypyridoxine on hippocampal end-blade neurons; an experimental study of "special pathoclisis" in the cerebral cortex. *J. Neuropath. exp. Neurol., 1960,* 19:421–432.

Purpura, D. P., Girado, M. and Grundfest, H. Synaptic components of cerebellar electrocortical activity evoked by various afferent pathways. *J. Gen. Physiol., 1959,* 42:1037–1066.

Purpura, D. P. and Grundfest, H. Nature of dendritic potentials and synaptic mechanisms in cerebral cortex of cat. *J. Neurophysiol., 1956,* 19:573–595.

Purpura, D. P. and Housepian, E. M. Morphological and physiological properties of chronically isolated immature neocortex. *Exp. Neurol., 1961,* 4:366–401.

Purpura, D. P., Girado, M., Smith, T. G., Jr. and Gomez, J. A. Effects of systemically administered ω-amino and guanidino acids on spontaneous and evoked cortical activity in regions of blood-brain barrier destruction. *Electroenceph. clin. Neurophysiol., 1958,* 10:677–685.

Purpura, D. P. and Shofer, R. J. Intracellular recording from thalamic neurons during reticulocortical activation. *J. Neurophysiol., 1963,* 26:494–505.

Purpura, D. P. and Shofer, R. J. Cortical intracellular potentials during augmenting and recruiting responses. I. Effects of injected hyperpolarizing currents on evoked membrane potential changes. *J. Neurophysiol., 1964, (In Press).*

Purpura, D. P., Shofer, R. J., Housepian, E. M. and Noback, C. R. Comparative ontogenesis of structure-function relations in cerebral and cerebellar cortex. *In:* D. P. Purpura and J. P. Schadé (Editors), *Growth and Maturation of the Brain.* Elsevier, Amsterdam, *1963, (In Press).*

Purpura, D. P., Shofer, R. J. and Musgrave, F. S. Cortical intracellular potentials during augmenting and recruiting responses. II. Patterns of synaptic activities in pyramidal and non-pyramidal tract neurons. *J. Neurophysiol., 1964 (In Press).*

Ramon y Cajal, S. *Histologié du systeme nerveaux de l'homme et des vertebres.* Consejo Superior de Investigaciones Cientificas, Madrid, 1911.

Ramon y Cajal, S. *Degeneration and Regeneration of the Nervous System.* R. M. May (Trans.), Reprinted by Hafner, New York, *1959a.*

Ramon y Cajal, S. *Studies on Vertebrate Neurogenesis.* L. Guth (Trans.). Charles C Thomas, Springfield, *1959b.*

Schmidt, R. Die postnatale Genese der Kleinhirndefekte rontgenbestrahlter Hausmause. *J. Hirnforschung, 1962,* 3:12–209.

Shofer, R. J., Pappas, G. D. and Purpura, D. P. Radiation induced changes in morphological and physiological properties of immature cerebellar cortex. *In:* T. J. Haley (Editor), *Second Symposium on Response of the Nervous System to Ionizing Radiation.* Academic Press, New

York, *1964, (In Press)*.

ULETT, G., DOW, R. S. and LARSELL, O. Inception of conduction in the corpus callosum and the corticoponto-cerebellar pathway in young rabbits with reference to myelinization. *J. comp. Neurol.*, 1944, 80:1–10.

VOELLER, K., PAPPAS, G. D. and PURPURA, D. P. Electron microscope study of development of cat superficial neocortex. *Exp. Neurol.*, 1963, 7:107–130.

VOGT, C. and VOGT, O. Erkrankungen der Grosshirnrinde im Lichte der Topistik, Pathoklise und Pathoarchitektonik. *J. Psychol. Neurol.*, 1922, 28.

DISCUSSION

DR. GRAFSTEIN: For some evoked responses, the configuration of the response in the immature brain may be determined by the properties of the sub-cortical centers. For example, in examining the development of the auditory system, Rose et al. (1957)[1] found that changes in the latency of the evoked response were determined by the maturation of subcortical stations and not by the development of the cortex itself. I think that this might also occur with some of the other evoked responses that you have considered, which are produced by peripheral stimulation and which thus involve activity transmitted through a whole series of relays before reaching the cortex. The fact that you get a purely negative response at first and later a positive-negative response may then indicate maturational changes at subcortical rather than cortical levels. In the case of the trans-callosal response, on the other hand, where activity is transmitted directly from one hemisphere to the other with no intermediary relay, you do in fact see a well-developed initial positive phase in the response immediately after birth. Also, the subsequent development of this positive phase during the first four postnatal weeks in the kitten seems to be in every way parallel with that of the negative phase, so one would guess that the time course of maturation of the neuronal elements involved is the same for both.

DR. GOLDRING: I think that this is a good point. However, we have stimulated and specifically tried to avoid the relay by stimulating the radiations, and if you stimulate the radiation to the somathesthetic cortex, you get also a predominantly negative response in the newborn animal. Later on, in the radiations of course, as I have shown in the adult animal, the positive wave comes in.

DR. KELLAWAY: How does this compare with what you see when you stimulate the optic radiations?

DR. GOLDRING: We have stimulated the white matter beneath the optic cortex in the cat and the white matter beneath different cortical areas in the human infant. I think that there is some species difference, but nevertheless in the postnatal kitten we do get a predominantly positive-negative response.

DR. SCHADÉ: Would it be possible to explain the difference between callosal stimulation and peripheral stimulation by major differences in the dis-

---

[1]*Acta Neurol. Latinoamer.*, 1957, 3:133–143.

tribution of the synaptic fields? Callosal fibers have their major synaptic fields at other spots in the cerebral cortex than the peripheral projections.

DR. GRAFSTEIN: The transcallosal evoked response is a typical positive-negative response of the kind that we have seen demonstrated by Dr. Purpura. The puzzling thing, however, is that it is apparent from a number of different studies of the distribution of the callosal fibers in the cortex (Nauta and Bucher, 1954[1]; W. R. Hayhow, personal communication, 1957) that these fibers have no terminations in the molecular layer, in spite of the fact that there is a very prominent negative phase in the evoked response. One possible explanation is that the negative phase is generated on the apical dendrites of third-order neurons activated by the cortical interneurons on which the callosal fibers end.

DR. CRAIN: I am wondering whether the evidence is adequate to eliminate the possibility that the ontogenetic development of the positive phase in these evoked responses might be due to local activation of later-maturing, inhibitory synapses, analogous to the interpretation of the negative response. Why have you not included this possibility instead of invoking only the idea of excitatory postsynaptic potentials developing in the cortical depth and appearing at the surface by volume conductor mechanism?

DR. PURPURA: You are raising the question of whether there is a differential development of an inhibitory system. I think this is a good point and probably has to be considered in external recording which is summating synaptic activities at all layers of the cortex.

DR. GOLDRING: But I think we have fairly good evidence that the initial positivity reflects postsynaptic excitatory potentials in the cortical depth. The evidence is especially good for identifying the positive spikes as postsynaptic discharges of the soma.

DR. PURPURA: Once you have recognized the existence of inhibitory postsynaptic potentials in all kinds of wave forms and responses, then you are in trouble with respect to interpretation of any external waves in terms of volume conductor. You are saying that a particular wave form represents depolarization—could it not also represent local inhibition or local excitation as well as some distant EPSP and IPSP? The existence of IPSP's in all wave forms makes such interpretations very difficult and Dr. Crain was raising an important point as to whether or not one should also consider differential development of excitation and inhibition as a determinate in the development of these wave forms. In the cerebellum there is an inverse developmental relationship to that of neocortex. That is to say, there is an external granular layer which is essentially occupying a zone which would otherwise be occupied by axodendritic synaptic contacts on Purkinje cells. In the newborn animal one could predict that surface stimulation would produce no negativity because there is no substrate for its production. Later on this system becomes more effective due to the fact that the external granule cells migrate inwardly and in part give rise to this system. We should see later a development of surface negativity going along with this morphogenetic change. With surface stimulation it is virtually impossible under three weeks to see a 20 millisecond graded negativity in the cerebellum of the kitten on local stimulation. Thereafter the negative wave is similar to that Dow described in 1949, a typical negativity which we have interpreted also as due to synaptic activation of superficial dendrites of the Purkinje cells. In other words, it is during this period that the dendrites of the Purkinje cells are growing upward toward the surface as superficial synaptic pathways are being formed. This is the inverse of that of the neocortex. In neocortex you get negative waves on local surface stimulation at birth because axodendritic substrate is present. In the cerebellum it requires three weeks for this substrate to appear under the pial membrane. The point is that the afferent pathway—definitely afferent from motor cortex through paramedian lobule—is well developed. Hence activation of the depth of the cerebellar cortex occurs with ease in the newborn animal in contrast to that of the neocortex. Since in the newborn animal it is impossible to evoke a negative wave with local stimulation in the cerebellum until this system appears, the superficial axodendritic system must be the substrate for the negativity. The local negative wave of cerebellum is generated axodendritically in the fine branchlets of the Purkinje cells. Secondly, the pathways in the depths of the cerebellum must already be present at birth in contrast to findings in the neocortex.

DR. WINDLE: I would just like to clarify one thing. You are talking about the newborn but you have mentioned the fetus from time to time. I would like you to clarify for the record how far back in prenatal life you have gone in these studies? Have you enough stages prenatally to know what the cortices are capable of doing in this regard?

DR. PURPURA: We have looked into the situation at about two and a half or three weeks before term in the kitten. You can get the local negative wave perfectly well.

DR. GRAFSTEIN: I would like to tell you about some interesting observations that have been made on fetal muscle, which may be appropriate here if we consider that the properties of the immature cortical synapse may resemble those of the immature neuromuscular junction. We may thus guess at a few of the mechanisms that may determine some of the features of the evoked responses that we have been examining.

For example, one property of fetal skeletal muscle described by Diamond and Miledi (1962)[1] is that its end-plate potential is more prolonged than that of the adult muscle. Similarly, as we have seen, the duration of evoked responses in the immature brain is longer than in the adult. In the case of the muscle, one of the reasons adduced for the prolongation of the end-plate potentials is that there is relatively little cholinesterase in the immature muscle, so that any acetylcholine released at the junction by the nerve end-

---

[1] *J. Physiol. (Lond.), 1962, 162:393–408.*

ing has a longer time to act, and I would like to suggest that the long duration of the evoked cortical response also may be determined to some extent by the absence of appropriate enzyme systems for destruction of chemical transmitters. Another characteristic feature of fetal muscle demonstrated by Diamond and Miledi is that it is sensitive to acetylcholine not only in the end-plate region, as adult muscle is, but over its whole length. As the neuromuscular apparatus matures, the sensitivity to acetylcholine decreases in the regions away from the end-plate, and the curious thing is that this decrease progresses from the tendinous ends of the muscle fiber toward the end-plate, till only the end-plate itself retains its high degree of sensitivity. I am now going to suggest that a similar process may occur in the maturation of the cortical neuron: in an early stage of its development it may be sensitive over its whole surface to any particular synaptic transmitter, and subsequently this sensitivity may become restricted to the actual synaptic regions. This might explain why the space constant of the transcallosal evoked response is smaller in the 16-day old kitten than in the newborn (B. Grafstein, unpublished results), and also why the area of cortex from which visual evoked responses can be recorded in the kitten diminishes between the 10th and 20th postnatal days (Marty et al., 1959).[1]

A final point that I want to make is the one that derives from observations made by Miledi (1960)[2] on denervated muscle, which resembles fetal muscle in that it also is sensitive to acetylcholine all along its length, and when it becomes re-innervated, the acetylcholine-sensitive region recedes from the tendon end toward the end-plate. In such a re-innervated muscle, block of neuromuscular transmission occurs readily when the newly regenerated nerve is stimulated repeatedly, apparently because of a failure of nerve impulses to traverse the terminal portion of the nerve fiber. Why this should happen is not entirely clear, but I would like to suggest that the same susceptibility to presynaptic blocking also exists in immature cortical neurons, and accounts for the fact that the cortical responses are extremely fatigable when repetitive stimulation is used.

In summary, then, I would like to suggest that on the basis of studies on newly-formed neuromuscular junctions, it seems probable that the immature cortical neuron has the following properties which may be important in determining some of the characteristics of evoked cortical responses in young animals: (1) long-lasting postsynaptic potentials due at least in part to the absence of enzyme systems for destruction of transmitter substances; (2) sensitivity to transmitter substances in extrasynaptic regions; (3) susceptibility to presynaptic blocking.

---

[1]Rev. Neurol., 1959, 100:376–377.
[2]J. Physiol. (Lond.), 1960, 154:190–205.

ELECTROENCEPHALOGRAM OF THE MONKEY FETUS IN UTERO, AND CHANGES IN IT AT BIRTH

MARIA I. ROBERT DE RAMIREZ DE ARELLANO

Laboratory of Perinatal Physiology, National Institute of Neurological Diseases and Blindness, National Institutes of Health, Public Health Service, U. S. Department of Health, Education and Welfare, and the University of Puerto Rico, San Juan, Puerto Rico

Numerous efforts to record spontaneous electrical activity of the human fetal brain prior to birth have been made with electrodes in the vagina or on the gravid abdomen at various times in gestation. The recordings showed very slow waves and low amplitude recognizable as EEG. Lindsley's early study (1942) of the intrauterine EEG is noteworthy.

Jasper, Bridgeman and Carmichael (Jasper *et al.*, 1937) were the first to observe spontaneous electrical brain activity in the fetal guinea pig. They have recorded the EEG from the fetuses of experimental animals; but no one has reported experiments in which the day-by-day course of EEG has been followed prenatally with electrodes. With exception of a preliminary abstract (Esquivel de Gallardo, 1962), this is the first report of such an experiment. It followed an investigation of the normal postnatal maturational changes in the EEG of the monkey (Robert de Ramirez de Arellano, 1961). After establishment of the characteristics of both fetal and neonatal EEG, the changes during arousal at birth were investigated.

Procedures

The present experiments were conducted on fetuses of sixteen pregnant monkeys (*Macaca mulatta*), most of which were of known gestational age. Five were used in an attempt to make day-by-day observations of the prenatal EEG and eleven for acute experiments during birth.

All surgical procedures for the chronic as well as acute experiments were conducted under local anesthesia. The Cesarian sections were performed after procaine infiltration of all layers of the abdominal wall, discomfort and pain being less evident with these procedures than during spontaneous vaginal deliveries.

Surgical preparation for the chronic experiments was in two stages: (a) a pedestal electrode holder of special design (Figure 1) was screwed into the gluteal side of the innominate bone near the iliac crest. An S-shaped incision permitted a tight closure of gluteal muscle and skin around the vertical column of the holder. A subcutaneous channel was made for a polyethylene tube running between the hip and the midline of the abdominal wall to carry electrode wires from the holder to the uterus; (b) a paramedian laparotomy

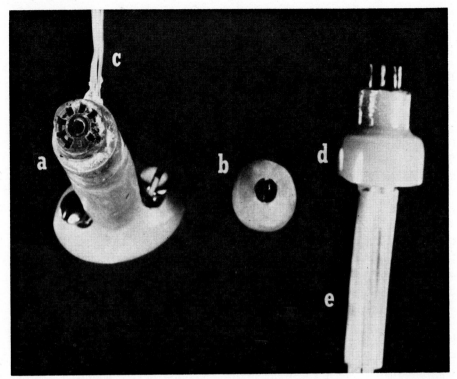

Fig. 1. Assemblies for intrauterine EEG recording. a) Acrylic resin pedestal electrode holder with subminiature transistor female socket; note the vitallium screws to hold the base of the pedestal to the bone. b) Cap to screw onto the female socket when not in use. c) Stainless steel wires in polyethylene tube; the wires are insulated with INSL varnish, but have bare tips. d) Connector male element of the subminiature assembly; from this, e) wires (Microdot) lead to the junction box of the EEG instrument.

was performed. The sites of the placentas and fetal heads were determined by palpation and the uterus was incised. The head was approximated to the amnion and held in place by an assistant while the amnion was incised. Thus, loss of amniotic fluid was prevented. Four insulated steel electrode wires with bare tips were hooked into the fetal scalp, two frontal and two parietal; a fifth electrode was attached to the ear for reference. (Electrode resistance was 2,000 to 2,500 ohms.). The amnion was then sutured around the tube which carried the electrode wires; the uterine and abdominal incisions were closed, and after an initial recording was made, the animal was returned to a cage.

The five monkeys were operated on at 112, 117, 127, 139, and 148 days of gestation, the median age at full term being 168.8 days (van Wagennen, 1958).

The EEG's were recorded with an eight-channel Grass instrument, "Microdot" wires (movement-artifact tested) being used to connect with the pedestal electrode holder when the monkey was restrained in supine position. Fetal monopolar and bipolar recordings were made daily until the experiment was ended by spontaneous abortion. In addition to the records from the fetal scalp leads, a maternal EKG was obtained from subdermal electrodes (Grass E2) and a pneumogram was recorded with a special device (Alvar).

Most acute experiments were performed at 145 to 158 days of gestation, but two monkeys were of unknown gestational age near full term. The head of the fetus in the amniotic sac was exposed at Cesarian section without touching the umbilical cord or tearing the membranes. In the first two experiments clip electrodes were clamped onto the amnion and scalp together, two frontal and two parietal, and a reference electrode was placed on one ear. In the rest of the monkeys the application of electrodes was carried out in the same manner as in the chronic experiments. Monopolar and bipolar EEG's were recorded for at least 5 minutes before delivery of the fetus; the fetal EKG sometimes appeared as an artifact. The fetus was then delivered from the uterus and membranes, but the placenta remained *in situ* and the umbilical cord was not clamped. At this time EKG electrodes were applied to the fetus. Recordings from the quiescent fetus continued as long as possible without fetal disturbance, avoiding unnecessary handling and excessive light or sound. Next, the umbilical cord was clamped. Some monkeys began to breathe before, and others after clamping. We recorded EEG, EKG and respiratory rate continuously at this stage, avoiding unnecessary handling. Usually it was possible to record events during arousal at birth, but sometimes the initiation of a neonatal EEG was obscured by movement artifacts from the squirming monkey infant. Finally, daily EEG and EKG records were made until the offspring had reached a stage equivalent to that of spontaneous full-term birth. These records were compared with those of monkey infants born spontaneously (Caveness, 1962; Kennard and Nims, 1942; Robert de Ramirez de Arellano, 1961).

Results

The earliest recording with electrodes chronically implanted on a fetus *in utero* was at 112 days of gestation. A spontaneous EEG was already present (Figure 2). The recording showed continuous irregular waves with frequency of about 0.5 to 1.0 cycle/sec, and amplitude varying between 8 and 15 μv. There were a few superimposed faster waves of very low voltage. The fetus was quiescent and produced no movement artifacts, but artifacts from maternal movements alternated with periods of undisturbed spontaneous fetal brain activity. Abortion occurred on the second day of the experiment. No difference between recordings on days 1 and 2 was noted.

The most successful effort to maintain pregnancy with chronically implanted electrodes resulted in recordings from 117 to 128 days of gestation. At 117 days the electrical brain activity was the same as at 112 days, frequencies of about 0.5 to 1.0 cycle/sec and amplitude of 8 to 20 μv being recorded (Figure 3A). No day-by-day changes were seen; interdependence of the two hemispheres did not exist; and no differences between anterior and posterior regions were observed. There were numerous gross fetal movments at 125 days of gestation and in one instance a notable change in the EEG coincided with a fetal

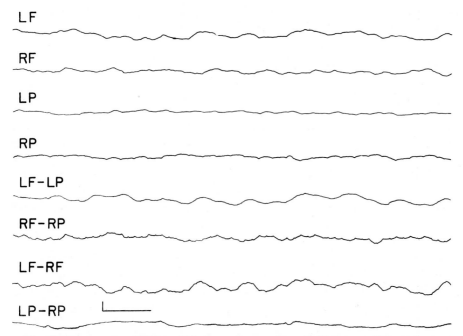

Fig. 2. Intrauterine EEG at 112 days of gestation. Calibrations: 50 μv; 1 sec.

movement artifact (Figure 3B). This consisted of a burst of waves of very low amplitude and 18 per sec. frequency lasting a little more than 1 second and followed by resumption of the slow activity previously seen.

A third fetus with electrodes implanted at 127 days of gestation showed a good EEG with poorly modulated wave frequencies of 1 to 1.5 cycle/sec and amplitude of 10 to 20 μv (Figure 4A). It occasionally displayed higher frequencies of about 1 to 5 μv superimposed on the type of records seen earlier. This fetus died *in utero* on the second day and the record thereafter showed an isolectric line with some maternal EKG artifacts (Figure 4B). The contrast between records before and after death demonstrated the validity of the intrauterine EEG.

Two other fetuses with electrodes implanted at 139 to 148 days were retained *in utero* until 141 and 151 days. The EEG of these differed in no way from those in the other experiments. The basic EEG remained unchanged from beginning to end.

The findings in the five experiments indicate that the spontaneous EEG of the monkey throughout the period studied is characterized by waves of low frequency and amplitude. No essential differences in the basic pattern between the oldest and the youngest were encountered. There were some variations in frequencies from 0.5 to about 2.0 cycle/sec, but these were unrelated to increase in gestational age.

The fetus became more active *in utero* as gestation progressed, and the EEG occasionally had faster waves of low amplitude superimposed on the background activity. The superimposed waves were more commonly found

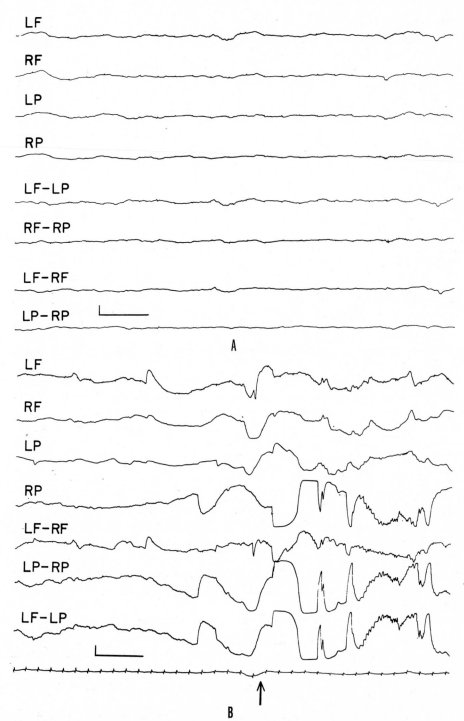

Fig. 3. A (top). Intrauterine EEG at 117 days of gestation. B (bottom). Intra-uterine EEG of the same monkey fetus at 12 days of gestation; fetal movement began to be seen at the arrow; maternal EKG lowest trace in B. Calibrations: 50 μv; 1 sec.

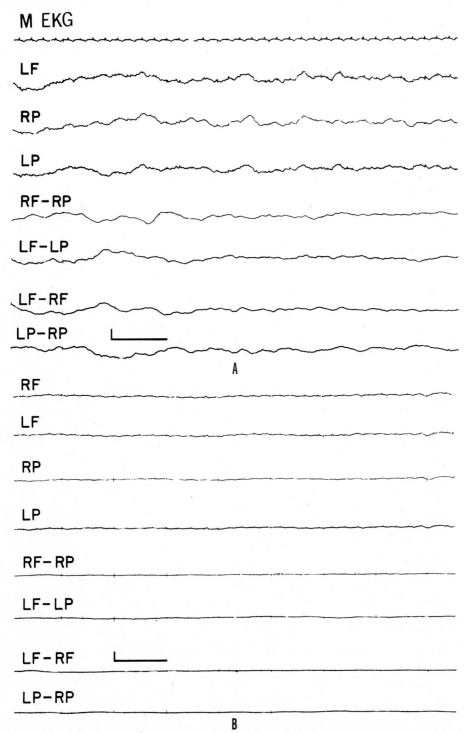

Fig. 4. A (top). Intrauterine EEG at 127 days of gestation; maternal EKG uppermost trace. B (bottom). The same fetus after death *in utero*. Calibrations: 50 μv; 1 sec.

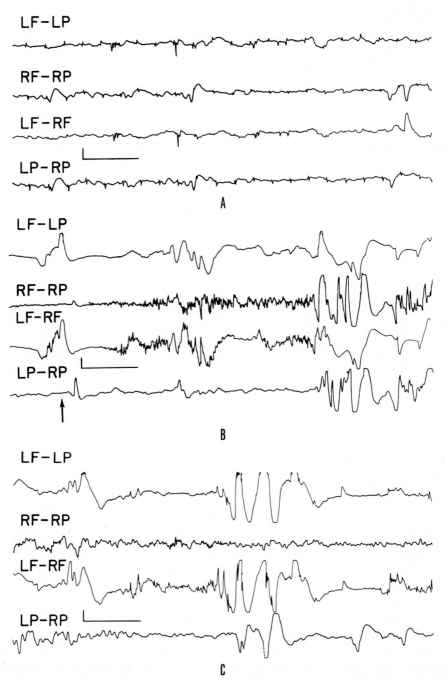

Fig. 5. A (top). Recording of fetal EEG *in utero* near term; maternal EKG of 180 per min. superimposed. B (middle). Changes in the EKG after delivery when the first gasping occurred (arrow). Time between records A and B was 25 sec. Calibrations: 50 μv; 1 sec. C (bottom). 20 sec. later EEG recording shown free of superimposed muscle potentials.

in the latter part of gestation than early in the third trimester. Generally they were associated with transient fetal movements.

Acute experiments were performed between 145 days and the end of gestation. The earlier stage may represent prematurity, the offspring weighing about 350 grams. The later stage was that of full-term monkeys weighing 400 grams or more.

The spontaneous electrical brain activity *in amnio* at Cesarian section did not differ in pattern from that recorded *in utero*; waves of low frequency and amplitude characterized it. The fetal EKG signals, recorded as artifacts, showed the heart rate to be 250 beats per minute which is a little higher than the basal value for the intrauterine fetal heart rate in the monkey.

The second stage of the experiment began when the fetus was delivered from the uterus. So long as it lay undisturbed, the EEG remained the same as *in amnio*, but as hypoxia developed fetal movements became pronounced and they imposed artifacts on the tracing. An EKG electrode was placed on the fetal precordial region at this time. The heart rate declined from 250 to 100 beats per minute, or even fewer beats per minute in some instances, at the end of this stage.

The third stage began when the umbilical cord was clamped or when the first gasp occurred, whichever event was first. A marked change took place in the spontaneous EEG when gasping appeared. This change consisted of an increase in both frequency and amplitude, as seen in Figure 5. The rate of the heartbeat at this time increased to 200 or more per minute. Breathing became regular and the EEG and EKG quickly took on the characteristics of the neonatal pattern. The changes in spontaneous electrical brain activity were not related to exposure of the offspring to air, nor were they caused by the act of clamping the umbilical cord, but they appeared simultaneously with gasping, whether this preceded or succeeded the clamping of the cord. There was no significant difference between the response of the premature monkey of 145 days gestation and those near full term.

Discussion

The technique of chronically implanting electrodes on the fetal scalp, which we have introduced, made it possible to register brain bioelectrical potentials from the intrauterine fetus for several days without anesthesia and with minimal excitement of the pregnant animal. Our experiments were limited to the last 8 weeks when the fetal head had attained adequate size for the method. Had more pregnant monkeys been available the number of observations could have been extended. However, the present series was large enough to demonstrate not only that there is no pronounced intrauterine maturational change in the monkey EEG during this period, but that the intrauterine recordings are not different from those obtained in acute preparations nearer full term.

The acute experiments of Givre (1957, 1961) in guinea pig fetuses revealed electrical brain activity resembling that which we encountered in the monkey fetus. Reports by Lindsley and others (Bernstine, 1961; Bernstine and Borkowski, 1956; Bernstine *et al.,* 1955; Lindsley, 1942; Okamoto and Kirikae, 1951) in human fetuses by recording from vaginal or abdominal electrodes bear out the fundamental similarity to the current findings in monkeys. It may be concluded that the prenatal EEG at all gestational ages up to full term is characterized by waves of low frequency and very low amplitude. Superimposition of faster waves occurs transiently, especially toward the end of gestation, with intrauterine movements of the fetus.

Bioelectrical events associated with the phenomenon of arousal at birth have not been previously related to the advent of respiration, in so far as we have been able to learn. The mere presentation of the fetus to the air did not effect arousal. Clamping the umbilical cord also did not effect arousal, but of course it induced hypoxia with concomitant biochemical changes as signaled by the slowing of the fetal heartbeat. At some point in this sequence of events the fetus gasped and its EEG changed dramatically from the fetal to the neonatal type. Since our experiment on arousal covered only the last 3 weeks of the gestational period we do not know when in development this change in the EEG can first occur. Nonviable premature human fetuses (as well as one monkey in our experience) have shown EEG of the fetal type, even though the fetuses were making respiratory movements (Dreyfus-Brisac, 1959; Dreyfus-Brisac *et al.,* 1962; Ellingson, 1958; Kasatin and Shepovalnikov, 1961; Sureau *et al.,* 1950). Correlations between morphological and biochemical maturation of the brain prenatally and electrical brain activity have been drawn in other species of mammals (Flexner, 1952). It will be instructive to explore this avenue in the rhesus monkey.

ACKNOWLEDGMENT

The research on which this report is based was conducted by Dra. F. O. Esquivel de Gallardo, Dra. M. I. Robert de Ramirez de Arellano and Dr. R. W. Fleischman. The investigators wish to thank all members of the Laboratory of Perinatal Physiology who aided in this work, especially Mr. Orlando Nieves and Mr. Calixto Jimenez for technical assistance in construction of special assemblies and recording the EEG. This communication reproduces the major part of an article about to appear in *Experimental Neurology;* permission of the publishers, Academic Press, Inc., is gratefully acknowledged.

REFERENCES

BERGSTRÖM, R. M. Brain and muscle potentials from the intrauterine foetus in unnarcotized, conscious animals. *Nature, 1962,* 195:1004–1005.

BERGSTRÖM, R. M., HELLSTROM, P. E., STENBERG, D. An intrauterine technique for recording the foetal EEG in animals. *Ann. Chir. Gynaecol.* Fenniae, 1961, 50:430–433.

BERNSTINE, R. L. *Fetal Electrocardiography and Electroencephalography.* Thomas, Springfield, Illinois, 1961.

BERNSTINE, R. L., BORKOWSKI, W. J. Foetal electroencephalography. *J. Obstet. Gynecol, Brit. Empire,* 1956, 63:275–279.

BERNSTINE, R. L., BORKOWSKI, W. J., PRICE, A. H. Prenatal fetal electroencephalography. *Amer. J. Obstet. Gynecol.,* 1955, 70: 623–630.

CAVENESS, W. F. *Atlas of Electroencephalography in the Developing Monkey. Macaca mulatta.* Addison-Wesley Publ. Co., Reading, Mass., 1962.

DREYFUS-BRISAC, C. Electroencephalography in Infancy. *In:* F. LINNEWEH (Editor) *Die physiologische Entwicklung* Springer-Verlag, Berlin, 1959, pp 29–40.

DREYFUS-BRISAC, C., FLESCHER, J., PLASSANT, E. L'Electroencephalogramme: critere d'age conceptionne du nouveaune a terme et premature. *Biol. Neonat.* 1962, 4:154–173.

ELLINGSON, R. J. Electroencephalograms of normal, full term newborns immediately after birth with observations on arousal and visual evoked responses. *Electroencephal. clin. Neurophysiol.* 1958, 10:31–50.

ESQUIVEL DE GALLARDO, F. O. The EEG of rhesus monkey fetuses *in utero* from chronically implanted electrodes. *Physiologist,* 1962, 5(3):128.

FLEXNER, L. B. Development of cerebral cortex: a cytological, functional and biochemical approach. *Harvey Lectures ser.,* 1952, 47:156–179.

GIVRE, A. Electroencefalograma fetal. In *Cong. Latinoam. Neurocirurgia, 9° Mexico, 1961,* pp 891–894.

GIVRE, A. Electroencefalograma materno y electroencefalograma fetal. *Prensa Med. Arg.,* 1957, 44:2578–2580.

JASPER, H. H. BRIDGEMAN, C. S., CARMICHAEL, L. An ontogenic study of cerebral electrical potentials in the guinea pig. *J. Exp. Psychol.,* 1937, 21:63–71.

KASATIN, N. I., SHEPOVALNIKOV, A. N. Some features of cerebral electrical activity in newborns. *Excerpta Med. Int. Congr. Series, 1961,* 37:35.

KENNARD, M. A., NIMS, L. F. Changes in normal electroencephalogram of *Macaca mulatta* with growth. *J. Neurophysiol., 1942,* 5:325–334.

LINDSLEY, D. B. Heart and brain potentials of human fetus *in utero. J. Psychol., 1942,* 55:421–416.

OKAMOTO, Y., KIRIKAE, T. Electroencephalographic studies of brain of foetus, of children, of premature birth and newborn, together with a note on reactions of foetus brain upon drugs. *Folia Psychiat. Neurol. Japan.,* 1951, 5:135–146.

ROBERT DE RAMIREZ DE ARELLANO, M. I. Maturational changes in the electroencephalogram of normal monkeys. *Exp. Neurol.,* 1961, 3:209–224.

SUREAU, M., FISCHGOLD, H., CAPDEVIELLE, G. L'EEG du nouveau-ne: normal et pathologique. *Electroenceph. clin. Neurophysiol.,* 1950, 2:113.

VAN WAGENNEN, G. Breeding and care of monkeys. W. F. Windle (editor) *Neurological and Psychological Deficits of Asphyxia Neonatorum,* Thomas, Springfield, Illinois. *1958,* pp 274–281.

STUDIES OF THE MATURATIONAL CHANGES IN THE EEG DURING SLEEP AND WAKEFULNESS IN THE MONKEY

WILLIAM F. CAVENESS

Department of Neurology, College of Physicians and Surgeons, Columbia University, New York, N. Y.

Introduction

In the study of the developing brain in the developing *Macaca mulatta* during the past six years, one of the parameters has been systematic electroencephalography. Such observations were accompanied by a growing appreciation of distinctive patterns associated with the natural states of wakefulness, drowsiness, and sleep that develop at different rates and from different areas of scalp recording. The most significant changes in each of these were noted between birth and puberty. These data have been set forth with selected samples that depict the principal characteristics of the electrical activity at successive age levels (Caveness, 1962). For this presentation, these findings will be summarized.

The material included 434 records, from 47 monkeys, between the age of one day and twenty-four months (Fig. 1). Employing a standard eight channel Grass Electroencephalograph, bipolar recordings were obtained from an array of six tungstenplatinum needle electrodes in three bilaterally symmetrical pairs over the frontal, temporal, and occipital regions (Fig. 2).

While it is self-evident that waking and sleeping states are different aspects of a continuum of brain activity, for clarity the patterns that reflect these states will be dealt with separately, with a subsequent indication of their composite nature.

Awake

Out of a mixture of fast and slow waves a spontaneous waking rhythm becomes apparent by the second to third week after birth. The frequency of this activity, at first 3 to 4 cycles per second, increases from 5 per second at six weeks to 6 per second at nine weeks, 8 per second at twenty weeks, and 9 per second at nine months. There follows a more gradual advance, with the frequency remaining close to 10 per second at twenty-four months. The amplitude of the early admixture of waves is 30 to 70 microvolts. The dominant waking activity is at first within this range, but its individual waves increase to 50 to 150 microvolts by the third week and 80 to 200 microvolts by the sixth week. After a plateau at this level, a decline begins at ten weeks that reaches 60 to 120 microvolts at twenty-four months. When first seen,

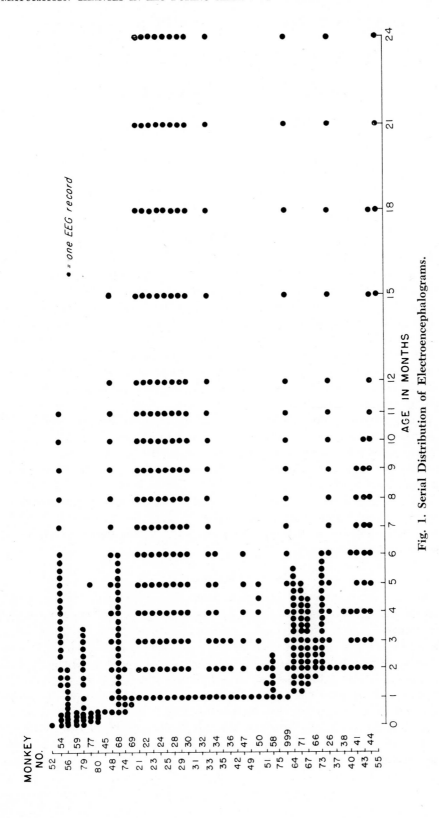

Fig. 1. Serial Distribution of Electroencephalograms.

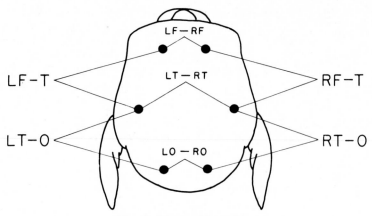

Fig. 2. Bipolar Recording.

the dominant waves are sparse, asynchronous in the anterior and posterior leads, and asymmetrical between the two sides of the head. As these waves evolve into a more persistent rhythm, some anterior-posterior synchrony is discernible at five weeks and is readily seen by nine weeks. Blocking of this activity by opening the eyes is demonstrable at four weeks. Symmetry in rate and amplitude between the two sides fluctuates, but becomes stable at nine to twelve months. The dominant rhythm appears diffusely in all leads at first, but a predilection for the posterior leads is apparent at five to eighteen weeks and is established at nine to twelve months. With the overall decline in amplitude, the greater voltage remains in the posterior leads. By twenty-four months constancy in the wave form is clearly defined.

There are relatively wide individual variations in the development of the central nervous system that are more marked in the earlier phases of this process. These variations are accompanied by differences in the time of appearance, prevalance, rate, amplitude, posterior dominance, and constancy in wave form for the dominant waking rhythm.

The range, as well as the average, in rate and in amplitude at successive age levels is indicated in Table 1. The average, with one standard deviation, is shown in Fig. 3.

Transition

In nature, the electrical forms that reflect the waking and sleeping states merge one into another in accordance with subtle or abrupt changes in brain function. Developmentally, the mode of transition is elaborated with the overall development of the waking and sleeping activity. At birth, when drowsiness and sleep are predominant, there is a slow drift between the rudimentary forms of sleep and the less prevalent and less well-defined waking forms. In the first few days and weeks, with the rapid development in expression of sleep, shifts in electrical activity are more easily recognized. After several months, with waking forms more prevalent and better defined, transition between waking and sleeping takes place in well-demarcated phases. There

Table 1.—*Frequency and Amplitude of Dominant Waking Rhythm*

AGE	NUMBER OF RECORDS	CYCLES PER SECOND		MICROVOLTS	
		AVERAGE	RANGE	AVERAGE	RANGE
Birth					
1 day	5	3.9	3.2– 5.0	43	30.0– 70.0
½ week	4	3.2	2.5– 3.5	39	32.5– 55.0
1 week	6	4.0	3.0– 5.0	56	30.0– 80.0
1½ weeks	5	3.9	3.0– 5.0	44	13.0– 85.0
2 weeks	9	4.1	3.5– 4.5	63	35.0–100.0
1 month	28	5.4	3.0–10.5	94	50.0–120.0
2 months	35	6.1	4.0–11.5	89	52.5–130.0
3 months	29	7.2	4.5–12.5	96	51.0–117.5
4 months	26	7.3	5.5–11.5	98	55.0–112.5
5 months	24	8.0	5.5–11.5	93	55.0–112.5
6 months	21	8.5	6.0–11.0	83	50.0–120.0
7 months	16	9.0	6.5–11.5	76	37.5–105.0
8 months	16	9.1	6.5–11.5	73	55.0– 88.5
9 months	16	9.6	6.5–11.5	72	42.5– 90.0
10 months	15	9.8	8.0–11.5	73	37.5–100.0
11 months	14	9.6	6.5–11.5	62	37.5–100.0
12 months	13	9.7	7.5–11.5	70	35.0–100.0
15 months	14	9.8	8.0–11.5	57	35.0– 85.0
18 months	13	9.8	9.0–11.5	50	35.0– 75.0
21 months	12	10.0	9.0–11.0	52	22.5– 62.5
24 months	12	9.8	9.0–11.5	45	27.5– 65.0

may be gradual and asymmetrical fluctuations between these phases, but such changes can occur with great rapidity. As puberty is approached, at eighteen to twenty-four months, transition into sleep is perceived more easily by the decomposition of the predominant waking activity than by the advent of sleeping forms, which have now become less well delineated.

Drowsy

Rhythmic activity, relatively well formed, is apparent in brief runs at one day of age. At first it is predominantly in the posterior leads, at one-half week it is diffuse, and at one week it is more clearly seen in the anterior leads. It remains predominantly frontal and central, with increasing duration of the runs, until twelve months of age. At fifteen months the bursts are short and variable; at eighteen months they are difficult to find and when found are more prominent in the posterior leads. At twenty-four months this rhythmic activity is no longer present.

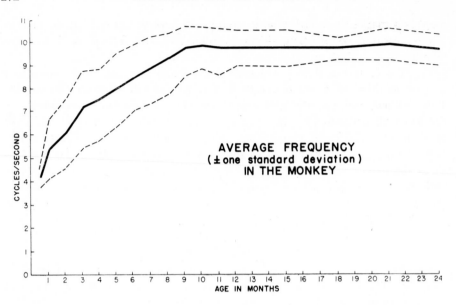

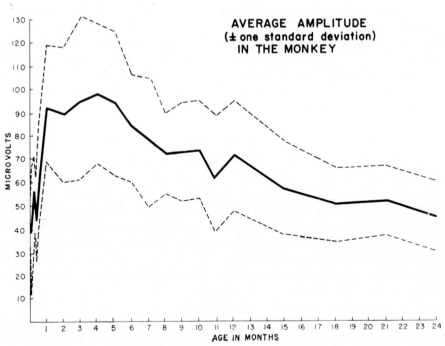

Fig. 3.—Average Frequency and Average Amplitude, Awake.

The amplitude, at first low to medium, increases to bursts of high voltage at two weeks and steady high voltage at two months. By three months, particularly in the frontal regions, it is very high. With some waxing and waning, the voltage remains at this level until twelve months. Thereafter there is a marked reduction, with medium to high voltage at fifteen months, low to medium voltage at eighteen months, and low voltage at twenty-four months.

Frequency, at first 4 to 5 per second gradually increases to 6 per second at four months. With some variation, this is maintained to twelve months. There follow, with the declining amplitude, shorter runs and wave forms that are less well defined. The rate remains around 6 per second until the eighteenth month. Thereafter there is low voltage, random slow and fast activity.

Bilateral synchrony from homologous areas is apparent from the first day. With increasing age, synchrony between the areas in which the rhythmic activity is most prominent becomes even more manifest. Beyond twelve months, as the rhythmic activity becomes less evident, so does its synchrony between the two sides.

Light Sleep

Spindles, the hallmark of light and medium sleep, are apparent from the first day. These are predominantly frontal throughout. Short and long runs of 15 to 18 per second waves, with smooth fluctuations from low to medium voltage, give way after a few weeks to more discrete bursts of high amplitude. These remain well delineated, with some variation in rate, for the first twelve months. Thereafter the bursts become less frequent, shorter in duration, lower in voltage, and slower in rate. By twenty-four months the spindle appears as a rare, 12 to 15 per second, low voltage remnant super-imposed on more prominent, less rhythmic sleep activity. Bilateral synchrony of spindles is often approximate, never exact, and on occasion these forms occur independently from either side.

Deep Sleep

Variable slow waves of medium to high voltage are at first scattered amidst activity of lower voltage and faster rate. By the end of the first week high amplitude, slow activity occurs in long runs, with a suggested symmetry between the two sides. This irregular slow activity predominates for the first six months, then occurs in episodes or bursts and by twenty-four months is far less constant. Its early frequency is 1.5 to 3 cycles per second, but the range is gradually extended after six months and may include 4, 5 and 6 per second waves by twenty-four months. The amplitude, high from the first week, increases gradually until twelve months, then declines to its original level by twenty-four months. Bilateral homologous synchrony, suggested in the first week, is more evident by the second. First noted between the posterior leads, at two months it is equally apparent between the anterior leads. Gaining in detail with age, this expression of symmetry becomes less evident as the activity it reflects becomes less constant.

Concomitant Development of Waking and Sleeping Activity

To summarize the parallel development of the principal wave forms, a

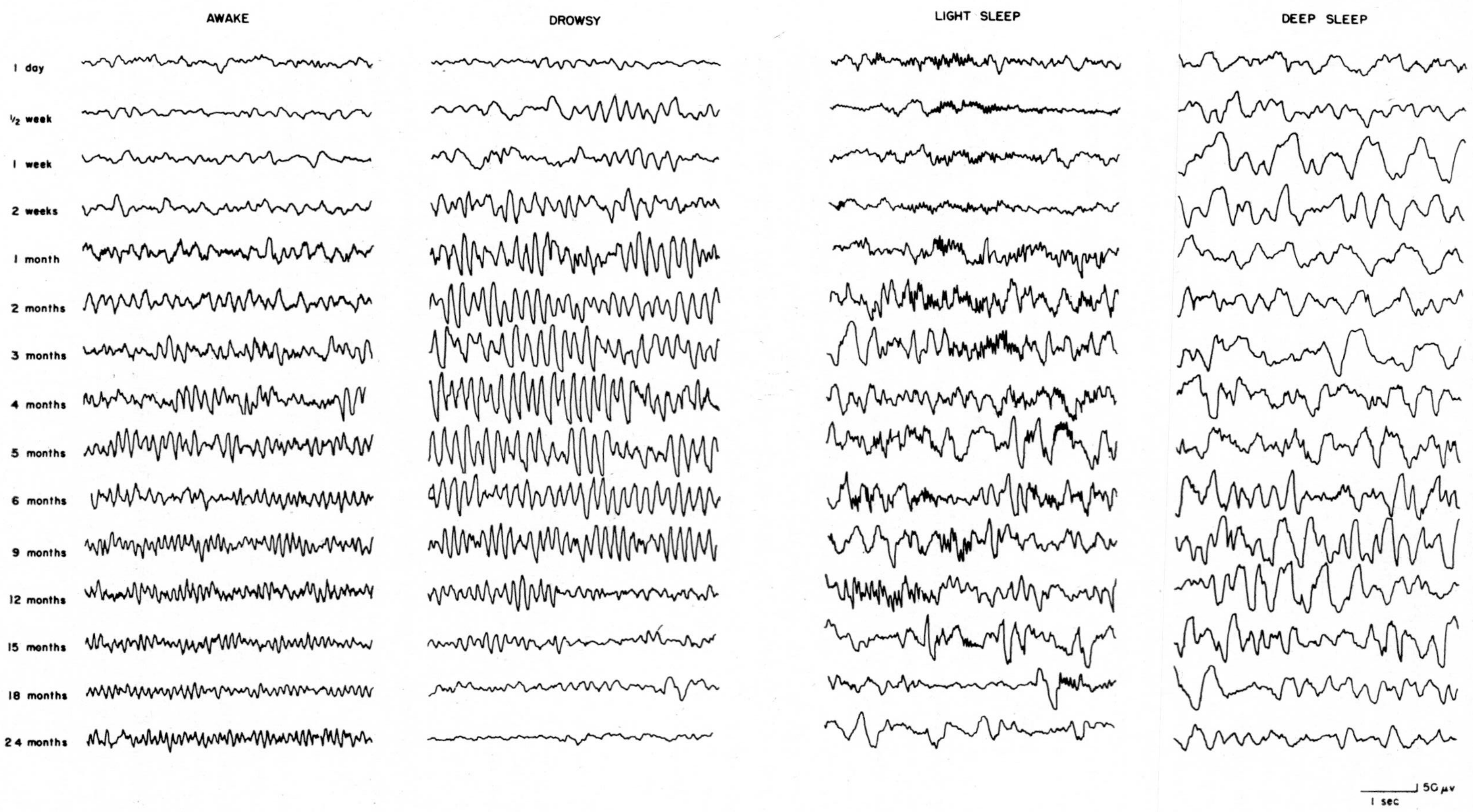

Fig. 4. Composite Summary of Waking and Sleeping Activity at Successive Age Levels. This figure, with a single run at each age level, depicts the principal forms in their concomitant development. Those representing waking and deep sleep are from the posterior leads, those representing drowsiness and light sleep are from the anterior leads.

single channel of recording is selected for waking activity, drowsiness, light and deep sleep at each age level. (Fig. 4).

When the developmental characteristics of the electroencephalogram in the monkey are set forth and compared to those of man, certain similarities and differences become apparent (Caveness, 1962). The telescoping of time in the monkey lends sharper definition to the changes that accompany the progressive growth, integration, and complexity of the central nervous system. The hypersynchronous waves of drowsiness, the spindles of light and medium sleep, and the bilaterally homologous, slow activity of deep sleep are seen shortly after birth and achieve their fullest expression in the young animal. Must not their projections be from those parts of the brain which are fully developed at that time: the brain-stem reticular formation, the midline nuclear structures, and the archicortex? These patterns, distinctly different in wave form, frequency, amplitude, and topography, suggest different sites of origin in the primordial brain. The more gradual devolopment of the waking patterns has a rough parallel in the maturation of the neocortex. The alpha activity does not achieve its stabilized characteristics until early pubescence, by which time the cerebral cortex of the monkey is well devoleped. Whatever the activating or suppressing influences from the subcortical structures, the role of the neocortex in the waking activity is evidently great. This is further borne out by the reciprocal relation between the sleeping and waking forms, not only at any given time but in developmental perspective as well. As the behavioral waking periods are lengthened and the electrical waking patterns are progressively elaborted, the concomitant reduction in behavioral sleep and alteration in the sleeping patterns is an integral part of the maturation of the *waking brain.*

REFERENCE

CAVENESS, W. F. *Atlas of Electroencephalography in the Developing Monkey,* Addison-Wesley Publishing Company, Inc., Reading, Massachusetts, *1962,* pp. 145.

DISCUSSION

DR. DREYFUS-BRISAC: If one compares the age at which the hypersynchronous high voltage slow waves of drowsiness appear and disappear, it is noted that the presence of this EEG pattern lasts much longer in monkey than in human when one considers the comparative time scale. This difference in the rate of maturation of the drowsy phase would seem to be of interest, in respect to comparative development.

DR. PAMPIGLIONE: Did you ever encounter in your normal series of monkeys any abnormal activities of the kind seen in man?

DR. CAVENESS: Only in one case—a single incidence of infection. But, other than the individual variations, we did not find any paroxysmal activity or other abnormalities.

DR. KELLAWAY: There are two very interesting points here. One is that the range of variation in the monkey is relatively narrow as compared to that of the human in which the range of normal variation at a given age level is relatively wide and varies tremendously at different ages. Also, the lack of symmetry quite late in age is another characteristic of the monkey. In other words, we get synchronous and symmetrical records in human infants fairly soon as compared to the monkey, for even the adult monkey does not show as good symmetry in homologous regions as does the young child.

THE ELECTRICAL ACTIVITY OF THE
BRAIN IN THE YOUNG DOG*

G. PAMPIGLIONE

*The Hospital for Sick Children, and The Medical Research Council,
Human Nutrition Research Unit, London, England*

The literature on the central nervous system of various laboratory animals is growing very rapidly, the cat and the monkey having been extensively studied. The dog was a favorite animal in experimental work during the nineteenth century and the beginning of the twentieth century, but it has become less fashionable in the last 20 to 30 years. The electrical activity of the brain of the adult dog was beautifully described in the pioneer work of Prawdicz-Neminski in 1913 and particularly in 1925. However, changes that occur in the electrical activity of the brain of the growing dog have received little attention. Two papers on limited material have recently been published (Charles and Fuller, 1956; Werner, 1960), suggesting that from the fifth week of life, the EEG of the dog had reached adult pattern. In a preliminary communication (Pampiglione, 1961), variance with the results of previous studies was mentioned, and it was suggested that changes continue to take place in the EEG of the dog well after the fifth week of life. The present paper includes and amplifies those preliminary observations, giving a general outline of the development of the EEG in the first half-year of life of the normal dog. Fuller details are given in a small monograph on the development of cerebral function in the dog, to be published (Pampiglione, 1963).

Material and Methods

A longitudinal investigation was carried out on a group of 42 normal animals. The dogs were largely bred from basset and beagle stock whose dietary and behavioral features before and during pregnancy were known to be normal. Animals which became ill during this study were not included in this group unless the illness was a mild one. The 42 dogs were grouped in 9 litters. Three of these litters were fed by the mothers for six weeks. One litter was artificially-fed from the age of 10 days, while the other litters were divided between mother-fed and artificially-fed pups.

The EEG's were taken at weekly and, later, fortnightly and monthly intervals from the end of the first week of life to the age of 6 months. In five dogs, records continued up to the age of 2 years.

A simple method of recording EEG's in growing animals was developed (Pampiglione, Platt and Stewart, 1959). Small stainless steel needle elec-

*Part of this work was supported by a grant of the National Spastics Society Medical Research Trust Fund.

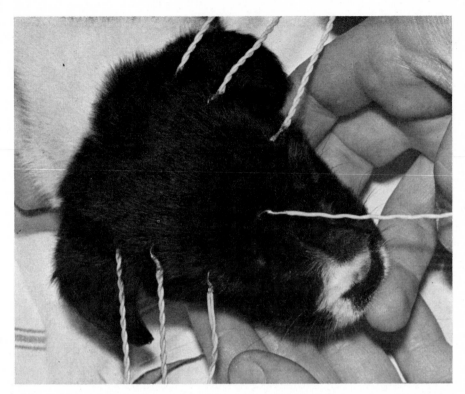

Fig. 1. Type of electrodes used in this study and their light insertion. For further details, see Pampiglione, 1963.

trodes (Lane's cleft palate, half-circle, ⅜″ needles) soldered to a flexible "deaf aid wire" were lightly inserted in the scalp over the anterior, middle, and posterior third of each hemisphere (Fig. 1). The tip of each small needle was inserted only one or two millimeters into the skin, avoiding deep insertion into the muscles of the scalp, which not only might be slightly painful but would also stimulate local and widespread muscle activity. Most pups usually did not appear to notice either the insertion or the presence of the small electrodes in the first few weeks of life, and later seemed fully adapted to the repetition of the test. The animal was gently held or nursed on the lap of the laboratory assistant, who covered the animal's eyes with his hand most of the time.

At first a two-channel Ediswan and later a four-channel O.T.E. ink-recording EEG apparatus was used with an amplification of 10 microvolts per millimeter pen-deflection, full H.F. response (15% down to 90 c/s), and a time constant of 0.3 seconds. On some animals, particularly toward the end of the second month of extra-uterine life, the amplification had to be diminished to 20 microvolts per millimeter pen-deflection. Natural stimuli (clapping of hands, short whistle, touching the tail or paw, smell of food, covering and uncovering of the eyes) were presented at various intervals.

Results

RESTING STATE

During the second and third weeks of life, there was in the EEG a fairly uniform pattern of continuous activity of rather low amplitude (10 to 40 microvolts), mostly rhythmic at about 11 to 12 c/s. Few slower components were occasionally seen, and there were no constant differences in either amplitude or frequency between the anterior and posterior halves of the hemispheres. Some moderate "spontaneous" fluctuations in frequency and amplitude of the traces occurred, usually generalized, but these changes did not appear to be related to variations in the animal's behavior. For example, the EEG changes did not occur more often when the animal appeared awake, moving about, or whining, or when sleep and bouts of trembling were observed. No clear correlations could be found between these "spontaneous" EEG fluctuations and periods in which the animal had his eyes either closed or open. Asymmetries between the activities of the two hemispheres were variable. Often the traces were of larger amplitude recording between the two hemispheres than on each one.

Toward the end of the first month, some slower waves began to appear in the EEG, while there was little increase in rhythmic components at 10 to 15 c/s. There was also an increase in amplitude of the traces, and there were more definite fluctuations in frequency and amplitude, both when the animal appeared awake and when he was asleep (Fig. 2). These changes, however, did not occur at regular intervals, and could appear independently of the behavioral changes. Alterations in frequency and amplitude of the traces could occur either in the anterior half or the posterior half of each hemisphere, although they were more commonly generalized. No definite "sleep spindles" were seen, even when the animals appeared soundly asleep. Long periods of predominant fast activity were also seen while the animals were fast asleep.

In the fifth and sixth weeks of life, and thereafter, the animals appeared very much interested in their environment; during the test, the eyes of the pups had to be kept covered much more continuously than those of the younger animals. The faster activities were not at all prominent, unless the animal was allowed to look around, and a greater amount of somewhat irregular 3 to 7 c/s activity was seen during the waking state. The amplitude of this activity was of the order of 100 microvolts and was greater over the posterior half than over the anterior half of the head. During drowsiness and sleep, however, larger slower waves appeared, often being more marked over the anterior half than over the posterior half of each hemisphere. No definite sleep spindles could be recognized, although mixed fast frequencies occasionally appeared.

Between the seventh and ninth week of life, a rhythmic activity, often of large amplitude (100 to 150 microvolts), at about 4 to 6 c/s appeared during the waking state when the animal was fairly relaxed with his eyes covered (Fig. 3). This activity was much larger and better formed over the posterior

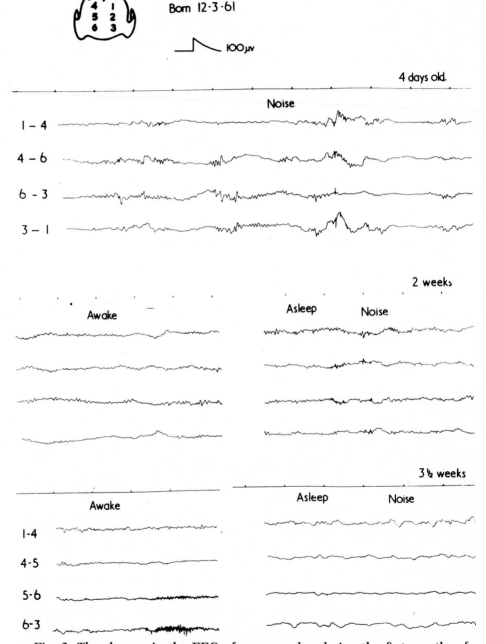

Fig. 2. The changes in the EEG of a young dog during the first months of extra-uterine life. Note that in the first week of life there is a tendency for the activity to appear in runs with variable distribution, with relatively equi-potential periods in the intervals. The effects of auditory stimuli are not obvious in the EEG and begin to appear only towards the end of the first month.

half than over the anterior half of the hemispheres, usually appearing at about the same time over both hemispheres though not necessarily in the same phase. The changes during drowsiness and sleep were more marked than in the previous stages, with the appearance of large slow waves now more marked over the anterior half than over the posterior half of the hemispheres. Faster activities were often seen during sleep, particularly over the anterior half of the head, without, however, well-formed sleep spindles.

From the tenth week, the rhythmic activity at 4 to 6 c/s was well established in all animals during the resting, waking state when vision was excluded. This activity, clearly arising from the posterior half of each hemisphere, often oppeared in long runs. Spontaneous sleep was less commonly seen at this age than in younger pups, but the differences in frequency and amplitude between the anterior and posterior regions of the hemispheres were well recognizable. Short runs of rhythmic 8 to 10 c/s waves were occasionally seen over the fronto-central regions during sleep ("sleep spindles").

In the fourth and fifth months of life, the rhythmic activity became slightly faster at 6 to 8 c/s, though appearing for somewhat shorter periods. The amplitude of the traces was more of the order of 20 to 40 than 100 microvolts, and lower amplitude faster activities were commonly seen both over the anterior and the posterior halves of the head. Sleep could be observed only infrequently and for very short periods, but clear changes occurred in the EEG, with a generalized increase in slower waves, disappearance of the rhythmic 6 to 8 c/s activity, and occasional appearance of sleep spindles.

By the sixth month of life, the traces during the waking state became of still lower amplitude, usually about 20 to 30 microvolts, with only infrequent activity at 4 to 6 c/s, and predominant faster activities at 7 to 8 and 12 to 20 c/s having reached the better known adult patterns (Fig. 3). No further changes were seen, however, in the sleep patterns of the fourth and fifth months apart from a moderate general decrease in amplitude of the traces in comparison with earlier age groups.

Effect of Sensory Stimuli

When simple sensory stimuli were presented, marked evolutional changes were noticed in the EEG responses obtained at various ages. Although individual differences were common, an auditory stimulus (a whistle, clapping hands loudly, or other noises) did not evoke consistent changes in the EEG either during sleep or during wakefulness in the first three to four weeks of life (Fig. 2). Later, however, particularly after the end of the second month, similar stimuli evoked marked changes in the EEG (blocking of the rhythmic 4 to 6 c/s activity during the waking, but resting, stage accompanied by the appearance of, or increase in, low amplitude faster activities; appearance of K complexes during sleep). Olfactory stimuli and mixed ones (smell of food, acetone, or ether) were, however, quite effective even in the first month of life, although the EEG changes might be variable and sometimes delayed. Tactile stimuli were sometimes effective, even in the first month of life, but seemed to produce a greater EEG change in the second and third months

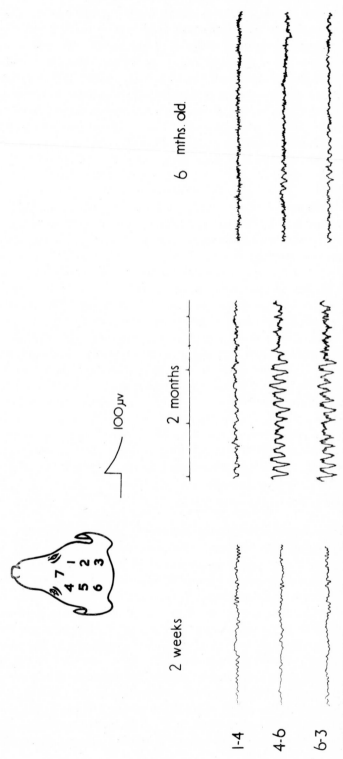

Fig. 3. Main EEG features during the waking state in the same dog at the age of 2 weeks, 2 months and 6 months while vision was occluded. There are marked changes in the amplitude and frequency of the traces during these periods.

of life. The effect of visual stimuli could not be systematically tested with our method of holding the animal, as the eyes were usually kept covered by the assistant's hand and removal of the hand was already, in itself, a powerful stimulus. However, when the animal was awake and vision was temporarily occluded, clear EEG changes could be noticed beginning at five to six weeks and becoming marked between eight and about sixteen to twenty weeks (facilitation of the appearance of rhythmic 4 to 6 c/s activity over the posterior half of the head). After the end of five months, however, the exclusion of vision, even if the animal remained very quiet, was not always followed by the appearance of, or increase in, rhythmic activity.

Discussion

Only a limited amount of information was found in the available literature on the development of EEG patterns in the growing dog. Charles and Fuller, in 1956, studied 5 young dogs (without narcosis), using only three electrodes on the scalp, and compared their records taken at weekly intervals with those of a single adult dog. They found at the age of three weeks an activity at 9 to 11 c/s (40 microvolts), which was said to be similar to the alpha rhythm and which would appear when their dogs were quiet. About the age of four to five weeks, they found a general increase in frequency during the waking state and some slowing during sleep. Moreover, Charles and Fuller, in the same paper, found that at eight weeks the main frequencies recorded were grouped as in the previous three weeks. Their conclusion was that the main change in the EEG of the dog was taking place between three and five weeks. Similar observations were made in a short communication by Werner (1960), who stated that "starting with the 5th week of life the waking and sleeping EEG's were identical with those of the adult dog". By contrast with the very limited literature, our observations suggest that a much more complex development of EEG pattern occurs in the dog, with various phases: 1) from birth to the end of the first week, 2) from 8 days to 3 weeks, 3) from 3 to 6 weeks 4) from 7 weeks to 4½ months, and 5) from 4½–5 months to maturity.

In view of the considerable discrepancies with previous work, the possibility that the progressive EEG changes found in our dogs might have been due to phenomena of "habituation to the test" had to be considered. The most remarkable feature was the establishment of 4 to 6 c/s rhythmic activity by the end of the second month of life. As controls, six normal dogs, previously untested, were examined at the age of 9 and 10 weeks. These dogs belonged to litters other than those used in the longitudinal study, and were held during the test by an assistant not usually in contact with them. The method of examination and the position of the electrodes, however, were similar to those of the main experiment. In all these animals, the rhythmic 4 to 6 c/s activity was well formed and similar in amplitude, frequency and distribution to that of the animals repeatedly tested. This finding, therefore, excluded the possibility that the establishment of the 4 to 6 c/s activity might have been due to conditioning phenomena of the animal to the test situation or to it's being handled by the same person over a period of many weeks. This activity has to be considered as part of the spontaneous maturation phenomena.

The records were usually taken after feeding. It was noticed that after the age of five to six weeks the pups were much more quiet with a full stomach than with a relatively empty one. This was even more obvious for the animals in whom artifical feeding started at the age of three weeks, as they rarely slept in the two hours preceding being fed. Some differences in behavior and, to some extent, in the EEG features were noticed, even in members of the same litter, between those that had been mother-fed and those that had artificial feeding. The tendency was for earlier and more marked differences between waking and sleeping patterns in the mother-fed animals. This might well be due to the fact that the mother-fed animals had a full stomach most of the time, while a more artificial time table had to be followed for artificial feeding. Toward the end of the second month the appearance of the rhythmic 4 to 6 c/s activity occurred slightly earlier in the mother-fed than in the artificially-fed animals of the same litter when considered as two groups.

No marked differences were noticed between male and female pups when considered over a long period, although some variations might be present in single records taken at the same age, particularly at about six to eight weeks. The trend was that the young bitches were slightly more forward than their brothers, a common occurrence also in other species.

The individual differences in EEG features both between members of the same litter and between various litters seemed to be mild in the first two to three weeks of life, but could become more obvious after four weeks or later. These differences were either in the form of asymmetries between the activities of the two hemispheres or in the amount of fast activity mixed with the predominant slow elements. In addition, slightly advanced or retarded degrees of EEG maturation could be noticed for a period in some animals, but these delays were only transitory.

There were no constant differences in frequency and amplitude of the traces between dogs that appeared active and restless and dogs that were quiet or whining.

The variations with age in the responses to simple sensory stimuli are probably in keeping both with anatomical development and with the changing importance and integration of various afferences in the growing animal. It is possible that in the first month of life olfactory stimuli are of greater importance than visual ones. Visual clues appeared to become important between two and five months, while auditory stimuli seem progressively more effective from the end of the first month of life onward.

ACKNOWLEDGMENTS

This work could not have been carried out without the encouragement and facilities kindly offered by Prof. B. S. Platt and his Medical Research Council Human Nutrition Research Unit.

REFERENCES

CHARLES, M. S. and FULLER, J. L. Developmental study of the electroencephalogram of the dog. *Electroenceph. clin. Neurophysiol.*, *1956*, 8:645–652.

NEMINSKI, W. W. Ein Versuch der Registrierung der elektrischen Gehirnerscheinungen. *Zentralbl. Physiol., Leipz. u. Wien*, *1913*, 27:951–960.

PAMPIGLIONE, G. The development of some rhythmic activity in the electroencephalogram of the young dog. *J. Physiol. (Proc. Physiol. Soc.)*, *1961*, 159:27–28.

PAMPIGLIONE, G. *Development of Cerebral Function in the Dog*. Butterworth, London, *1963*.

PAMPIGLIONE, G., PLATT, B. S. and STEWART, R. J. C. Longterm EEG and ECG studies of young rats, pigs and dogs. *Electroenceph. clin. Neurophysiol.*, *1959*, 11:603.

PRAWDICZ-NEMINSKI, W. W. Zur Kenntnis der elektrischen und der Innervationsvorgange in der funktionellen Elementen und Gewehen des tierischen Organisms. Elektrocerekrogramm der Saugetiere. *Pflüg. Arch. ges Physiol.*, *1925*, 209: 362–382.

WERNER, J. Concerning the ontogenesis of brain potentials in the spontaneous EEG's of newborn dogs. *Electroenceph. clin. Neurophysiol.*, *1960*, 12:256.

DISCUSSION

DR. KELLAWAY: One interesting feature of these observations is the relatively rapid emergence of certain rhythms in the electrogram of the young pup. In following human babies over a period of time I think the thing that strikes you is how little they change from time to time. At certain stages, week after week, there is practically no change awake or asleep.

DR. PAMPIGLIONE: Yes, this is what I was trying to emphasize. For example, over a period of up to about three months nothing changes in the EEG and then over a relatively short period, probably a couple of weeks in that particular individual, the rhythmic patterns emerge.

THE ELECTROENCEPHALOGRAM OF THE PREMATURE INFANT AND FULL-TERM NEWBORN
Normal and Abnormal Development of Waking and Sleeping Patterns*

C. DREYFUS-BRISAC

*Clinique Baudelocque, Maternity Hospital Saint Antoine,
EEG Department of the Hôpital de la Pitié, Paris, France*

Study of the ontogenesis of the electroencephalogram has become a very useful tool in evaluating the functional development of the central nervous system. It is also a very good method for assessing the contribution of the various regions of the nervous system, and of each nervous component to its electrical activities (Scheibel and Scheibel, 1961). In this regard it is interesting to note that only since 1957 at the Fourth International Congress of Electroencephalography and Clinical Neurophysiology (Kellaway, 1957) has interest been raised in ontogenesis of the electroencephalogram.

Waking and Sleeping Patterns

During our initial studies originating in 1953 (Dreyfus-Brisac and Blanc, 1956; Dreyfus-Brisac *et al.*, 1956), we were concerned with the development of the waking and sleeping patterns of bio-electrical activity of the brain. Since that time our knowledge in this field has been extended, and in a recent publication we have defined more accurately the sleeping patterns which appear at eight and nine months of conceptual age respectively (Dreyfus-Brisac, 1962).

It appears that until eight months of conceptual age, the absence of differentiation between waking and sleeping patterns is one of the most important features of the normal early human premature electroencephalogram (Dreyfus-Brisac, 1959).

The morphology and topographical distribution of the electrical activity changes between the fifth and seventh months of fetal life, and this development of the bio-electrical activity is extraordinarily rapid.

This evolution has already been described in previous papers (Dreyfus-Brisac and Blanc, 1956; Dreyfus-Brisac *et al.*, 1956, 1961, 1962), and this is shown in Figures 1 and 2. During these three months of early prematurity the salient features of the EEG remain as follows:

---

*This work has been fulfilled with the aid of the Institut National d'Hygiène and of the Délégation Générale à la Recherche Scientifique.

a. The recordings made during the wakeful and asleep states have a similar morphology and spatial distribution.

b. Electrical activity is discontinuous and sometimes paroxysmal. In addition, long lasting silent periods can be recorded.

3. There is an absence of interhemispheric synergy.

At the beginning of our studies it was thought that the EEG remains stable during the last month of conceptual age, until full term birth. However, this early observation has been invalidated by more recent findings of an important change in pattern occurring during the ninth month of conceptual age, and allowing the differentiation of the late premature eight month old from a full neonate (Dreyfus-Brisac, 1962).

The salient feature at eight months is the appearance of the differentiation between the electrogram during the sleeping and waking state. At the same time there appear the following new characteristics:

a. Continuous electrical activity.

b. Some degree of interhemispheric synergy.

c. Diffuse electroencephalographic reactivity to any stimulation.

At eight to nine months of conceptual age the waking electrogram has lost the rhythmic and spatial organization surprisingly present at seven months, and has become uniform, arrhythmic and continuous (Figure 3).

To the description of the waking pattern should, however, be added that the concomitant appearance of a specific sleep pattern is a most important feature in ontogenesis. Indeed, the conceptual age of eight to nine months is the first period where the EEG findings can be correlated with the infant's behavior. From this time to the beginning of the second month after full-term birth, three specific electroencephalographic patterns may be recognized when the infant is awake, drowsy or deeply asleep. In addition, at eight months a puzzling phenomenon has been observed: the EEG in drowsiness or light sleep is similar to the waking or sleeping EEG of a seven month conceptual age infant. In deep sleep, however, the pattern changes to a discontinuous, sometimes paroxysmal activity with asynergism between the two hemispheres.

At eight and a half to nine months conceptual age the typical differentiation described by many authors is present (Samson-Dollfus, 1955; Dreyfus-Brisac et al., 1956; Ellingson, 1958; Fischgold et al., 1959; Glaser, 1959). At this time the differences between the electroencephalographic findings during the states of wakefulness and deep sleep are obvious. In addition, a rhythmic Rolandic pattern and occasional slow waves may be noted during drowsiness and light sleep.

Polygraphic Studies of the Sleep Cycle

Prolonged electroencephalograms with simultaneous recordings of the EEG, respiration, body activity, and sometimes myography are adding valuable information to our knowledge of new born infants. Attention has been drawn by the work of Kleitman and his associates (Kleitman, 1939; Kleitman and Engelman, 1953; Aserinsky and Kleitman, 1955) on the occurrence of ocular movements and EEG cycles during sleep. These authors have demonstrated

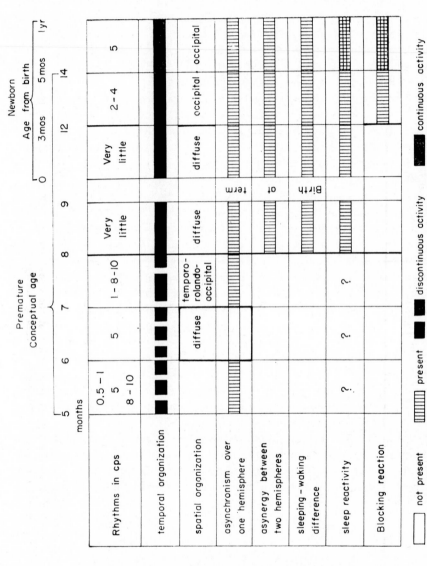

Fig. 1. A table summarizing the characteristic features of the EEG in prematures, full-term newborns, and infants (Dreyfus-Brisac, 1962).

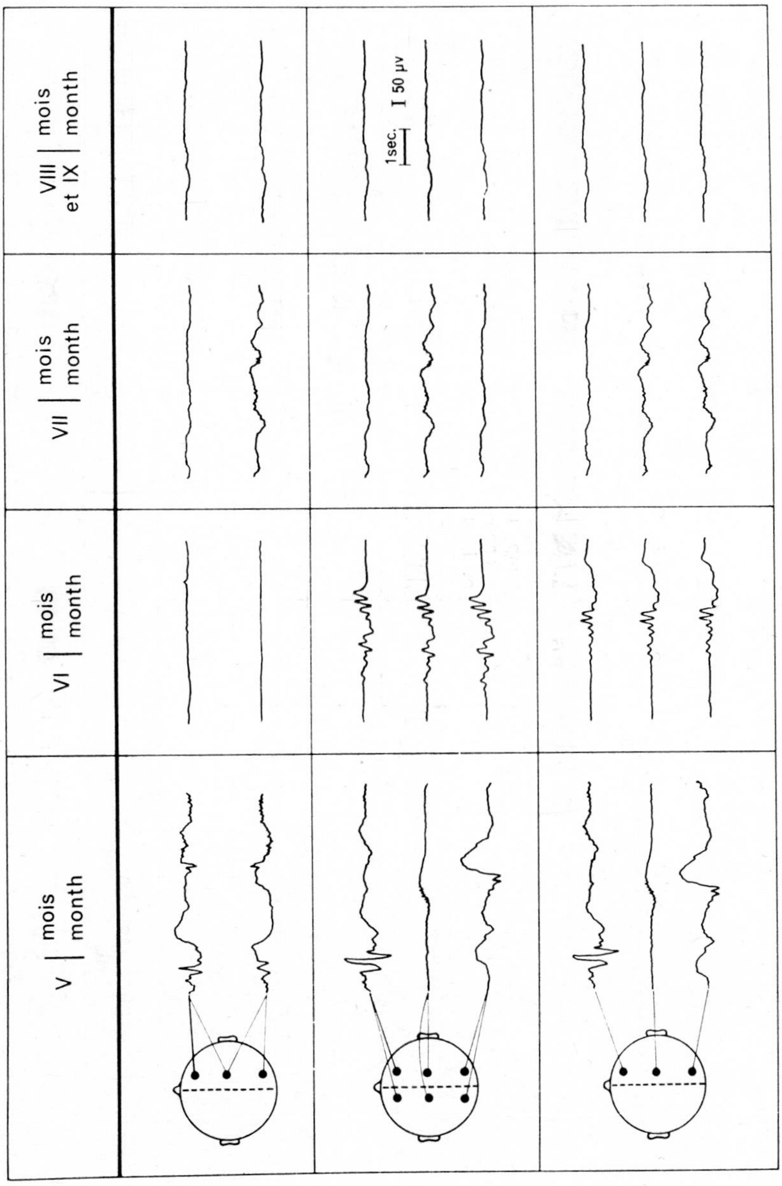

Fig. 2. Schematic representation of the bio-electrical patterns and their spatial organization from 5 to 9 months of conceptual age.

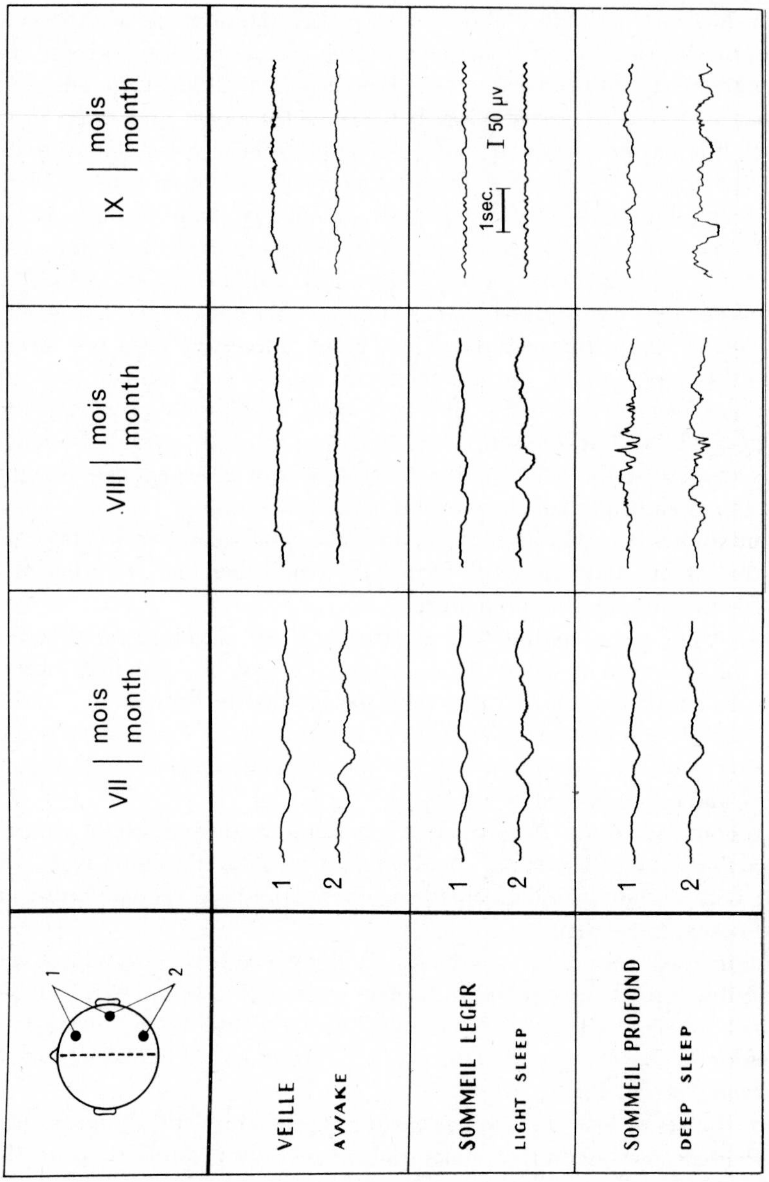

Fig. 3. Waking and sleeping patterns at 2, 8 and 9 months of conceptual age. The patterns are the same at 7 months, and are different at 8 and 9 months (for description, see text).

cyclic variations of night sleep in human adults. Others (Dement and Kleitman, 1957; Schwartz and Fischgold, 1960; Fischgold and Schwartz, 1961; Jouvet et al., 1961; Jouvet, 1962; Oswald, 1962) have more recently stressed the importance of such findings in normal and pathological conditions.

Prolonged polygraphic recordings are interesting in many respects. In the premature they may provide a clue as to whether the absence of differentiation between the electroencephalogram during sleep and the wakeful state can be correlated with absence (or presence) of other vegetative and somatic parameters of differentiation between wakefulness and sleep in the premature. For example, Gesell and Amatruda (1945) have stated that it is difficult to appreciate whether the premature is awake or asleep. In this regard, the simultaneous recording of these parameters, many of them already being studied independently (de Toni, 1933; Wagner, 1939; Brazelton, 1960; Stechler et al., 1960; Parmelee et al., 1961, 1962; Vallbona et al., 1961, 1963; Roffwarg et al., 1963) will probably provide valuable data in the approach to this problem. It should be mentioned that much interesting data has already been published by various authors both in animal and human newborns (Scherrer and Oeconomos, 1954; Scherrer et al., 1960; Jouvet et al., 1961; Delange et al., 1962; Ruckebusch, 1963; Roffwarg et al., in press). Prolonged recordings of two to three hours duration, generally between two feedings, permitted the identification of sleep cycles in the newborn.

From our studies we shall discuss the differences between two electrograms, one recorded at five days in a full-term baby, the other one recorded at 11 days in a 7½ month gestation premature.

The differences between the two electrograms are striking. As described above, in the full-term newborn when asleep (Figure 4), we may observe two main electrical patterns: 1) rhythmic, (described in drowsiness) and 2) "alternant" or discontinuous slow waves, (described in deep sleep). Less typical patterns of short duration can also be detected (mixed rhythmic and slow waves, and continuous slow waves).

In a two hour recording (Figure 5), it is possible to distinguish very clearly two periods of "tracé alternant," of 15 to 20 minutes duration which are associated with a state of quiescence, regular respiration, regular pulse and absence of ocular movement.

In addition, two periods of rhythmic activity were observed which were quite opposite to preceding recordings. The degree of responsiveness at this stage cannot be stated. It appears certain, however, that a sleep cycle is already present in the first week of life of a full-term infant. (Delange et al., 1962; Roffwarg et al., 1963).

Thus far, studies of long duration sleep in the premature still do not provide sufficient evidence for definitive conclusions, but it is possible to state that the cyclic organization of sleep seems to appear only at full term. It is present in the single record taken in a premature at a period corresponding to the normal term (1½ months after the birth of a 7½ month gestation infant), the law of parallelism of maturation for newborn and premature being exemplified in this case.

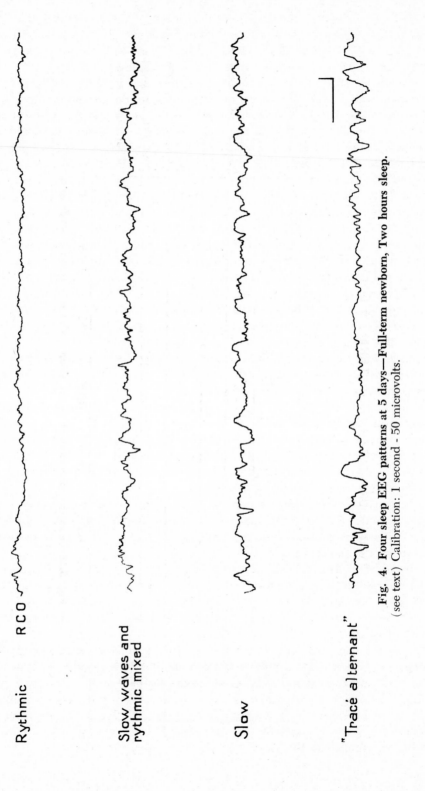

Fig. 4. Four sleep EEG patterns at 5 days—Full-term newborn, Two hours sleep. (see text) Calibration: 1 second - 50 microvolts.

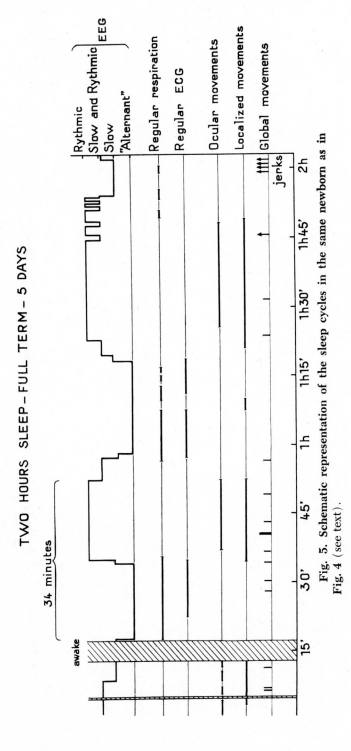

Fig. 5. Schematic representation of the sleep cycles in the same newborn as in Fig. 4 (see text).

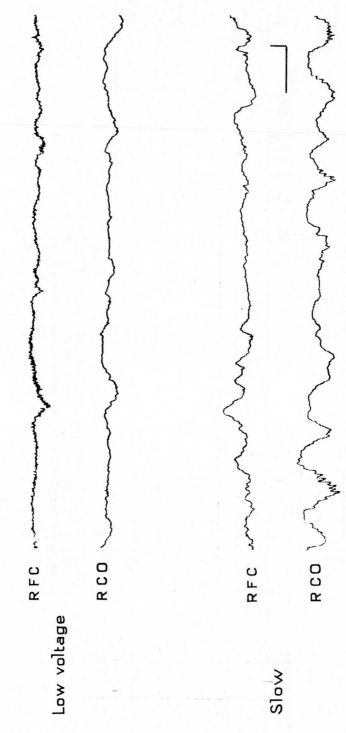

Fig. 6. Two sleep EEG patterns at 11 days. Premature born at 7½ months. Two hours sleep (see text).

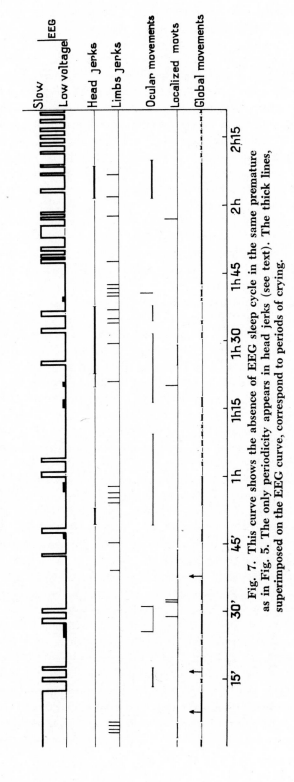

Fig. 7. This curve shows the absence of EEG sleep cycle in the same premature as in Fig. 5. The only periodicity appears in head jerks (see text). The thick lines, superimposed on the EEG curve, correspond to periods of crying.

In the electrogram of the premature (Figure 7), no electrographic patterns suggestive of cyclic organization are revealed. Only two patterns are recognized, low voltage electrogram and a slow wave record (Figure 6) and it is difficult to correlate them with the different stages or types of sleep.

During the two hour recording (Figure 7) the electrocardiogram is regular, and respiration appears quite irregular. During short periods of quiet, localized or generalized movements are present most of the time. In addition, there are short periods of crying with or without movements. During these episodes the ocular movements are rare, sporadic and appear distinguishable only for 10 minutes at the end of the record with the infant remaining quiet.

Sporadic limb movements are also noted, and there also occurs episodes of movements of the head and chin associated with gustatory behavior manifestations, reminiscent of some patterns of temporal lobe epilepsy, and also of movements obtained by stimulation of the amygdala which is incidently well developed at this time (Delmas, 1955). Movements of this type occur once synchronously with the ocular movements; they are found during sleep in prematures of 7 to 8 months conceptual age and are absent in full-term and old premature infants.

It is possible that the difference between the two types of electrograms can be interpreted essentially as an absence of a "tracé alternant" phase of sleep in the premature infant. However, the presence of some periodicity of the head movements is suggestive of a kind of cycle in the control of the axial musculature during sleep which is not apparent in vegetative and electroencephalographic recordings. Additional studies are necessary to validate our results.

Reactivity

Further studies of the reactivity in the newborn premature would also seem to be indicated to determine at which period and at which level the phenomenon of habituation and summation appear for the first time; "flattening" responses to various kinds of stimuli have been described in full-term and 8 months gestation newborns (Dreyfus-Brisac et al., 1957; Ellingson, 1958; Fischgold et al., 1959). It would seem that the polygraphic method would be most helpful in a study of this type, although some difficulties inherent in this technique must be emphasized.

It is very difficult to appreciate reactivity of the EEG when electrical patterns are paroxysmal or of low voltage, for the flattening response and also the "burst response" may be inapparent or misinterpreted.

Respiration and pulse rate are so irregular that their variations seldom seem reliable as a test of reactivity, except in the periods of "tracé alternant" when regular respiration and pulse are noted in full-term infants. In this regard myographic studies, as well as studies of the galvanic skin response and the arterial blood pressure, would perhaps be more helpful (Candia et al., 1962), but to the present no valuable data has been added to the conclusions already published. Furthermore, it has been impossible to show whether the level or responsiveness during the period of low voltage activity with ocular movements differ in any way from that seen during slow discontinuous waves. Perhaps the study of myographic responses during sleep of early prematures could provide a means of recognition of somatic reactivity, while electro-encephalographic reactivity is still absent. Still another approach to the problem is afforded by the study of the development of evoked potentials in humans and animals (Hunt and Goldring, 1951; Scherrer and Oeconomos, 1954; Ellingson, 1960; Marty, 1962; Engel and Butler, 1963).

The Influence of Birth Weight in EEG

Electroencephalographic evaluation of the conceptual age and the developmental patterns during the wakeful and sleeping states has been used in babies showing discrepancy between the conceptual age and the birth weight. Fifty neonates were studied in this respect (Dreyfus-Brisac, 1962) and, as mentioned above, the criteria of maturation proved to be valuable since the electroencephalogram corresponded to the conceptual age (Figure 8).

Control studies were performed with 5 pairs of twins, whose weights varied at birth (Figure 9). In some cases a follow-up study provided confirmation to the above mentioned observation. This relation between conceptual age and the electroencephalographic characteristics remains valuable if subsequent electrographic studies are taken into account (Figure 10).

If the electroencephalogram of a full-term baby is compared with that of a 3 month old premature born at 6 months conceptual age, they will be similar (Dreyfus-Brisac, 1962). This parallelism between *"in utero"* and incubator electrical maturation, matches that seen for neurologic data (Sainte-Anne Dargassies, 1955) evoked potentials (Ellingson, 1960; Engel and Butler, 1963) and conditioned reactivity.

The Electroencephalogram in Abnormal Conditions

Abnormal conditions generally do not disturb the recognition of the conceptual age in a full-term infant. They rather give rise to superimposed features, as already described (Harris and Tizzard, 1960; Loiseau et al., 1960; Monod et al., 1962) which do not modify the differentiation between sleep and the wakeful state.

At times, high voltage monomorphic activity appears in drowsiness and the sudden change between the waking and drowsy records appears too important and rapid (Monod et al., 1960). This abnormal activity of drowsiness, however, is often followed by a normal sleep record. In some very serious cases the absence of differentiation between the electroencephalogram during the wakeful state and sleep exist in full-term neonates. The electrograms then are very abnormal, consisting of paroxysmal activity or complete inactivity (Dreyfus-Brisac et al., 1961; Monod and Dreyfus-Brisac, 1962) (Figure 11). At times a slow continuous diffuse electrogram is found during both the wakeful and sleeping states, especially in cases of prolonged anoxia (Loiseau et al., 1960; Monod et al., 1960) (Figure 11).

In premature infants, a differentiation between the wakeful and sleeping

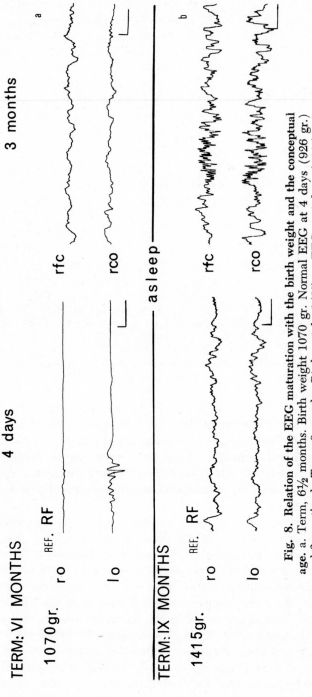

Fig. 8. Relation of the EEG maturation with the birth weight and the conceptual age. a. Term, 6½ months. Birth weight 1070 gr. Normal EEG at 4 days (926 gr.) and 3 months. b. Term, 9 months. Birth weight 1415 gr. EEG at 4 days (1285 gr.) and 3 months. There is an important discrepancy between the conceptual age and the birth weight in b. The electrical development corresponds to the conceptual age. The EEG at 4 days of the full-term newborn is similar to the 6 months (28 weeks) premature's EEG at 3 months.

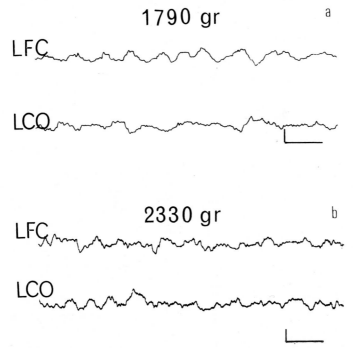

Fig. 9. Comparison of the EEG recorded at 5 days. Twins. Different birth weight—Term: 8 months. a. Birth weight: 1790 gr. Height: 41 cm. Cephalic perimeter: 31 cm. b. Birth weight: 2330 gr. Height: 41 cm. Cephalic perimeter: 31 cm. The EEG's were quite similar in the two babies, and corresponded to the conceptual age of 8 months.

states which appears too early with respect to the conceptual age and to other features of the electrogram has been previously described as a common abnormality. Indeed, the coexistence on the same record of bio-electrical patterns which should not be found together corresponds to heterochronism of bio-electrical maturation, which seems the most common pathological pattern in cerebral electrogenesis of prematures (Dreyfus-Brisac, 1962).

Discussion

The ontogenesis of bio-electrical activity in the human during the second half of gestation follows a rapid and precise development, which can be a useful criterion of conceptual age.

Comparative studies of development in different species should be very interesting, especially if one considers that the stages of development at birth are different in each species. For example, a comparison between the electroencephalogram of a full-term newborn monkey and that of a full-term newborn human infant (whose neurological development at birth are quite different) reveals important differences, in that the sleep spindles are already present in the monkey (Caveness, 1962) and are not found until approximately six weeks of age in the human infant.

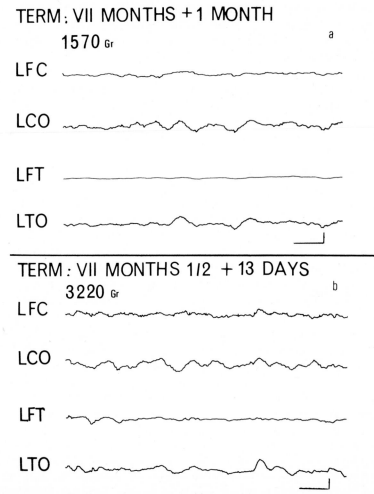

Fig. 10. Comparison of two infants born at the same conceptual age, with a different birth weight, recorded after 1 month and 13 days of life in incubator. a. 7 months (1570 gr.) EEG at 1 month. b. Term: 7½ months (3220 gr.) EEG at 15 days. The EEG's were similar, though term, birth weight and age were different. The EEG maturation is in concordance with the conceptual age (8 months) which is the same for the two infants.

In addition, the study of different species in the early periods of gestation or life (Scherrer and Oeconomos, 1954; Charles and Fuller, 1956; Garcia-Austt, 1957; Bernhard, 1959; Verley, 1959; Laget and Delhaye, 1961; Pampiglione, 1961; Caveness, 1962) has provided a means of discovering paroxysmal patterns that are encountered in the electroencephalogram of the premature infant (Garcia-Austt, 1957; Pampiglione, 1961). According to Metcalf (1963) the origin of these paroxysmal discharges in humans seems to lie in the central gray nuclei although some authors argue against this interpretation. The studies of Kennard on the developmental EEG of the *Macaca mulatta,* and on the EEG's of decorticate monkeys argues for a subcortical origin of these paroxysms (Kennard and Nims, 1942). However, the recent description of Bergstrom (Bergstrom and Bergstrom, 1963) who recorded continuous activity in the brain stem of a three month gestation human fetus, is somewhat disturbing.

Paroxysmal patterns of this type have also been noted in some coma states (coma dépassé), hypothermia (Weiss and Arfel, 1960) and barbiturate anesthesia (Schneider and Thomalske, 1956). Interhemispheric asynchrony is very uncommon in such abnormal situations but has been found in some cases of barbiturate anesthesia with a parasagittal deep lesion (Schneider and Thomalske, 1956).

The respective roles of the maturation of the deep structures, cortex and ascending reticular fibers in the differentiation of sleep and wakefulness cannot be precisely assessed (Scheibel and Scheibel, 1962, 1963). Following the original studies of Bremer (1935), Jouvet's description (Jouvet et al., 1961; Jouvet, 1962) of aperiodicity and absence of slow waves in the sleep of decorticate animals and of decorticate comatose patients is an important finding. One interpretation may be that at eight months conceptual age, the cortex is for the first time able to maintain a state of wakefulness, thus being receptive to specific and nonspecific afferent stimulation. Experiments on decorticate animals or "cerveau isolé" preparations are also important in the interpretation of the appearance of cyclic sleep in the newborn period. Although his conclusions are not in agreement with those of other investigators (Batsel, 1960), the experimental work of Jouvet strongly suggests that the electroencephalogram of early prematures is of subcortical origin, and further support to this conclusion is provided by anatomical data (Dodgson, 1962).

Systematic anatomical studies on the development of neurones in the human brain during the last four months of pregnancy should provide aid in the interpretation of the stages of electrical maturation (Rabinowicz, 1961; Schadé, 1961). In our group, Larroche (1962) has noted rapid changes in the morphology of the brain after the sixth month of gestation. Between the third and sixth month maturation is prominent in the grey nucleus. After the sixth month cortical maturation progresses very rapidly but at different rates in each area.

Rabinowicz (1961) studied the cyto-arhitectonic development of the cortex, following the research of Connel (1939).

Schadé's observations have shown that at the cortical level biochemical and dendritic development are parallel (Schadé and Baxter, 1960; Schadé, 1961). These findings concerning the development of cortical dendritic development of human newborns (Schadé, 1961) are consistent with the findings of Purpura, who has demonstrated the respective roles of apical and basal dendrites (Purpura et al., 1960; Purpura, 1962). Scheibel (1962) insists on the role of Golgi II cell development.

Although much work remains in the fields of comparative developmental anatomy, biochemistry and electrogenesis, the literature already contains many findings which have improved our knowledge or suggested useful hypotheses. It is to be noted that the original work of Jasper (Jasper et al., 1937) and Flexner (Flexner et al., 1950) have been confirmed.

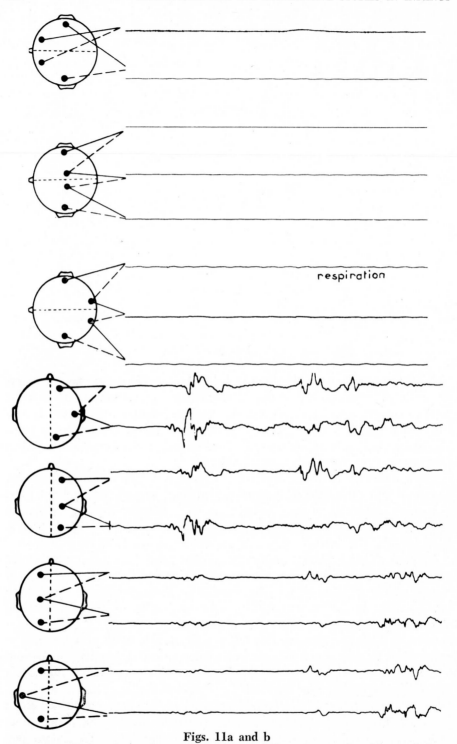

Figs. 11a and b

Fig. 11. Abnormal patterns, with absence of differentiation of waking and sleeping patterns in full-term newborns. a (top). Inactivity. b (bottom). Paroxysmal bursts. c (facing page). Diffuse slow activity.

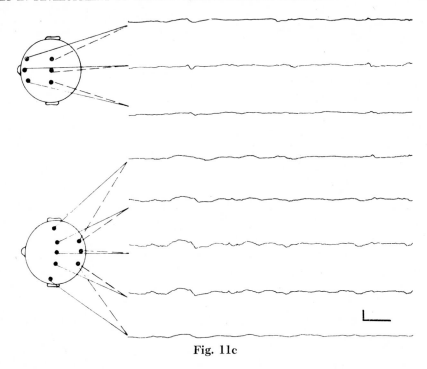

Fig. 11c

Polygraphic studies should provide a new tool in the recognition of different levels of neuro control at the different stages of maturation. It is to be hoped that research in the galvanic skin response should improve our knowledge concerning reactivity. Simultaneous studies in animals of strech reflex and electroencephalographic activity have already provided interesting data (Bernhard *et al.*, 1959; Bergstrom, 1962).

The parallelism of neurologic bio-electrical and anatomical findings has already been emphasized. It is to be added that the author would not insist so much on the value of the EEG as a useful tool in determining conceptual age were it not supported by other data, particularly the neurological observations.

It appears that postnatal maturation of the premature infant follows the same rate in the incubator as it would do *in utero* (Figure 8A), and is not fundamentally influenced by environment. This characteristic has been found in all aspects of the nervous development and seems to be a fundamental phenomenon.

At the present, it seems that this rule is still valuable in the establishment of cyclic sleep. Conceivably some interference due to feeding rhythms or environmental variations might cause the development of the sleep cycle to match less closely the development of the EEG.

Intra-uterine studies would be necessary to gather definitive evidence about the stages of early electrogenesis. In this regard, the recent work of Bergstrom (1962), comparing intra- and extra-uterine development in the guinea pig, emphasizes the possible reaction of anoxia, already discussed in our records of five month prematures (Dreyfus-Brisac, 1957).

The author does not consider that such intra-uterine or even vaginal records are permissible in the human being.

Summary and Conclusions

Electroencephalograms of premature and full-term newborn infants have been studied in the postnatal period with respect to the states of wakefulness and sleep. It appears that the postnatal bio-electrical maturation of the premature infant follows the same rate in the incubator as it would *in utero*. The appearance of a waking-sleeping differentiation at eight months of conceptual age is one of the most important phenomena during electroencephalographic development, corresponding to an important change in behavior at the same period. A cyclic rhythm during prolonged sleep can be detected in the full-term newborn infant. The duration of each period is shorter than that of the adult. Such a cycle is not present in the premature.

The role of some peculiar factors (abnormal birth weight, abnormal conditions) on sleeping and waking patterns was studied. Abnormalities of these patterns were described, with special reference to the premature.

ACKNOWLEDGMENTS

I am indebted to Doctor N. Monod for her contribution in the research, and to Miss N. Pajot, F. Morel-Kahn, J. Flescher and Mrs. E. Plassart, for their technical assistance.

REFERENCES

Most of the references anterior to 1958, studying the EEG of newborns, are cited in Dreyfus-Brisac (1958–1959).

ASERINSKY, E. and KLEITMAN, N. A motility cycle in sleeping infants as manifested by ocular and gross body activity. *J. Appl. Physiol.*, 1955, 8:11–18.

BATSEL, H. L. Electroencephalographic synchronization and desynchronization in the chronic "cerveau isolé" of the dog. *Electroenceph. clin. Neurophysiol.*, 1960, 12:421–430.

BERGSTROM, R. M. Prenatal development of motor functions. *Ann. Chir. Gyn. Fenn.*, 1962, 51 (suppl. 112):5–48.

BERGSTROM, R. M. and BERGSTROM, L. Prenatal development of stretch reflex functions and brain stem activity in the human. *Ann. Chir. Gyn. Fenn.*, 1963, 52 (suppl. 117):1–21.

BERNHARD, C. G., KAYSER, I. H. and KOLMODIN, I. H. On the development of cortical activity in fetal sheep. *Acta. Physiol. Scand.*, 1959, 47:333–349.

BRAZELTON, T. B. Some experiences with the neonatal period. *Symposium on Infancy*, Boston Univ., 1960.

BREMER, F. Cerveau isolé et physiologie du sommeil. *Compt. Rend. Soc. Biol.*, 1935, 118:1235–1241.

CANDIA, O., FAVALE, E., GIUSSANI, A. and ROSSI, G. F. Blood pressure during natural sleep and during sleep induced by electrical stimulation of the brain stem reticular formation. *Arch. Ital. Biol.*, 1962, 100:216–233.

CAVENESS, W. F. *Atlas of Electroencephalography in the Developing Monkey. Macaca mulatta.* Addison-Wesley Publ. Co., Inc. Mass., London, 1962, pp 145.

CHARLES, M. S. and FULLER, J. L. Developmental study of the electroencephalogram of the dog. *Electroenceph. clin. Neurophysiol.*, 1956, 8:645–652.

CONNEL, J. *The postnatal development of the human cerebral cortex*, Vols. I–VI. Harvard Univ. Press, Cambridge, Mass., 1939–1960.

DELANGE, M., CASTAN, PH., CADILHAC, J. and PASSOUANT, P. Les divers stades du sommeil chez le nouveau-né et le nourrisson. *Rev. Neurol.*, *1962*, 107:271–276.

DELMAS, A. Lobe ou complexe temporal. *Les grandes activites du lobe temporal.* Masson ed., Paris, *1955*, pp 1–55.

DEMENT, W. and KLEITMAN, N. Cyclic variations in EEG during sleep and their relation to eye movements, body motility, and dreaming. *Electroenceph. clin. Neurophysiol.*, *1957*, 9:673–690.

DODGSON, M. C. H. *The Growing Brain.* Wright and Sons Ltd., Bristol, *1962*.

DREYFUS-BRISAC, C., FISCHGOLD, H., SAMSON-DOLLFUS, D., SAINTE-ANNE-DARGASSIES, S., MONOD, N. and BLANC, C. Veille, sommeil, réactivite sensorielle chez le prématuré, le nouveau-né. Activite électrique cérébrale du nourrisson. *Electroenceph. clin. Neurophysiol.*, *1957* (suppl. 6):417–440.

DREYFUS-BRISAC, C. and BLANC, C. Electroencéphalogramme et maturation cérébrale. *Encephale*, *1956*, 45:205–241.

DREYFUS-BRISAC, C. Activité électrique cérébrale du foetus et du trés jeune prémature. IVe Congr. Int. Electroenceph. Neurophysiol. Clin. *Acta Med. Belg. ed.*, Bruxelles, 1957, 163–171.

DREYFUS-BRISAC, C., SAMSON-DOLLFUS, D., BLANC, C. and MONOD, N. L'électroencephalogramme de l'enfant normal de moins de 3 ans. Aspect fonctionnel bio-électrique de la maturation nerveuse. *Et. Neonat.*, *1958*, 7:143–175.

DREYFUS-BRISAC, C. Electroencephalography in infancy. *Die Physiologische Entwicklung des Kindes.* Springer-Verlag, *1959*, pp 29–40.

DREYFUS-BRISAC, C., MONOD, N., SALAMA, P., DUCAS, P. and MAYER, M. L'EEG dans les 6 premiers mois de la vie, aprés réanimation prolongée et état de mal néonatal. Recherches d'éléments de pronostic. Vth Int. Congr. Electroenceph. clin. Neurophysiol. *Excepta Med. Int. Congr. Series.*, *1961* Rome 37:228–229.

DREYFUS-BRISAC, C. The electroencephalogram of the premature infant. *World Neurol.*, *1962*, 3:5–15.

DREYFUS-BRISAC, C., FLESCHER, J. and PLASSART, E. L'électroencéphalogramme. Critère d'âge conceptionnel du nouveau-né à terme et du prématuré. *Bio. Neonat.*, *1962*, 4:154–173.

ELLINGSON, R. J. Electroencephalograms of normal full-term newborns immediately after birth with observations on arousal and visual evoked responses. *Electroenceph. clin. Neurophysiol.*, *1958*, 10:31–50.

ELLINGSON, R. J. Cortical electrical responses to visual stimulation in the human infant. *Electroenceph. clin. Neurophysiol.*, *1960*, 12:663–677.

ENGEL, L. R. and BUTLER, BR. V. Appraisal of conceptual age of newborns by electroencephalographic methods. *J. of Pediat.*, *1963*, 63:386–393.

FISCHGOLD, H., DREYFUS-BRISAC, C., MONOD, N., SAMSON-DOLLFUS, D. KRAMARZ, P. and BLANC, C. L'EEG au cours de la maturation cérébrale-Aspects physiologiques, in *XVIIe Congr. de l'Assoc. des Pédiat. de langue francaise.* Montpellier. Dehan ed., *1959*, 1–66.

FISCHGOLD, H. and SCHWARTZ, B. A. A clinical, electroencephalographic, and polygraphic study of sleep in the human adult. *The Nature of Sleep.* Ciba Found. Symp., Little Brown Co. Boston, *1961*, 209–236.

FLEXNER, L. E., TYLER, D. B. and GALLANT, L. G. Biochemical and physiological differentiation during morphogenesis, onset of electrical activity in developing cerebral cortex of fetal guinea-pig. J. Neurophysiol., *1950*, 13:427–430.

GARCIA-AUSTT, J. R. Ontogenetic evolution of EEG in human and animals. IVe Congr. Int. Electroenceph. Neurophysiol. Clin. *Acta Med. Belg. Int. Congr. Series*, *1957*, 173–177.

GESELL, A. and AMATRUDA, C. J. *The Embryology of Behavior.* Paul Hobber, New York, *1945*, p. 289.

GLASER, G. H. The neurological status of the new-born: neuromuscular and electroencephalographic activity. *Yale J. Biol. Med.*, *1959*, 32:173–191.

HARRIS, R. and TIZZARD, J. P. M. The electroencephalogram in neonatal convulsions. *J. Pediat.*, *1960*, 57:501–520.

HUNT, W. E. and GOLDRING, S. Maturation of evoked response of the visual cortex in the postnatal rabbit. *Electroenceph. clin. Neurophysiol.*, *1951*, 3:465–471.

JASPER, H. H., CARMICHAEL, L. and BRIDGMAN, C. S. An ontogenetic study of cerebral electrical potentials in the guinea pig. *J. Exp. Psych.*, *1937*, 21:63–71.

JOUVET, D., VALATX, J. and JOUVET, M.

Etude polygraphique du sommeil du chaton. *Comp. Ren. Soc. Biol., 1961,* 155:1660–1664.

JOUVET, M. PELLIN, B. and MOUNIER, D. Étude polygraphique des différentes phases du sommeil au cours des troubles de conscience chronique (comas prolongés). *Rev. Neurol., 1961,* 105:181–186.

JOUVET, M. Recherche sur les structures nerveuses et les mécanismes responsables des différentes phases du sommeil physiologique. *Arch. Ital. Biol., 1962,* 100:125–206.

KELLAWAY, P. Ontogenic evolution of the electroencephalogram in humans and animals. IVe Congr. Electroenceph. clin. Neurophysiol. *Acta Med. Belg. Ed.* Bruxelles., *1957,* 141–154.

KENNARD, M. K. and NIMS, L. F. Changes in the normal electroencephalogram of *Macaca mulatta* with growth. *J. Neurophysiol., 1942,* 5:325–333.

KLEITMAN, N. S. *Sleep and wakefulness.* Univ. Chicago Press, Chicago, *1939,* p. 638.

KLEITMAN, N. and ENGELMAN, T. G. Sleep characteristics of infants. *J. Appl. Physiol., 1953,* 6:269–282.

LAGET, P. and DELHAYNE, N. Quelques données sur le développement de l'activité électrocorticale spontanée chez le lapin. *J. Physiol., 1961,* 53:393–394.

LARROCHE, J. C. Quelques aspects anatomiques du développement cérébral. *Bio. Neonat., 1962,* 4:126–153.

LOISEAU, P., AUSSARESSES, M. and VERGER, P. Essai de correlations electroclinques dans la période immédiatement post-natale chez le prématuré. *Rev. Neurol., 1960,* 103:236–242.

MARTY, R. *Developpement post-natal des réponses sensorielles du cortex cérébral chez le chat et le lapin.* (238 references) Thèse, Faculté des Sciences, Masson ed. Paris, *1962.*

METCALF, D. R. *Observation on the development of EEG sleep patterns in infants.* Private communication. Assoc. of Psycho. Physiol. study of sleep, *1963.*

MONOD, D., DREYFUS-BRISAC, C., DUCAS, P. and MAYER, M. L'EEG du nouveau-né à terme. Etude comparative chez le nouveau-né en présentation céphalique et en présentation de siège. *Rev. Neurol.,*

1960, 102:375–379.

MONOD, N. and DREYFUS-BRISAC, C. Le tracé paroxystique chez le nouveau-né. *Rev. Neurol., 1962,* 106:129–130.

OSWALD, I. *Sleeping and waking; physiology and psychology.* Elsevier, *1962.*

PAMPIGLIONE, G. Developmental pattern in the EEG of young dog and pig. Vth Int. Congr. Electroenceph. clin. Neurophysiol. Rome. *Excerpta Med. Int. Congr. Series, 1961,* 37–40.

PARMELEE, A. H. JR., SCHULZ, H. R. and DISBROW, M. A. Sleep patterns of the new-born. *J. Pediat., 1961,* 58:241–250.

PARMELEE, A. H. JR., BRUCK, K. and BRUCK, M. Activity and inactivity cycles during the sleep of premature infants exposed to neutral temperatures. *Biol. Neonat., 1962,* 4:317–339.

PURPURA, D. P., CARMICHAEL, M. W. and HOUSEPIANE, M. Physiological and anatomical studies of development of superficial axodendritic synaptic pathways in neocortex. *Exp. Neurol., 1960,* 2:324–347.

PURPURA, D. P. and HOUSEPIAN, E. M. Morphological and physiological properties of chronically isolated immature neocortex. *Exp. Neurol., 1961,* 4:377–401.

PURPURA, D. P. Analysis of axodendritic synaptic organizations in immature cerebral cortex. *Ann. N. Y. Acad. Sci., 1961,* 94:604–654.

PURPURA, D. P. Synaptic organization of immature cerebral cortex. *World Neurol., 1962,* 3:275–298.

RABINOWICZ, TH. L'écorce cérébrale du prematuré du 8 ème mois. Etude systématique. *IVe Congr. Int. de Neuropathol.* Munich. Abstracts. Thieme Verlag, *1961,* 58.

RAMIREZ DE ARELLANO, M. I. R. Maturational changes in the electroencephalogram of normal monkeys. *Exp. Neurol., 1961,* 3:209–224.

ROFFWARG, H. P., DEMENT, W. C. and FISCHER, CH. Observations in the sleep dream-pattern in neonates, infants, children and adults. *Child Psychiatric Monographs,* In press.

ROFFWARG, H. P., DEMENT, W. C. and FISCHER, C. *A sleep EEG rapid eye movement cycle in newborn infants associated with specific physiological variations.* Preliminary data presented to A. P. S. S. New York, *1963.*

RUCKEBUSCH, Y. Activité corticale au cours du sommeil chez la chèvre. *Comp. Ren. Soc. Biol., 1962,* 156:867–871.

RUCKEBUSCH, Y. Etude polygraphique et comportementale de l'évolution postnatale du sommeil physiologique chez l'agneau. *Arch. Ital. Biol., 1963,* 101:111–132.

SAMSON-DOLLFUS, D. *L'EEG du prematuré jusquà l'âge de 3 mois et du nouveau-né à terme.* Thèse, Paris, Foulon ed., 1955.

SAINTE-ANNE-DARGASSIES, S. La maturation neurologique du prematuré. *Et. Neonat., 1955,* 4:71–116.

SCHADÉ, J. P. and BAXTER, C. F. Changes during growth in the volume and surface area of cortical neurons in the rabbit. *Exp. Neurol., 1960,* 2:158–178.

SCHADÉ, J. P. Aspetti della maturazione della corteccia cérébrale nell uomo. *Mine. Med., 1961,* 52:3042–3048.

SCHEIBEL, A. B. Neural correlates of psychophysiological development in the young organism. *In:* J. Wortis (editor). *Recent advances in biological psychiatry.* New York, Plenum Press, 1962, 4:313–327.

SCHEIBEL, M. E. and SCHEIBEL, A. B. Some structuro-functional correlates of maturation in young cats. *Electroenceph. clin. Neurophysiol., 1962,* 4:313–327.

SCHEIBEL, M. E. and SCHEIBEL, A. B. Some structuro-functional correlates of maturtion in young cats. *Electroenceph. clin. Neurophysiol., 1962,* 14:429.

SCHEIBEL, M. E. and SCHEIBEL, A. B. Some neural substrates of postnatal development. Pre-print for publication in *1st Ann. Rev. of Child Development.* Hoffman ed. (105 ref.), 1963.

SCHNEIDER, J. and THOMALSKE, G. L'exploration pharmacodynamique cortico-sous-corticale et ses critéres électrographiques. Détermination d'un foyer lésionnel chez l'homme par la technique pentothalique. *Electroenceph. clin. Neurophysiol., 1956,* 8:353–369.

SCHERRER, J., CONTAMIN, F. and VERLEY, R. Maturation comparée des réponses électro-corticales et des activités motrices et neuro-végétatives chez les Mammifères (primates exceptés). *Rapport Ier. Congr. Européen Pedo-Psychiatrie,* Paris, Spei. ed., 1960, 61–76.

SCHERRER, J. and OECONOMOS, D. Reponses corticales somesthésiques du Mammifère nouveau-né comparées à celles de l'animal adulte. *Et. Neonat., 1954,* 3:199–216.

SCHWARTZ, B. A. and FISCHGOLD, H. Introduction a l'étude polygraphique du sommeil de nuit (mouvements oculaires et cycles de sommeil). *Vie Médic., 1960,* 41:39–46.

STECHLER, G., GALLANT, D. and BRAZELTON, T. B. Some aspects of the sleeping EEG in the human newborn. *Ann. Meet. of the Amer. EEG Soc.,* 1960.

TONI, (DE) G. I movimenti pendolari dei bulbi oculari dei bambini, durante il sonno fisiologica, ed in alcuni stati morbosi. *La Pediat., 1933,* 41:489–498.

VALLBONA, C., DESMOND, M. M., PAP, L. F., HILL, R. M. and VON MINDEN, M. C. Studies on the regulation of the heart rate in newborn infants. *Amer. J. Dis. Child., 1961,* 102:563–564.

VALLBONA, C., DESMOND, M. M., RUDOLPH, A. J., PAP, L. F., HILL, R. M., FRANKLIN, R. R. and RUSH, J. B. Cardiodynamic studies in the newborn. II. Regulation of heart rate. *Bio. Neonat., 1963,* 5:159–199.

VERLEY, R. *Développement des activités électro-corticales des mammifères nouveaux-nés.* Thèse, Méd. Paris, 1959.

VERLEY, R. and SCHERRER, J. Etudes expérimentales des relations entre réactions motrices et réactions électro-corticale aux stimulations au cours du développement post-natal du lapin. *Rev. Neurol., 1960,* 102:311–315.

WAGNER, I. F. Curves of sleep depth in newborn infants. *J. Gen. Psychol., 1939,* 55:121–135.

WEISS, J. and ARFEL, G. Sequences EEG de l'hypothermie profonde. *Rev. Neurol., 1960,* 103:220–222.

EEG OF THE HUMAN INFANT DURING SLEEP AND WAKEFULNESS DURING THE FIRST YEAR OF LIFE

Normal Patterns and Their Maturational Changes; Abnormal Patterns and Their Prognostic Significance*

D. SAMSON-DOLLFUS, J. FORTHOMME AND E. CAPRON

*Laboratoire d'EEG et Anatomie Pathologique du
Centre Hospitalier et Universitaire, Rouen, France*

Introduction

The information provided by a study of infant electroencephalography increases yearly. However, interpretation of this data is difficult because of the following factors: (a) The special configuration of the young infant's EEG, and (b) the problem of evaluation of the significance of the collected available data. Because of the cerebral maturation factor (Minkowski, 1938; Connel, 1955) a particular electrographic finding or symptom can be evaluated only when followed over a prolonged period of time. In this report the electrogram of the normal infant during the states of wakefulness, drowsiness and sleep will be considered. In addition, certain pathologic features and findings of questionable abnormality will be discussed.

1. THE NORMAL ELECTROGRAM

The Electrogram of Wakefulness. These findings are often difficult to interpret because of artifacts due to crying and movements of the infant. Periods of calm may signify that the infant is drowsy even when the eyes remain open.

Between the ages of one month and three months rhythmic activity of the waking electrogram with the infant's eyes closed makes its appearance very gradually. Often only low voltage random activity is noted during the first weeks of life. On the other hand, there exists during wakefulness a clear differentiation of occipital rhythms. At times, these rhythms radiate toward Rolandic regions, but this may be a sign of light drowsiness (Henry, 1944; Hughes et al., 1949; Gibbs and Gibbs, 1952; Samson-Dollfus, 1955).

At three months of age a new phenomenon appears in the waking electrogram of the infant: the arousal reaction upon opening of the eyes (Dreyfus-Brisac and Blanc, 1956; Dreyfus-Brisac et al., 1958). Conversely, as the eyes

---

*With acknowledgments to R. Laumonier of the Laboratory of Pathology of the School of Medicine at Rouen.

of the infant close there is an increase in the amplitude of the EEG as well as of its rhythmicity in occipital regions. The frequency of the basic rhythm increases somewhat and varies between 4 and 6 cycles per second (Henry, 1944; Gibbs and Gibbs, 1952). By five months of age the waking electrogram of the infant is well organized: it is rhythmical, differentiated in occipital leads, has an amplitude of 50 to 100 microvolts with the eyes closed and disappears upon opening of the eyes.

After six months of age the predominant changes in the electrogram during the state of wakefulness are those of increase in the basic occipital rhythms, or rather the appearance of new rhythms of 6–7 cycles per second and sometimes even 8 cycles per second. The electroencephalogram during the state of wakefulness consists of rhythmic 5–8 cycles per second activity of rapidly changing amplitude. Thus, the waking electrogram even of a child one year old should not be too regular, of too great an amplitude, or too rhythmical, if it is to be considered within the range of normal variation.

At the age of five or six months photic stimulation evokes occipital responses at frequencies of the basic occipital rhythm (5–6 cycles per second). Responses of this type seem to appear only when the child is somewhat drowsy. Very rarely, responses in the frequency range of 8–10 cycles per second are encountered, and these are perhaps abnormal. EEG responses to single flashes are difficult to see, but it is obvious that they can exist as early as the first weeks of life (Ellingson, 1958, 1960; Engel and Butler, 1963).

2. THE ELECTROGRAM DURING DROWSINESS

Upon examination of the wakeful electrogram of an infant below the age of 3 to 4 months it is often difficult to differentiate between a well behaved baby who is awake and one who is drowsy. This is important, however, because there exists in the state of drowsiness a rhythm which does not yet appear clearly in the wakeful state (Henry, 1954; Kellaway and Fox, 1952). This rhythm which appears in Rolandic regions can be completely absent as the child passes immediately from the random activity of wakefulness to sleep (Fig. 1) (Samson-Dollfus, 1955; Dreyfus-Brisac et al., 1957; Engel, 1961; Delange et al., 1962).

At the ages of five or six months the drowsy stage is nearly always present, and is manifested by continuous 4–5 cycles per second activity in occipital and Rolandic regions. The amplitude of this activity is moderate, around 50–100 microvolts.

After seven months of age there occurs an increase in the amplitude of this Rolandic activity which gives it a hypersynchronous appearance (Kellaway, 1952, 1957; Dreyfus-Brisac and Blanc, 1956; Dreyfus-Brisac et al., 1958; Fischgold et al., 1959; Samson-Dollfus et al., 1963). Although an increase in amplitude is observed the activity remains relatively slow and does not reach the frequencies of 5–6 cycles per second which are encountered in the wakeful electrogram. Certain variable features are present in electrograms of children between the ages of seven months and two years. The two principal variables seem to be: a) simple rhythmical frequencies without real hypersynchrony;

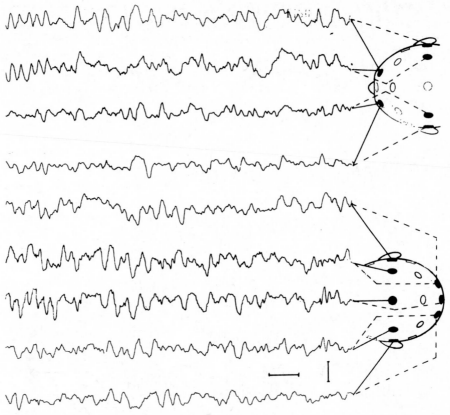

Fig. 1. V. V., 3 months. Just asleep. This electrogram was recorded before the spindle stage, and the baby is still drowsy. (Scale: the horizontal line indicates 1 second; the vertical line indicates the deflection per 100 microvolts).

this is seen especially between seven and twelve months of age and again after 18 months, and b) slower rhythms of 3–4 cycles per second, at times localized to posterior leads but sometimes manifesting themselves centrally and even diffusely. Finally, attention should be called to the low voltage fast activity seen during light sleep (Kellaway and Fox, 1952; Kellaway, 1957). This activity appears at the beginning of the disorganization phase of the sleep electrogram in a child from eight to nine months onwards. This low voltage fast activity, almost exclusively occipital in origin and very probably physiological, is to be differentiated from other types of fast activity encountered in certain types of brain pathology.

3. The Electrogram During Sleep

In contrast to the electrograms noted during the wakeful and drowsy states, the essential characteristics of the electrogram during sleep are encountered much earlier. The essential features of the sleep electrogram are its disorganization, slowness, amplitude, and posterior-dominant delta waves, which exist as early as the second month of life (Fig. 3) (Kellaway and Fox, 1952).

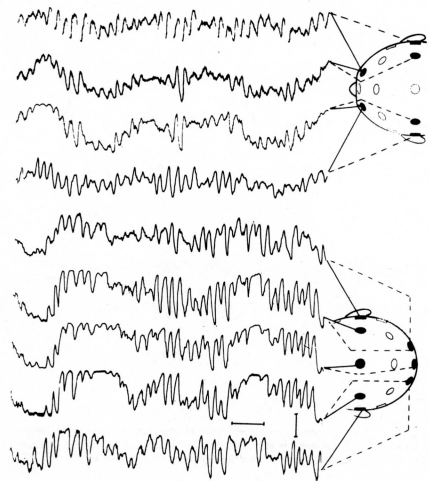

Fig. 2. J. L. G., 8 months. Drowsy state. Typical EEG with spread of hyper-synchrony. (Scale: 1 second and 100 microvolts).

The Rolandic or frontorolandic spindles are always noted at six weeks of age. The vertex and parietal humps, classically recognized from five to six months, in fact appear earlier. At the time of their appearance they are asymmetrical, often of higher amplitude on the right or left side. Finally, they are observed in a deeper stage of sleep than that at which spindles first appear.

These Rolandic and vertex humps become more and more prominent, and at 8 months of age they appear before the sleep stage of the spindles. We shall not discuss at this time the very large spikes characteristic of sleep in the young child from 18 months to two years (Kellaway and Fox, 1952).

Very deep sleep is characterized by the disappearance of spindles and Rolandic humps, an increase of amplitude and slowing of the occipital rhythms. These features of deep sleep are common to all ages from the first months of life. However, for this stage of sleep to be obtained it is necessary to have at one's disposal a silent laboratory and a patient technician, since it can hard-

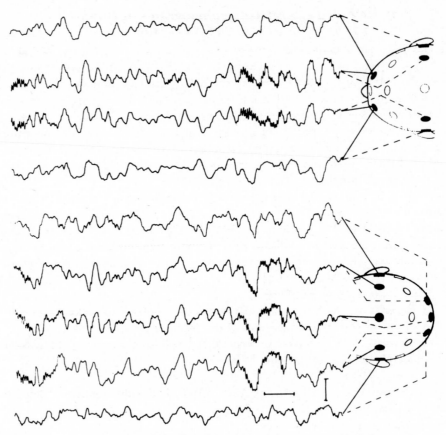

Fig. 3. P. T., 2 months. Sleepy. The spindles appear clearly and disorganization of the EEG during the sleep is noted. (Scale: 1 second and 100 microvolts).

ly be observed in less than a quarter of an hour after sleep has ensued. As the patient enters a lighter stage of sleep due to extraneous stimulation, the stages of hypersynchrony are once again observed. This awakening stage is ordinarily shorter than the drowsy stage but it can also be greater in amplitude, slower and of greater duration. Before this stage of awakening the EEG shows diffuse and often isolated "humps" in the central regions (Kellaway and Fox 1952; Kellaway, 1957; Samson-Dollfus and Samson, 1961). These awakening potentials are always seen from five to six months but some babies have them earlier, occasionally even in the second month of life.

Knowledge of the normal characteristics of a wakeful, sleeping and drowsy electrogram of an infant according to its age allows us to formulate criteria which are indispensible for the interpretation of these tracings. The electrographic differentiation of the various states of consciousness exists for all ages. In this connection we shall stress the abnormal electrograms which are considered pathologic not only because of their adjunction of abnormal patterns, but also because of the dissociations in their maturational stages or because there is no differentiation between the states of wakefulness and sleep.

Pathologic Electroencephalograms of Infants Less Than One Year Old

Having examined the characteristics of the normal electrograms of babies under one year old, let us now consider the diverse patterns of pathologic records, and compare them with their clinical etiology and evolution. It is necessary to first explain that concerning the children or infants involved in this study a) the first electrogram was recorded before the age of one year, b) the EEG was requested for clinical symptoms but never systematically, c) the clinical and electrographic evolution of these children has been followed in more than 100 cases over a period of several months to the ages of six or seven months.

Of these 120 infants we have observed 37 patients whose first EEG, recorded when under one year old, was pathologic. Thirty of these records have been noted on children whose clinical evolution has resulted in death or in mental retardation, with seizure problems or neurologic abnormalities. These findings point out the scale of severity of the records which we consider as pathologic patterns.

These pathologic findings are:

1) Records in which the abnormal waves or abnormal patterns are in complete disorder. The classical example of this is hypsarhythmia.

2) Records with localized or generalized spikes and waves but without the general disorganization noted above;

3) Fast rhythms;

4) Over-organized patterns, or those in which the differentiation between sleep and wakefulness does not exist;

5) Records which are too slow;

6) Records with generalized depression.

I. The Disorganized EEG

A. *Description.* The best known disorder of this type is hypsarhythmia (Gibbs and Gibbs, 1952; Gibbs et al., 1954; Aicardi, 1955; Druckman and Chao, 1955; Thiebaut et al., 1955; Bernard et al., 1956; Burnett et al., 1958; Low et al., 1958; Robuffet-Deschamps, 1958; Samson-Dollfus, 1958; Thieffry and Aicardi, 1958; Kellaway, 1959; Launay et al., 1959; Samson-Dollfus, 1959; Tucker and Solitare, 1963). In this disorder the electroencephalogram shows generalized spikes and slow waves of high amplitude which are poorly organized and occur during wakefulness and light sleep. During deep sleep the record assumes an almost periodic appearance. The recording of massive spasm seizures is often accompanied by a sudden depression with low voltage fast activity which persists for a few seconds (Samson-Dollfus, 1958; Kellaway, 1959).

B. *Evolution.* Hypsarhythmia resolves after several months, this occurring more quickly when the patient is treated with ACTH (Gibbs et al., 1954; Sorel and Dusaucy-Bouloye, 1958; Kellaway, 1959; Low, 1959); some cases become normal while others show persistent spike foci or fast rhythms (Kellaway, 1959; Vallat and Lepetit, 1959; Dailly et al., 1961).

It seems that hypsarhythmia does not appear before the age of four months, and has not been seen in its full-blown form before this time. But "incomplete hypsarhythmia" has been seen as early as the second month of life. This type of disorder has been recognized by the almost paroxysmal quality of the record; in these cases the discharges are not as great in amplitude as in the typical form, but they show irregular and polymorphic discharge patterns. These abnormal discharges appear during the drowsy stage and increase during sleep. These paroxysmal records resemble electrograms seen during sleep in the newborn, but they cannot be called hypsarhythmia (Monod and Dreyfus-Brisac, 1962). They are sensitive to ACTH in the same manner as the typical form, but this apparent improvement does not prevent evolution toward the typical hypsarhythmia (Fig. 4, 5 and 6).

SIGNIFICANCE

Whether in a complete form or not, a record of this type before the age of one year has almost always signified, in our experience, a very serious cerebral pathologic process, and perhaps a very long standing one. Of seven children who began to breathe regularly between 20 minutes and 1½ hours after birth six had a record of this type; of 18 children whose first clinical symptoms were noted before the age of five months, five have shown this abnormality; of eight children whose clinical features were noted for the first time between five months and one year, only one has had hypsarhythmia, and this is the only patient who has evolved toward a completely normal wakeful and sleep EEG. All the others still have spike and wave or fast dysrhythmias. To measure the severity of these electrographic abnormalities it is necessary to compare them with the etiologic and clinical features, and to follow the patients in order to study the appearance of EEG sequelae. It would appear that electrographic abnormalities of this type are testimony of structural brain damage. For example, the child P had hypsarhythmia between five and 15 months. Later the EEG became symmetrical and almost normal, with the exception of a right temporal spike and wave focus (Fig. 7). He died at age four years, and neuropathologic examination revealed severe porencephaly of the right hemisphere and toxoplasmosis. However, it is to be noted that the histopathologic features are not always so clearly evident (Poser and Low, 1960; Harris and Pampiglione, 1962; Tucker and Solitare, 1963).

The persistence of a spike and wave focus is often the sign of an epilepsy which will be refractory to treatment, in addition to being a sign of mental retardation.

II. Spikes and Spikes and Waves

Apart from those observed in association with hypsarhythmia, spikes and spike and wave abnormalities are much less common in infant electroencephalography. Only rarely have they been noted to be localized (Dreyfus-Brisac et al., 1962). In general they do not appear on a normal electrogram but have been seen in association with excessive fast activity or slow rhythms.

They can be recorded like seizures in which the localization may change during the same recording; however, these are chiefly alterations of a very immature brain (Ribstein and Walter, 1958).

Finally paroxysmal bursts of spikes and waves or slow waves are exceptional, having been observed by this group only once (Fig. 8). This was a case of epilepsy of unknown etiology which appeared at five months and resulted in death, with the patient having gone through an intermediate stage of a diffusely slow electrogram.

FAST RHYTHMS

Pathologically fast electrograms have not been observed before the age six to seven months. In these cases the fast activity has peculiar characteristics and can easily be differentiated from the physiologic fast rhythms of light sleep, in that pathologic fast activity is somewhat higher in voltage, and resembles the "extreme spindles" described by Gibbs and Gibbs (1962). Fast activity of this type seems to appear during wakefulness, chiefly when the eyes are open (Fig. 9). It increases and becomes greater in amplitude during deep sleep, but in these cases the electrogram shows almost no change and the physiological spindles of sleep do not appear.

This would appear to be associated with a special disorder of maturation. It has been observed in two very abnormal children (one who was never able to hold up his head and who died when four years old, the other one having a severe cerebral palsy). In addition, abnormalities of this type can progress to hypsarhythmia (Fig. 10). Their pathologic significance has become obvious as activity of this type has been observed to be asymmetrical and to be seen only on the pathologic hemisphere (in a child of two or three years).

IV. Over-organized Electrograms and Electrograms Which Do Not Show a Change between Wakefulness and Sleep

It appears that in this type of abnormality there is premature organization which occurs during wakefulness or drowsiness; in these cases 7 cycles per second activity may be observed during drowsiness and sleep (Fig. 11). The slow activity during sleep is not easily observable, and if spindles exist they are usually either too great in amplitude or have to sharp a configuration.

Electrograms of this type have been encountered in children with microcephaly, with or without craniostenosis, and with unknown etiology.

The above electrographic findings, all of which are certainly pathologic, have in addition a very severe prognostic significance when they have been recorded for the first time before the age of one year.

V. The Slow EEG

During the wakeful state the slow electrograms are usually characterized by monomorphic delta rhythms of 2–3 cycles per second. During drowsiness they become somewhat slower and polymorphic. During sleep they can be differentiated from the normal electrogram in that they are particularly slow. These

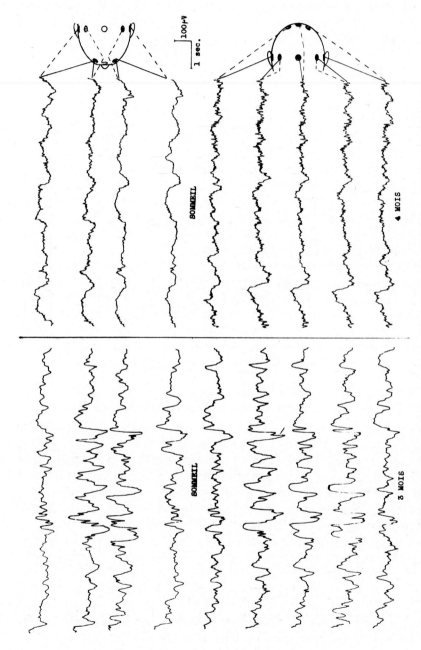

Fig. 4. N. D., On the left: partial hypsarythmia at 3 months. On the right: the same child after 3 weeks of treatment by ACTH. (Scale: 1 second and 100 microvolts).

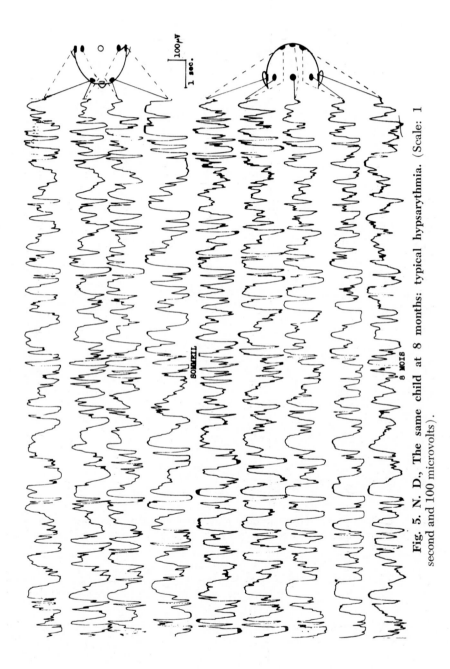

Fig. 5. N. D., The same child at 8 months: typical hypsarythmia. (Scale: 1 second and 100 microvolts).

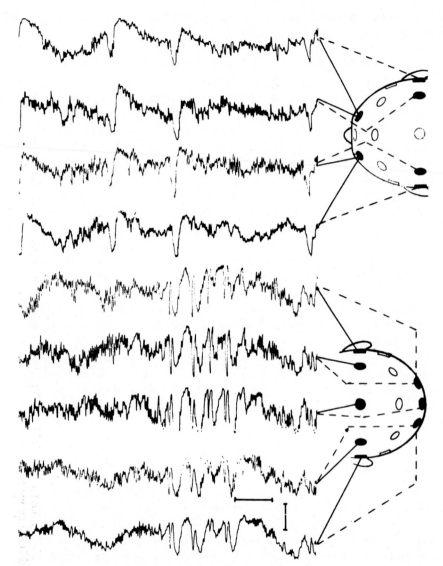

Fig. 6. N. D., 2 years. Rapid rhythms and occipital spike-and-waves. (This child had hypsarythmia when she was 8 months old). (Scale: 1 second and 100 microvolts).

slow waves are frequently localized to the occipital regions (Fig. 12A), but are much more diffuse and asymmetric, and there are no physiologic humps or spindles associated with them.

The etiology of these cases with the slow electrograms appears to be quite different from the abnormalities mentioned above; for example, in one case the etiology was craniostenosis (Fig. 12), on one occasion subacute encephalitis and in two cases hematoma. In two cases these slow electrograms have changed very little in infants who have had epilepsy resulting in death within

a few months. In one of these two cases the etiology has not been made clear
from the neuropathologic examination.

VI. Electrograms With Generalized Depression

Even when noted very early in life these records, with very little activity
during either wakefulness or sleep, bear a very poor prognosis (Dreyfus-Brisac
et al., 1961; Monod et al., 1962).

It must be mentioned as part of the discussion of pathological EEG's that
all children resuscitated between 20 minutes and 1½ hours after birth who
have severe clinical and EEG findings will die before they are five years old.
The electroclinical evolution of those who have begun to breathe regularly
before 15 minutes or in whom the first symptoms were noticed some days after
a normal birth is not so severe. On the other hand, out of 8 infants who have
become ill after the age of five months five have died, and the other three one
has undergone surgery for a hematoma (he presently has a right hemiplegia)
and at four years of age shows electrographic sequelae with spikes and fast
rhythms over the left hemisphere only.

It is necessary to emphasize the very pejorative value of a deteriorated
electrogram before the age of one year. a) Of 20 children having died subsequently, there were 16 abnormal records; b) of 21 cases of encephalopathy 14
pathological records were noted; c) but of 39 children who have grown up
to be normal (that is, until school age) only two pathologic records have
been observed (one hypsarhythmia and one very asymmetrical EEG with a
localized temporal slow wave focus). If an abnormal EEG is found in an
infant it is then of greatest importance to investigate thoroughly to establish
an etiology.

Doubtful Records

ELECTROGRAPHIC FINDINGS OF QUESTIONABLE ABNORMALITY

It is in this field that the problem is most difficult and where discussion and
statistical study will be most useful. In certain cases while an electrogram
cannot be considered completely pathological it does not seem to be strictly
normal. There are many electrographic findings which would appear to be not
completely pathologic and of these we shall discuss only some special aspects:
a) spikes during sleep, and b) modifications of hypersynchrony during the
drowsy state.

1. Spikes in sleep under the age of three months. As has been observed these
are physiologic when observed in the central areas from the age of five to six
months. However, these humps have been observed much earlier, from two
months of age. It seems that their significance is completely different, depend-
ing upon whether they are Rolandic or occipital. A. Rolandic spikes. Even
when they have been considered questionably abnormal in the electrograms
of children from one to three months old they do not appear to have pathological significance: all of these children have been shown to be normal.
B. Occipital spikes. Here the significance is definitely different; in fact, of six

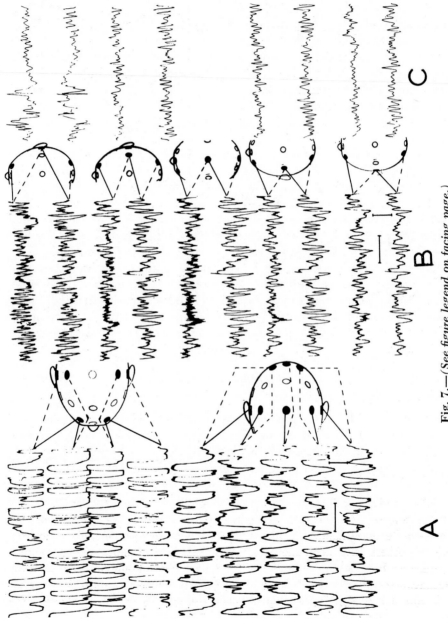

Fig. 7.—(*See figure legend on facing page.*)

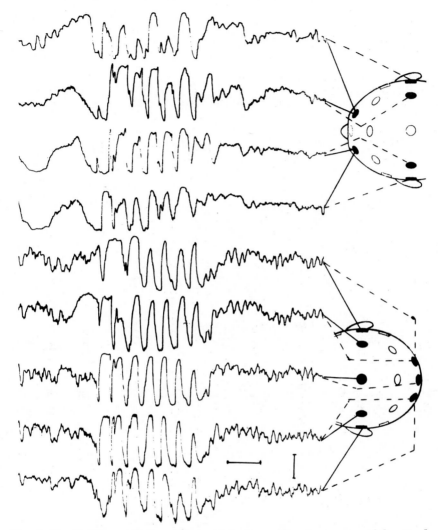

Fig. 8. Po. Epilepsy (died at 12 months). 5 months. A paroxysmal burst when awake. (Scale: 1 second and 100 microvolts).

children, age two to three months, with occipital spikes three had unsatisfactory clinical courses (one died of a serious epilepsy at the age of two, another has an infantile encephalopathy, and the third has become mentally retarded), but the others have been shown to be normal. The number of cases here is insufficient but they do show that a particular electrogram can have doubtful significance and that the child's development must be carefully observed.

2. *Absence of hypersynchrony between the ages of 8 and 12 months.* The

Fig. 7. D. P., This child died and the neuropathologic examination revealed porencephaly of the right hemisphere and the left hemisphere macroscopically normal. A. 12 months, hypsarythmia. B. 2 years; EEG almost normal, but the rhythms are a little too diffuse. C. 3½ years old: spike-and-waves on the temporal area. (Scale: 1 second and 100 microvolts).

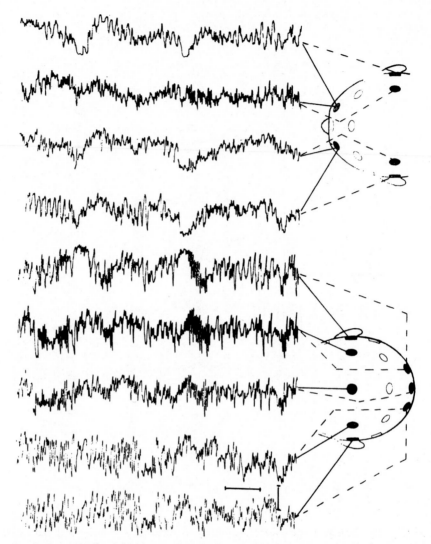

Fig. 9. Bo. Cerebral palsy. Rapid rhythms when awake and when asleep at 8 months. (Scale: 1 second and 100 microvolts).

ordinarily observed drowsy rhythm with moderate radiation into Rolandic regions should not be considered suspicious. This type of activity is frequently observed, especially at this age, at the beginning of the appearance of hypersynchrony. On the other hand, a direct progression from the electrogram of wakefulness to one of sleep without an intervening drowsy period has been observed six times in infants between the age of eight and 12 months (Fig. 13). In five of these cases the children presented neurological after-effects.

3. *The exaggeration of hypersynchrony.* These hypersynchronous rhythms appear in a diffuse fashion normally, or may predominate in Rolandic regions. However, from six months of age the hypersynchrony can be too slow, or too great in amplitude or too prolonged. This characteristic should not be under-

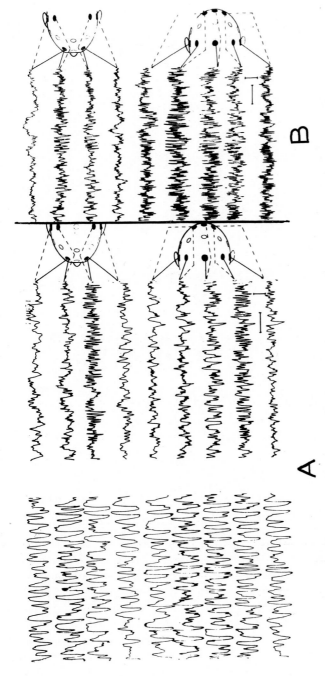

Fig. 10. Ju. Cerebral palsy with mental retardation. This child died when 2 years old. A. 6 months: EEG with hypsarythmia and Rolandic seizure. B. 19 months: fast rhythms during wakefulness and sleep. (Scale: 1 second and 100 microvolts).

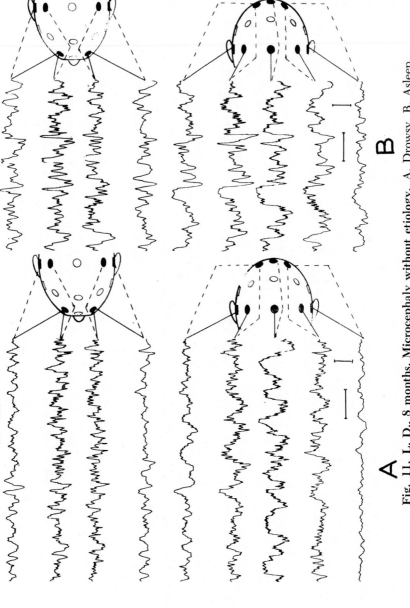

A

B

Fig. 11. L. D., 8 months. Microcephaly without etiology. A. Drowsy, B. Asleep. These are almost the same: they show Rolandic rhythms of about 7 c/s and some spikes. (Scale: 1 second and 100 microvolts).

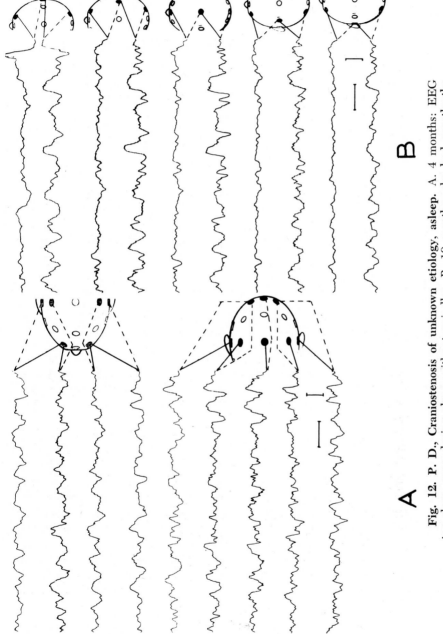

Fig. 12. P. D., Craniostenosis of unknown etiology, asleep. A. 4 months: EEG too slow, even during sleep without spindles. B. 19 months: she had exactly the same EEG; still much slower on the occipital area. (Scale: 1 second and 100 microvolts).

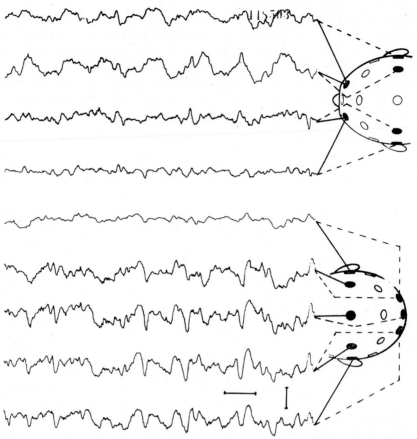

Fig. 13. C. G., 8 months. Cerebral palsy. Patient has recently fallen asleep without rhythmicity or hypersynchrony of the drowsy state (the two first channels show some artifacts due to breathing). (Scale: 1 second and 100 microvolts).

estimated because at the ages of two to three years, sometimes at this stage of drowsiness, spikes and waves which are not typical can be recorded. These electrograms are recorded in the cases of children who are subject to isolated convulsions, very often of febrile origin. Up to this time, the electro-clinical evolution of this disorder has seemed satisfactory, but the data for ages six to seven months which is now in our possession seems to be definitely insufficient since epilepsy appears much later and after some years of silence.

We shall not discuss deep sleep electrograms which are too slow or of too great an amplitude nor records with few spindles nor those which are asymmetric, but these possibilities must be considered since they may explain a number of doubtful EEG's which are observed and to which, however, we attach no more importance than to a normal tracing. It is our opinion that our results are in accord with most of the earlier studies (Kellaway, 1957; Lerique-Koechlin et al., 1958; Fischgold et al., 1959; Passouant et al., 1959; Gibbs, 1959; Kellaway, 1959; Dreyfus-Brisac et al., 1961; Kellaway, 1961).

The normal and abnormal EEG's in the first year of life is particularly interesting for all the stages of maturity which it offers. It is encouraging to note that electroclinical correlations established during the first months can, in a large number of cases, be confirmed by longitudinal studies in the same children. However, it is very important to remember that most of those have records for a period of time which does not exceed 10 years, and generalized and essential epilepsy are afflictions which overcome adolescents and adults: for this reason more light will perhaps be shed upon etiology when our infants become adults.

Summary

The appearance of the principle characteristics of the normal electroencephalogram has been discussed for a period during the first year of life.

1. It has been shown that rhythmicity and the arrest reactions on opening of the eyes during wakefulness appear clearly between the ages of three and five months. After five months the predominant developmental feature is the progressive increase in the frequencies of the basic rhythms.

2. Between six and eight months a new phenomenon appears, namely that of central hypersynchrony during drowsiness.

3. Spindles are noted during sleep between the ages of 4 and 6 weeks and Rolandic humps always from the age of six months, and from time to time, earlier.

4. Diverse types of abnormal electrograms have been shown during the first year of life, and their patterns of evolution have been explored.

The abnormal EEG seems in our experience to bear a poor prognosis. On the other hand, the normal or doubtful patterns may be seen in many different cases (whether they develop normally or abnormally).

REFERENCES

AICARDI, J. *Etude de 200 observations de convulsions dans la première année de la vie.* These Vezin imp. Paris., *1955*.

BERNARD, R., MANASSERO, J., GASTAUT, H., and ROGER, A. La dysrythmie majeure ou syndrome des spasmes en flêxion. *Sem. Hop.*, *1956*, 29, 30:322–328.

BURNETT, L. L., GIBBS, E. L., and GIBBS, F. A. Prognosis in infantile spasms. *Pediat.*, *1958*, 21:719–721.

CONNELL, L. *The Postnatal Development of Human Cerebral Cortex.* Harvard Univ. Press. Cambridge, Mass., 1939, 1941, 1947, 1951, 1955.

DAILLY, R., DE MENIBUS, C. H., NICOLLE, F., LE TRIVIDIC, J., and SAMSON,-DOLLFUS, D. Vingt quatre observations de "spasmes en flexion." Bilan clinique, EEG. therapeutique. *Sem. Hop.*, *1961*, 50–51:2503–2511.

DELANGE, M., CASTAN, PH., CADILHAC, J., and PASSOUANT, P. Les divers stades du sommeil chez le nouveau-né et le nourrisson. *Rev. Neurol.*, *1962*, 107:271–276.

DREYFUS-BRISAC, C., FISCHGOLD, H., SAMSON-DOLLFUS, D., SAINTE-ANNE-DARGASSIES, S., MONOD, N., and BLANC, C. Veille, sommeil, réactivité sensorielle chez le prematuré, le nouveau-né et le nourrisson. *Electroenceph. clin. Neurophysiol.*, *1957*, Suppl. 6:417–419.

DREYFUS-BRISAC, C. and BLANC, C. Electro-encephalogramme et maturation cérébrale. *Encephale*, *1956*, 45:205–241.

DREYFUS-BRISAC, C., MONOD, N., SALAMA, P., DUCAS, P., and MAYER, M. L'EEG dans les six premiers mois de la vie aprés réanimations prolongées et état de mal néo-natal. Recherches d'elements de pronostic. Vth int. Congr. Electroenceph. clin. Neurophysiol. *Excerpta med. Int.*

Congr. Series, 1961, 37:223–225.

DREYFUS-BRISAC, C., MONOD, N. and MOR-EL-KAHN, F. Pointes focalisées chez l'enfant. Correlations electrocliniques dans le cadre d'études longitudinales systematiques. *Rev. Neurol., 1962,* 106:129.

DREYFUS-BRISAC, C., SAMSON-DOLLFUS, D., BLANC, C., and MONOD, N. L'électroencephalogramme de l'enfant normal de moins de 3 ans. Aspect fonctionnel bio-électrique de la maturation nerveuse. *Et. Neonat., 1958,* 7:143–175.

DRUCKMAN, R. D., and CHAO, D. M. Massive spasms in infancy and childhood. *Epilepsia, 1955,* 4:61–72.

ELLINGSON, R. J. EEG of normal full-term newborn immediately after birth with observations on arousal and visual evoked responses. *Electroenceph. clin. Neurophysiol., 1958,* 10:31–50.

ELLINGSON, R. J. Cortical electrical responses to visual stimulation. *Electroenceph. clin. Neurophysiol., 1960,* 12: 663–677.

ENGEL, R. Evaluation of electroencephalographic tracings of newborns. *J. Lancet, 1961,* 81:523–532.

ENGEL, R., and BUTLER, B. Appraisal of conceptual age of newborn infants by electroencephalographic methods. *J. Pediat., 1963,* 62:786–793.

FISCHGOLD, H., DREYFUS-BRISAC, C., MONOD, N., SAMSON-DOLLFUS, D., KRAMARZ, P., and BLANC, C. L'EEG au cours de la maturation cérébrale. Aspects physiologiques. XVIIe Cong. de l'Ass. des Pediat. de Langue Francaise, Imp. Dehan, Montpellier, *1959,* 2–66.

GIBBS, F. A. *Molecules and Mental Health,* J. B. Lippincott Company, Philadelphia, 1959, 189 pp.

GIBBS, F. A. and GIBBS, E. L. *Atlas of Electroencephalography,* Addison-Wesley Press, Cambridge, Mass., 1952.

GIBBS, E. L., FLEMING, M. M. and GIBBS, F. A. Diagnosis and prognosis of hypsarythmia and infantile spasms. *Pediat., 1954,* 13:66–73.

GIBBS, E. L. and GIBBS, F. A. Extreme spindles: correlation of electroencephalographic sleep pattern with mental retardation. *Science, 1962,* 138:1106–1107.

HARRIS, R. and PAMPIGLIONE, G. EEG and histopathology of eleven children with infantile spasms. *Electroenceph. clin. Neurophysiol., 1962,* 14:283.

HENRY, C. H. E. Electroencephalograms of normal children. Society for research in child development. National Research Council Washington. *1944,* 71.

HUGHES, J. G. EHEMAN, B. and HILL, F. J. Electroencephalography of the newborn. II. Studies on normal, full term infants while awake and while drowsy. *Amer. J. Dis. Child., 1949,* 77:310–314.

KELLAWAY, P. Myoclonic phenomena in infants. *Electroenceph. clin. Neurophysiol. 1952,* 4:243.

KELLAWAY, P., and FOX, D. J. EEG diagnosis of cerebral pathology in infants during sleep. *J. Pediat., 1952,* 41:262–287.

KELLAWAY, P. Ontogenic evolution of the electrical activity of the brain in man and in animals. IV int. Cong. Electroenceph. clin. Neurophysiol., *Acta Med. Belg.* ed. Bruxelles, *1957,* 141–154.

KELLAWAY, P. Neurologic status of patients with hypsarythmia. *In:* F. A. Gibbs (editor), *Molecules and Mental Health,* J. B. Lippincott Co., Philadelphia, Montreal, 1959, pp 134–149.

KELLAWAY, P. The transition of epilepsy from infancy to childhood. Vth Int. Congr. Electroenceph. clin. Neurophysiol. *Excerpta med. Int. Congr. Series, 1961,* 37:150–153.

LAUNAY, C., BLANC, C., REBUFFAT-DES-CHAMPS, M. Spasmes en flexion et hypsarythmia; mise au point àpropos de six observations personnelles. *Presse med., 1959,* 67:887–890.

LERIQUE-KOECHLIN, A. ET AL. Colloque sur l'EEG dans les convulsions de le première enfance. Rev. Neurol., *1958,* 99:1–168.

LOW, N. Treatment of hypsarhythmia with ACTH and cortisone. *In:* F. A. Gibbs (editor), *Molecules and Mental Health,* J. B. Lippincott Co., Philadelphia, Montreal, 1959, pp 124–127.

LOW, N. L., BOXMA, J. F., ARMSTRONG, M. M. and MADSEN, J. A. Infantile spasms with mental retardation. 1. Clinical observations and dietary experiments. *Pediat., 1958,* 22:1152–1164.

MINKOWSKI, M. *L'élaboration du système nerveux.* Encyclopédie Francaise E. L., 1938.

MONOD, N., SALAMA, P. and DREYFUS-BRISAC, C. Le tracé du deuxième trimestre de la vie, sa valeur pronostique, ses relations avec le trace néonatal. *Rev. Neurol.,* 1962, 106:131–133.

MONOD, N., and DREYFUS-BRISAC, C. Le tracé paroxystique chez le nouveau-né. *Rev. Neurol.,* 1962, 106:129–130.

PASSOUANT, P., CADILHAC, J. and RIBSTEIN, M. L'EEG au cours de la maturation cérébrale. Aspect pathologique, le décharge epileptique. XVIIe Congr. de l'Ass. des Pediat. de Langue Francaise. Montpellier. Imp. Dehan, Montpellier., 1959, 67–148.

POSER, C. M. and LOW, N. L. Autopsy findings in three cases of hypsarythmia. *Acta Pediat.,* 1960, 49:695–706.

PURPURA, D. P. Developmental electrocortical physiology and the EEG. Vth int. Congr. of Electroenceph. clin. Neurophysiol. *Excerpta med. Int. Congr. Series.,* 1961, 37:25–26.

REBUFFAT-DESCHAMPS, M. *Spasmes en flexion et hypsarythmia.* Thèse médecine Foulon Ed. Paris, 1958.

RIBSTEIN, M. and WALTER, M. Convulsions du premier mois. *Rev. Neurol.,* 1958, 99:91–99.

SAMSON-DOLLFUS, D. *L'EEG du prématuré jusqu'à l'âge de trois mois et du nouveau-né à terme.* Thèse Foulon Ed. Paris, 1955.

SAMSON-DOLLFUS, D. Aspects électrocliniques de crises enregistrées chez des enfants présentant un tracé d'hypsarythmia. *Rev. Neurol.,* 1958, 99:126–132.

SAMSON-DOLLFUS, D. Limites et évolution électrique de l'hypsarythmia. *Electroenceph. clin. Neurophysiol.,* 1959, 11: 578–581.

SAMSON-DOLLFUS, D., DELANGE-WALTER, M. and MISES, J. L'Electroencephalogramme de l'enfant. *Rev. Neurol.,* 1963, 108:138–141.

SAMSON-DOLLFUS, D. and SAMSON, M. Traduction électroencephalographique des réactions d'éveil chez l'enfant. Vth int Congr. of Electroenceph. clin. Neurophysiol. *Excerpta med. Int. Congr. Series,* 1961, 37:60–61.

SMITH, J. R. EEG during infancy and childhood. *J. Gen. Psychol.,* 1938, 53: 431–469.

SOREL, L. and DUSAUCY-BOULOYE, A. A propos de 21 cas d'hypsarythmia de Gibbs; son traitement spectaculaire par l'ACTH. *Acta Neurol. Psychiat. Belg.,* 1958, 58:130–141.

SOREL, L. Treatment of Hypsarhythmia with ACTH. *In:* F. A. Gibbs (editor), *Molecules and Mental Health,* J. B. Lippincott Co., Philadelphia, Montreal, 1959, pp 114–120.

STAMPS, F., GIBBS, E., GIBBS, F. A. and ROSENTHAL, I. Experience with ACTH treatment of hypsarrhythmia. *In:* F. A. Gibbs (editor), *Molecules and Mental Health,* J. B. Lippincott Co., Philadelphia, Montreal, 1959, pp. 121–123.

THIEBAUT, F., SACREZ, R., ROHMER, F. and ISCH-TREUSSARD, L. Corrélations electrocliniques dans 25 cas d'hypsarythmie de Gibbs. *Rev. Neurol.,* 1955, 93:455–460.

THIEFFRY, S. and AICARDI, J. Les spasmes en flexion du nourrisson. *Sem. Hop.,* 1958, 19:1168–1178.

TUCKER, J. S. and SOLITARE, G. B. Infantile myoclonic spasms. Clinical Electrographic and neuropathologic observations. *Epilepsia,* 1963, 4:45–59, (Bibliogr.)

VALLAT, J. N., LEPETIT, J. M. Encephalopathies de la première enfance avec hypsarythmia ou avec dysrythmie rapide d'allure paroxystique. *Rev. Neurol.* 1959, 101:708–721.

VASQUEZ, H. J. and TURNER, M. Epilepsia en flexión generalizada. *Arch. Argent. Pediat.,* 1951, 35:111–141.

THE NATURAL HISTORY AND CLINICAL CORRELATES OF OCCIPITAL FOCI IN CHILDREN*

JEAN M. B. SMITH† AND PETER KELLAWAY

*Department of Physiology, Baylor University College of Medicine,
and The Blue Bird Clinic, The Methodist Hospital,
Texas Medical Center, Houston, Texas*

The occipital region is the most common locus for focal electrographic abnormalities in children younger than three years of age. The younger the child, the more likely it is that any focus present will be occipital in localization. In the newborn period, occipital and, to a lesser degree, central (Rolandic) foci are commonly seen but frontal and temporal foci are rare.

The purpose of this study was to determine the clinical significance and natural history of occipital foci in children by means of a longitudinal and retrospective investigation of a large number of cases.

Gibbs, Gillen and Gibbs (1954) and Blanc *et al.* (1959) have presented evidence that occipital foci are not only the most common type of foci occurring in the infant and very young child but also that there is a tendency for these foci to disappear early in childhood. Thus, in a series of 45 cases, Gibbs and his associates found that in only 23 per cent was the occipital focus still present at the age of nine years. These workers, on the basis of their findings, suggested that occipital foci show a tendency to migrate with the passage of time or increasing age to the temporal region or to transform into the 14 and 6 per second positive spike pattern.

The clinical significance and, to a lesser degree, the natural history of occipital foci in children have been studied by Blanc, Rebufat and Dreyfus-Brisac (1959) who analyzed 200 cases. One hundred of these cases were less than three years of age and, in these, both waking and sleep records were obtained. In the other one hundred cases (age 3–15), only waking records were made. Of the children under three years, 57 cases showed "delta polymorphic occipital foci" in deep sleep but no evidence of foci in the waking record. (The possibility that the "delta polymorphic foci" are not abnormalities but part of a normal sleep pattern seen in this age group will be discussed at the end of the paper.)

Of the other 43 cases below the age of three years, 33 had seizures and 8 were seizure-free but had "evidence of a cerebral lesion." In the older group, 59 had seizures and, of these, 40 were generalized, 17 Jacksonian and 2 absence attacks. Of the 41 who were not subject to seizures, 18 had evidence of

---

*This work was supported by the Cannafax Fund of The Methodist Hospital, Houston, Texas.

†Fellow in Electroencephalography.

a severe cerebral lesion and 23 had cataracts or various "neurotic" symptoms. Serial follow-up studies showed disappearance of the foci in 30 cases, replacement by a temporal focus in 10 and by a paroxysmal generalized abnormality in 5 cases.

Children with ocular abnormalities dating from birth have been reported to show a high incidence of occipital foci. Frequently these children have no other neurological abnormalities and there appears to be a definite cause and effect relationship between the visual defect and the occipital focus. In 1950, Levinson and Stillerman reviewed the clinical and electroencephalographic records of 915 children under the age of sixteen years and reported that patients with eye disorders but no evidence of brain injury ("cerebral palsy") showed a 23 per cent incidence of occipital electrographic abnormality as compared with only 0.6 per cent of normal controls. Children with evidence of both ocular disorder and brain damage showed occipital abnormalities in 85 per cent as compared with an incidence of only 52 per cent in subjects with cerebral palsy and seizures but no eye disorder. In contrast to the high incidence of occipital foci, the patients with ocular disorders showed very few electrographic foci elsewhere. Subsequently, this same group (Stillerman et al., 1950; Levinson et al., 1951) made a study of the types of ocular abnormality which were most often associated in children with occipital spike foci. In this study, they found that otherwise normal children with strabismus showed a 30 per cent incidence of occipital abnormalities and that these were twice as frequent in the exotropic as in the esotropic type.

A high incidence of occipital spike foci in children with retrolental fibroplasia was reported by Kellaway, Bloxsom and MacGregor and by Gibbs, Fois and Gibbs in the same year (1955). An earlier study of a much smaller series of cases by Jim and Kraus (1954) had, however, failed to reveal evidence of EEG abnormalities in children with RLF and, more recently, Parmelee, Fisk and Wright (1959) found that in only two of six cases of RLF were they able to find any suggestion of EEG abnormality. However, Cohen et al. (1961) and Gastaut (1961), in studies of larger groups, have confirmed the association of RLF and occipital foci and have indicated that there is a relationship between the existence of such foci and the severity of visual impairment. Kellaway and his associates (1955) have, furthermore, pointed out that existence of occipital foci is dependent upon loss of retinal function and not upon the character of the disease, as the same type of occipital foci may be present in other conditions, such as enucleation for retinoblastoma or congenital glaucoma in which the retinas are absent or severely damaged. The only essential feature of the retinal damage is that it occurs in infancy, as damage later in childhood or in adult life does not result in the appearance of occipital spike foci.

Material and Method

For the purposes of the present study, 452 cases were culled from a much larger number of children with occipital foci. This selecting of cases was done in order to obtain as "pure" a sampling as possible—that is, one in which all the patients had only the particular electrographic abnormality being studied; namely, an occipital focus. Thus, cases having, in addition to an occipital focus, other specific electrographic abnormalities such as foci elsewhere, generalized spike and wave patterns or 14 and 6 per second positive spikes, were excluded even when these abnormalities had been demonstrated in the past and were no longer evident. Nonspecific abnormalities, such as slow or fast background rhythms, were not, however, considered grounds to exclude a case from the study. The age range of the children in the series was 12 days through 16 years.

In all instances, the foci were clearly defined and were manifested by recurrent discharges of spike, spike and wave, sharp wave or slow wave activity located in the region of the electrodes designated as O_1 or O_2 in the international system. All the slow wave foci were unilateral; some of the spike, spike and wave and sharp wave foci were bilateral and independent on the two sides. Samples of the type of foci included in the study with illustrative case histories are given below.

Illustrative Case Histories and EEG Samples

R. S., male: Age 9 yr. 1 mo. Seizures since age 6 years beginning with vomiting and abdominal pain followed by intermittent jerking of the eyes to the right, jerking of right hand and twitching of right face lasting up to seven hours. Two months premature; birth weight 3 lb. 14 oz. Hydrocephalus from birth but not progressive. Right spastic hemiparesis since birth. Normal intelligence. EEG revealed an active spike focus *left* occipital region and independent lower voltage spike activity in the right occipital lead (Fig. 1).

L. R., female: Age 2 yr. 6 mo. Bilateral cataracts and congenital heart disease. No seizures. EEG revealed independent foci of polyspike and slow wave discharges in the right and left occipital regions (Fig. 2).

R. C., male: Age 2 yr. 5 mo. Congenital anophthalmia and mental retardation. Onset at age 28 months of seizures of three different types: "limp" attacks, left focal motor and generalized tonic-clonic. EEG revealed a spike and slow wave focus in the *right* occipital region occasionally showing reflection in the left homologous region (Fig. 3).

C. S., male: Age 8 yr. 5 mo. Short stature. Referred for school failure. Normal intelligence. EEG revealed independent spike foci in the right and left occipital regions (Fig. 4).

J. S., female: Age 1 yr. 8 mo. Retrolental fibroplasia. No seizures. EEG revealed independent spike foci in the left and right occipital regions (see Fig. 5).

B. L. P., female: Age 5 yr. Seven-week history of headache, vomiting, loss of weight. Early papilledema, nystagmus, right occipital glioblastoma. EEG revealed a focus of high voltage slow activity in the right occipital region (see Fig. 6).

Clinical Correlations

Ocular Abnormalities. Sixty-one of the 452 children in this series had ocular abnormalities of some type (strabismus, supression amblyopia, retrolental fibroplasia, congenital glaucoma, anophthalmia, ocular enucleation, congenital cataracts, etc.). This is probably a higher number than would normally be obtained in a general sampling of occipital foci due to the fact that at one time we made a special effort to collect a large group of children with ocular abnormalities and many of these were children who would not otherwise have had EEG studies.

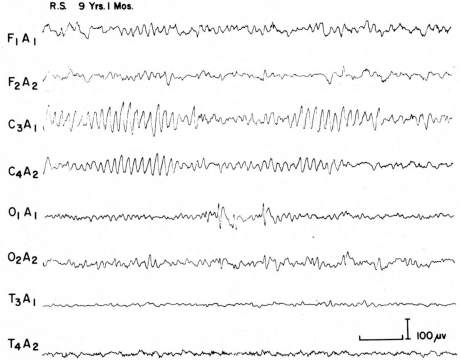

R.S. 9 Yrs. I Mos.

F_1A_1

F_2A_2

C_3A_1

C_4A_2

O_1A_1

O_2A_2

T_3A_1

T_4A_2

$100\,\mu v$

Fig. 1. Homolateral ear-to-scalp recording during "drowsiness' in R. S., child with seizures and right spastic hemiparesis, showing focus of fairly high voltage spike and wave discharge in the left occipital region with some similar synchronous and asynchronous low voltage activity in the right occipital lead.

Seizures. Two hundred and fifty-four, or 56.2 per cent, of all the cases in the series had had seizures, and 198, or 43.8 per cent, had had no seizures up to the time they were last studied. In the group with ocular abnormalities, the incidence of seizures was less than for the group as a whole, 32.8 per cent having had and 67.2 per cent not having had seizures.

The incidence of seizures in the whole group was studied in relation to the type of focus present: Three hundred and eighteen cases had spike or sharp wave foci and 134 had slow wave foci. The incidence of seizures in the spike and sharp wave group was 54.4 per cent and in the slow wave group, 60.4 per cent. If the children with ocular abnormalities (a group with a lower seizure incidence) are excluded, 59 per cent with spike or sharp wave foci and 61 per cent with slow wave foci had seizures (see Tables 1 and 2).

The age of onset of attacks in the 254 patients with seizures has been plotted graphically in Fig. 7. It can be seen that more patients had their first seizures during the first postnatal year than in any other period. For comparison, the age at which the EEG focus was seen is plotted at the top of the figure.

Generalized seizures without localizing features were the most common type of attack, occurring in 39.8 per cent of the epileptic group. Purely focal

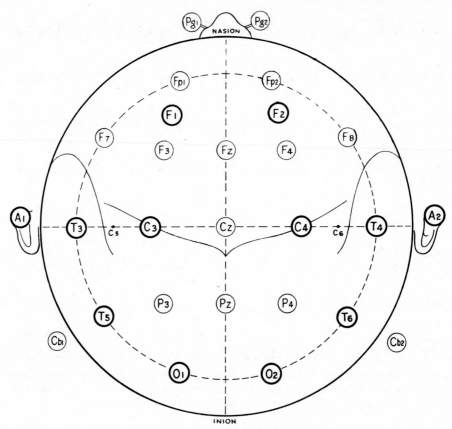

Fig. 1A. The darkly outlined circles indicate the electrode placements employed for routine studies in children. The International System is used for all measurements with the exception that the electrodes designated F_1 and F_2 are positioned at a point above the nasion 20 per cent of the nasion to inion distance and 10 per cent of the circumferential distance from the midline. When extra electrodes are used for localization purposes the placements are made in the standard International System positions.

seizures occurred in 34.3 per cent and generalized attacks with focal onset or focal features in 13.8 per cent. Head and eye turning was a feature of the attacks in 24.15 per cent and visual disturbances in 9.1 per cent (see Fig. 8).

Paroxysmal autonomic phenomena occurred in a significant number of all the cases in the study,* but because the pathophysiological basis of such attacks has not been clearly established, these were considered separately from the seizure group. Paroxysmal episodes of autonomic dysfunction and pain occurred in 91, or 21 per cent, of the 452 patients with occipital foci included in this study. Typically, these attacks consisted of recurrent episodes of headache and/or abdominal pain with associated autonomic disturbances,

---

*Case R. S. is an example except that, in this instance, the autonomic phenomena were followed by frank convulsive movements.

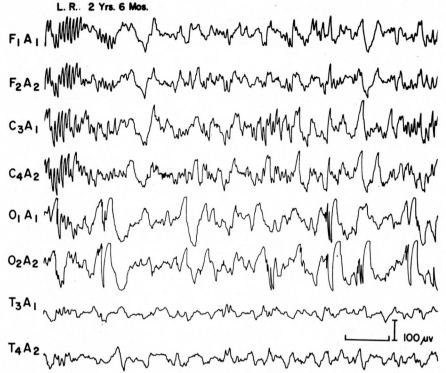

L. R. 2 Yrs. 6 Mos.

F_1A_1

F_2A_2

C_3A_1

C_4A_2

O_1A_1

O_2A_2

T_3A_1

T_4A_2

100 μv

Fig. 2. Homolateral ear-to-scalp recording during sleep showing independent polyspike and slow wave foci in the right and left occipital leads in L. R., child with bilateral cataracts, congenital heart disease and no history of seizures.

such as nausea, vomiting, pallor, sweating and alterations of body temperature.

Other Signs and Symptoms of Cerebral Disorder. Evidence of some degree of mental retardation was present in 121, or 26.7 per cent, of the patients, and speech difficulties, usually consisting of a marked delay in the development of speech out of proportion to general intelligence (even if the latter was low), were found in 42, or 9.2 per cent, of the group.

Only 60, or 13.2 per cent, of the cases had abnormal motor findings on neurological examination. Gross abnormalities, such as hemiplegia, were present in 43 and more subtle abnormalities, such as incoordination, in 17. Disorders of behavior, such as temper tantrums, hyperactivity and discipline problems, were a significant feature in 94, or 20.8 per cent, of the children (see Table 3).

Etiology of Occipital Foci. The etiology of the occipital focus (see Fig. 9) could not be established in nearly half the cases. However, in this regard, the age at which neurological abnormality was first manifested may be pertinent. This is shown graphically in Fig. 10. It will be seen that nearly three times as many of the children had onset of signs and symptoms of neurological disorder during the first year of life than at any other time, suggesting that in many cases the causative agent was operant in the peri-

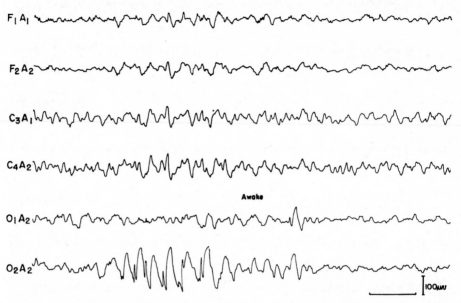

Fig. 3. Homolateral ear-to-scalp recording showing a spike and slow wave focus in the right occipital region in R. C., child with congenital anopthalmia. The right occipital focal discharge was occasionally reflected at low voltage in the left occipital lead.

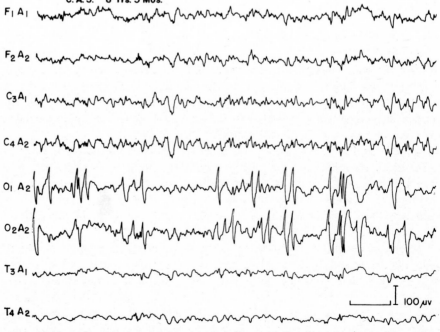

Fig. 4. Homolateral ear-to-scalp recording during light sleep showing independent spike foci in the right and left occipital leads in C. A. S., child with normal intelligence referred for school failure.

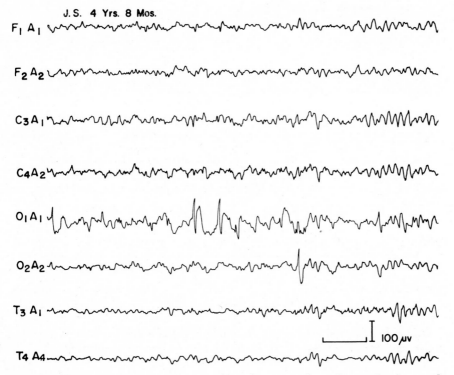

J. S. 4 Yrs. 8 Mos.

F₁ A₁

F₂ A₂

C₃ A₁

C₄ A₂

O₁ A₁

O₂ A₂

T₃ A₁

T₄ A₄

100 μv

Fig. 5. Homolateral ear-to-scalp recording showing independent spike foci in the right and left occipital leads in J. S., child with RLF and no history of seizures.

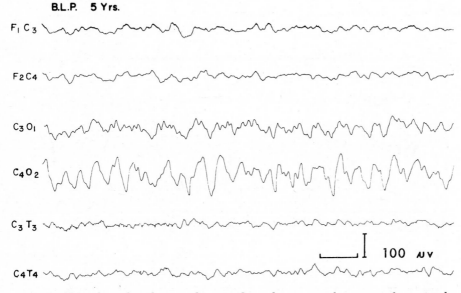

B.L.P. 5 Yrs.

F₁ C₃

F₂ C₄

C₃ O₁

C₄ O₂

C₃ T₃

100 μv

C₄ T₄

Fig. 6. Homolateral scalp-to-scalp recording showing a slow wave focus in the right occipital lead in B. L. P., child with glioblastoma in the right occipital region.

Table 1. *The Incidence of Seizures in the Entire Group and the Incidence in the Groups With and Without Ocular Abnormalities*

NO. OF CASES WITH OCCIPITAL FOCI

INCLUDING THOSE WITH OCULAR ABNORMALITIES TOTAL— 452	
WITH SEIZURES 254 (56.2 %)	WITHOUT SEIZURES 198 43 %
EXCLUDING THOSE WITH OCULAR ABNORMALITIES TOTAL-391	
WITH SEIZURES 234 (59.8 %)	WITHOUT SEIZURES 157 (40.2 %)
INCLUDING ONLY CASES WITH OCULAR ABNORMALITIES TOTAL-61	
WITH SEIZURES 20 (32.8 %)	WITHOUT SEIZURES 41 (67.2%)

Table 2. *The Incidence of Spike and Slow Wave Foci in Children With or Without Ocular Abnormalities or Seizures*

CASES WITH NO SEIZURES · NO OCULAR ABNORMALITY TOTAL 157	
SPIKE FOCI 106 (67.2%)	SLOW WAVE FOCI 51 (32.8%)
CASES WITH NO SEIZURES · OCULAR ABNORMALITY TOTAL 41	
SPIKE FOCI 39 (95.1%)	SLOW WAVE FOCI 2 (4.9 %)
CASES WITH SEIZURES · NO OCULAR ABNORMALITY TOTAL 234	
SPIKE FOCI 153 (65.3%)	SLOW WAVE FOCI 81 (34.6 %)
CASES WITH SEIZURES · OCULAR ABNORMALITY TOTAL 20	
SPIKE FOCI 20 (100%)	SLOW WAVE FOCI 0 (0%)

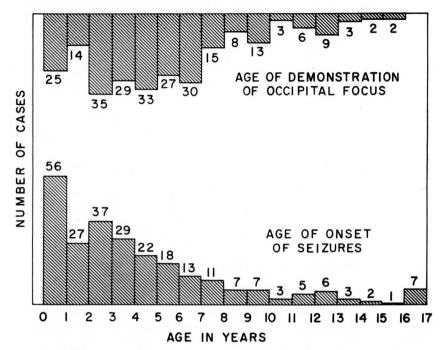

Fig. 7. Block graph showing the age at which the 254 children with seizures started to have attacks and the age at which the EEG focus was first revealed.

TYPES OF SEIZURES OCCURRING IN 254 CHILDREN WITH OCCIPITAL FOCI

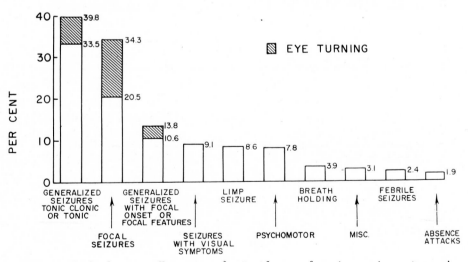

Fig. 8. Block diagram illustrating the incidence of various seizure types in children with occipital foci. Note the relatively high incidence of eye or head and eye turning.

Table 3. *The Incidence of the Various Neurological Signs or Symptoms in the Entire Series of 452 Children*

		CASES		PER CENT
MENTAL RETARDATION		1 2 1		26.7 %
ABNORMAL NEUROLOGICAL FINDINGS	DEFINITE	43	60	13.2 %
	MINOR	1 7		
SPEECH DISTURBANCE		4 2		9.2 %
BEHAVIOUR DISORDER INCLUDING HYPERACTIVITY		9 4		20.8 %

natal period. Anoxia at birth appeared by history to be a factor in 9.6 per cent but even in some of these there was some doubt as to whether the anoxia was sufficient to have been responsible. Encephalitis had preceded the onset of symptoms in 4.4 per cent and 12.3 per cent had suffered a significant injury to the head before the development of the symptoms and focus. The relationship of occipital spike foci and certain ocular abnormalities in children has been clearly established (Gibbs, Fois and Gibbs, 1955; Kellaway, Bloxsom and MacGregor, 1955), but the pathophysiological basis of the association has not as yet been determined. The 13.5 per cent of our cases who had ocular abnormalities probably somewhat distorts the percentage incidence of the various etiologies because there is a large number of such patients in our group than would appear in a general population due to the fact that at one time we specifically sought out ocular cases for study.

The Natural History of Occipital Foci. Longitudinal studies were made of 216 patients, 31 of whom had ocular abnormalities. Figs. 11 and 12 demonstrate our observations that occipital foci tend to disappear with time. This tendency is present in both the ocular and non-ocular group but in the latter the foci seem to disappear more quickly—in over 50 per cent of the cases within the first year. The foci in the ocular group, however, tend to persist for a longer time with about 50 per cent of the cases continuing to show foci for four years or longer.

Discussion

In children, *slow wave* foci occur more commonly in the occipital than in any other region. In the present series, 30 per cent of the cases had slow wave foci and in many of these the focal activity was very high in voltage and very slow. The fact that only 2 per cent of the cases in our entire series were found to have brain tumors is of particular significance in this regard. It would appear that, statistically, the presence of a high voltage very slow focus in the occipital region of the young child should not *in itself* be con-

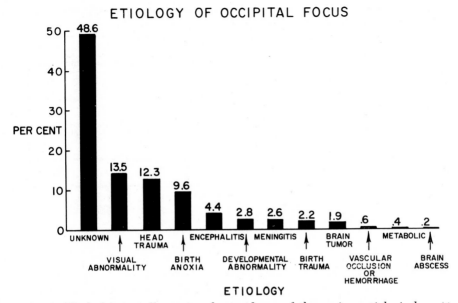

Fig. 9. Block diagram illustrating the incidence of the various etiological agents which were thought to contribute to the development of the occipital focus.

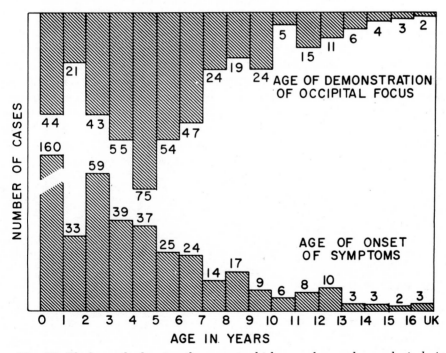

Fig. 10. Block graph showing the age at which any abnormal neurological sign or symptom first became apparent in the 452 children and the age at which these children's EEG's first revealed an occipital focus.

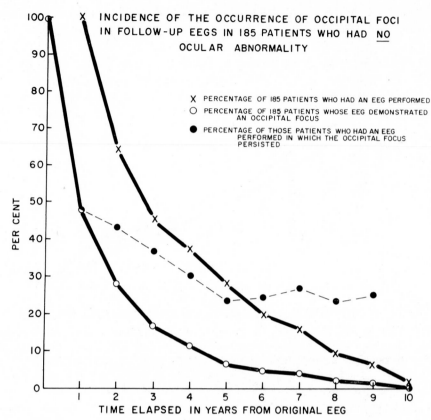

Fig. 11. Graph demonstrating the tendency of occipital foci in children who do no have ocular abnormalities, to disappear within a short time. Note that the critical part of this curve is more steeply inclined than that seen in Figure 12 indicating that foci in the non-ocular group disappear more quickly than do those of the ocular group.

sidered evidence to warrant contrast studies and that such a decision should always be weighted much more by the clinical evidence than by the character of the EEG focus (see also Holowach *et al.*, 1958). Our longitudinal studies have, indeed, shown that in most cases such foci tend to disappear or be replaced by spike foci with time, often within a relatively short period.

In our experience, foci of spike or sharp wave type commonly show increased activity during sleep whereas slow wave foci tend to disappear or be obscured in sleep. The converse effect reported by Blanc et al. (1959) of slow wave foci appearing *only* in sleep has not been observed by us. An illustration of the focal activity which they describe as "delta polymorphic" is not given by these workers and it is, therefore, difficult to make comparisons, but we have observed as a common finding in normal children of this age level high voltage slow wave transients in the occipital leads which may be mistaken for focal abnormality because of a tendency which they show to occur asynchronously on the two sides. An example of this type of activity

INCIDENCE OF THE OCCURRENCE OF OCCIPITAL FOCI IN FOLLOW-UP
EEGS IN 31 PATIENTS HAVING OCULAR ABNORMALITIES

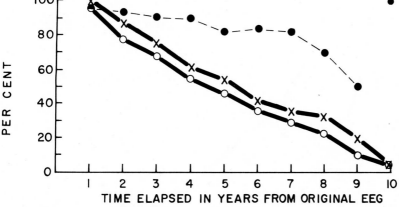

X   PERCENTAGE OF THE 31 PATIENTS WHO HAD AN EEG PERFORMED

O   PERCENTAGE OF THE 31 PATIENTS WHOSE EEG DEMONSTRATED AN OCCIPITAL FOCUS

●   PERCENTAGE OF THOSE PATIENTS WHO HAD AN EEG PERFORMED IN WHICH
     AN OCCIPITAL FOCUS PERSISTED

Fig. 12. Graph demonstrating the tendency of occipital foci in patients who have ocular abnormalities to disappear with time but to persist longer than the occipital foci in the non-ocular group. (See Figure 11).

in a normal child is shown in Fig. 13. Because of the high incidence of such occipital slow wave transients in moderately deep sleep in normal young children, we do not consider them an abnormal finding.

In middle and late childhood, temporal foci predominate (Gibbs and Gibbs, 1952; Scott and Kellaway, 1958), but in infants and in young children, occipital foci are more common. Indeed, in the newborn, whereas occipital and, to a lesser degree, central foci are often seen, foci elsewhere are a great rarity. This high incidence of occipital and central localizations almost to the exclusion of all other sites is not, we believe, a reflection of a greater proclivity of the cerebral insults of infancy to be localized to these areas, but rather of a maturational factor which permits expression of dysfunction in electrical terms earlier in these regions than in any other. The precocious morphologic maturation of the central and occipital cortices and their subcortical connections in man is well established (Conel, 1939). It is suggested that this early differentiation renders the cortical elements in these areas more capable of producing and sustaining abnormal electrical discharge than those of any other area. As a corollary of such a hypothesis, it would follow that the causative lesion would not necessarily have to be localized to the central or occipital cortex, and, indeed, in terms of statistical probability, would, in most cases, be relatively diffuse.

The relatively low incidence of seizures in children with occipital foci (only 56.2 per cent) may be explained, at least in part, on the basis of the experimental evidence that the occipital cortex has a high epileptogenic

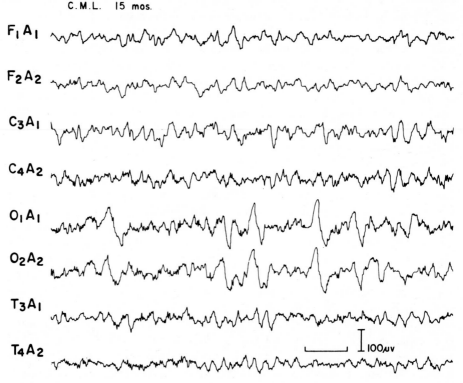

Fig. 13. Occipital slow activity of sharp, diphasic wave form and often occurring as isolated transients (as in the example above) is common in certain stages of sleep in normal young children.

threshold.* Another factor may have to do with the character or pathophysiology of the mechanism responsible for the focal abnormality. This is probably true in the case of the occipital foci associated with ocular defects where the malfunction responsible for the discharge is probably confined to the specific thalamocortical connections of the visual system and undoubtedly differs in its pathogenesis and structuro-functional characteristics from the usual epileptogenic lesion.

The etiology of most occipital foci in children and the nature and the exact site of the causative lesions are all factors which are still obscure. In nearly 50 per cent of the cases, no obvious historical cause can be found to account for the focus. The initial question which must, therefore, be answered is: Does this reflect a lack of understanding or recognition of the causative factors, particularly those which might be operant in the perinatal period which can produce such "lesions," or are many of these foci an expression of a biochemical or other functional defect as yet unidentified? This ques-

---

*Note: In the *clinical* sense. Actually, in monkeys the occipital cortex has the lowest threshold of all cortical areas to electrical after-discharge, but even when prolonged, such discharges are not accompanied by overt clinical changes (unpublished observations).

tion as to etiology is also linked with the problem of the nature and site of the lesion. It is clear from the available autopsy and surgical evidence that at least a small percentage of these foci are associated with atrophic cortical lesions of the type described by Penfield (1953) and others, but in the larger number, the lack of a clear etiologic cause, the course of the clinical and electrographic history and, in some instances, the failure to demonstrate a surgical lesion, point to some other type of pathophysiological process. The point should also be made that that the focal discharge in the occipital region may not be of cortical origin but may be of projected type arising from thalamic nuclei having specific projections to the occipital cortex. (See, for example, Jasper, 1955.)

Consideration of this possibility is particularly appropriate in the case of the occipital spike foci associated with ocular abnormalities. It appears that destruction of the retina from whatever cause (RLF, glaucoma, enucleation, etc.) will result in the appearance of the occipital spike abnormality as long as the damage occurs early enough in life and the foci are more likely to appear if both retinas are involved (Kellaway et al., 1955). Direct retinal damage is not, however, essential to the production of such abnormalities, for factors which result in light or form deprivation from birth are also likely to be associated with the appearance of spike foci. Thus, in cases of congenital cataract with intact retinas and in strabismus with suppression amblyopia, such foci may also occur (Stillerman et al., 1950; Kellaway and Scott, unpublished). The foci are not, however, present from birth but take time to develop. Regardless of the type of ocular abnormality, the earliest occipital spike focus which we have recorded was in an infant of ten months with RLF (Kellaway et al., 1955). It is, however, much more common for the foci to appear later than this—sometime between the ages of two and four years in cases of direct retinal damage and between five and eight years in cases of strabismus and suppression amblyopia. Two infants with anophthalmia also showed spike foci, suggesting that the neurol system involved in the production of the occipital foci develops in the absence of trophic influences from the retina and that it is laid down early in life. Similar conclusions concerning the development of the optic nuclei and pathways in the cat have recently been reported by Hubel and Wiesel (1963) who, on the basis of a study of receptive fields of single cells in the striate cortex of the newborn kitten, have concluded that many of the connections responsible for the highly organized behavior of such units must be present at or near the time of birth and that the development of these connections occurs even in the absence of patterned visual experience.

The mechanism responsible for the generation of focal occipital spike discharge in the child with retinal damage or visual deprivation has not yet been defined. It has been suggested (Kellaway et al., 1955) that the discharges may arise in the calcarine cortex as a result of a "denervation sensitization" effect. In man, following enucleation, transneuronal degeneration in the lateral geniculates has been found to be rapid and extreme (Clark and Penman, 1934; Cook et al., 1951) and, in animals, this process is accelerated and is more pronounced if eye removal is carried out during fetal or neonatal life (Hess, 1958). More recently, it has been demonstrated that visual deprivation in the young kitten results in marked atrophic changes in the lateral geniculate body of the deprived eye. This atrophy, which is present in all layers receiving input from the deprived side, is most pronounced in animals deprived from birth, less marked in kittens deprived at later ages, and absent in the adult cat (Wiesel and Hubel, 1963b).

Thus, both direct retinal damage and visual deprivation will produce similar degenerative changes in the lateral geniculate bodies. Furthermore, studies of single unit responses in the striate cortex (Wiesel and Hubel, 1963a) and lateral geniculate in the young kitten deprived of vision in one eye have shown that while geniculate cells respond well to stimulation of the deprived eye, the cortical units are completely unresponsive. Wiesel and Hubel suggest that there is a defect of function in the region of the synapse between the axon terminals of the geniculate cells and the cortical cells on which these terminals end.

Thus, the basic mechanism underlying the EEG foci in unilateral argamblyopia, visual deprivation (cataracts) and direct retinal damage or loss may be unitary.

A slowly developing increase in excitability to the point of spontaneous epileptiform discharge is a characteristic feature of neuronally isolated cortex (Echlin, 1959). This phenomenon has been variously attributed (Echlin, 1959) to a denervation sensitization effect similar to that which occurs in effector organs (Thesleff, 1960) or to a proliferation of recurrent axon collaterals (Purpura and Housepian, 1961). The latter phenomenon has been demonstrated to be a constant finding when the isolation is carried out in the infant animal and must, therefore, be considered a possible factor in the genesis of the cortical spiking associated with visual deprivation or retinal damage, as these, too, are only effective if they occur very early in life.

That there might be a basic pathophysiologic difference between occipital foci engendered by ocular defects and those of other cause is also suggested by the fact that foci associated with visual deficits tend to persist for a much longer period than do the others (Fig. 12). That there is a tendency for all EEG foci in children to disappear with increasing age has been observed by several investigators. We have found that the curve describing the time course of this trend has essentially a similar general shape for all areas. The curve has an initial steep slope followed by a more gradual hyperbolic inflection. How much this curve is a reflection of maturational changes and how much of the evolution of the pathologic process itself is not clear, but it would appear that the initial steep part of the curve, the slope of which is the most constant feature regardless of location of the focus, may be ontogenetically determined.

The hypothesis of Gibbs et al. (1954) that occipital foci characteristically migrate to the midtemporal region or transform into the 14 and 6 per second positive spike pattern is based entirely on their observation that children who originally showed occipital foci may, in later life when the occipital abnormality has disappeared, show, instead, either one of the two findings. Similar observations have been made by Blanc et al. (1959), and we also have seen such changes, but their incidence and regularity of occurrence are not statistically impressive in our series. Furthermore, the choice of the term "migrate" is unfortunate because of the implication, probably unintended, that the pathologic process responsible for the focus actually moves its location from one site to another.

We believe that the evolution of electrographic findings in children in time, with the confusing shifts in the site of foci which sometimes occur, may be, in large part, a reflection of maturational changes. It is suggested that when shifts of location, transformation in character, or diffusion of the discharge pattern occur, such changes are evidence that the original lesion was not focally delimited but "diffuse"—the initial focalization of electrographic abnormality is conceived as being determined by the maturational state of the involved brain structures in terms of their "readiness" to express the effect of the insult in the form of abnormal electrical discharge. The apparent "migration" or "transformation" of foci is conceived as merely the result of a "coming of age" of other neuronal systems (which were directly or indirectly involved in the initial causative insult) in terms of their ability to express dysfunction in the form of abnormal electrical activity. Another factor which might also be considered is the possibility that the original foci might, during their lifespan, induce "conditioned" discharges (Morrell, 1959), which eventually become self-sustained, in related cortical and diencephalic systems.

Summary

Four hundred and fifty-two children with occipital foci, ages 12 days through 16 years, have been studied. The occipital focus was the only focal abnormality in all cases. Sixty-one of the children had visual or ocular abnormalities. In 318 cases, the focus was either a spike or sharp wave and, in 134, a slow wave. Seizures were present in 54.4 per cent of cases with a spike focus and in 60.4 per cent of cases with a slow wave focus. A total of 254 of the children had cerebral seizures. Generalized tonic or tonic-clonic seizures occurred in 39.8 per cent, pure focal seizures in 34.3 per cent, and generalized seizures with focal onset or focal features in 13.8 per cent. There was an aura of blindness or flashing lights in 9.1 per cent and, in 24.2 per cent, head and eye turning occurred either before or during a seizure.

One hundred and twenty-one, or 26.7 per cent, of the cases were mentally retarded. Speech problems were evident in 9.2 per cent of cases and behavior disorders in 20.8 per cent.

Occipital foci were the most common type of foci in the newborn period, and 35.4 per cent of cases had onset of symptoms during the first year of life.

Longitudinal studies were made in 216 patients and it was confirmed that such foci tend to disappear in time, but less rapidly in the group who have ocular abnormalities.

Identification of the etiological factors responsible for the production of occipital foci could not be made in 48.6 per cent of the patients. Even in the remaining cases the etiological factor was not always certain.

The early onset of signs and symptoms of neurological disorder is suggestive that in many cases the causative agent was operative in the perinatal period. It also appears that the foci seen in patients with visual defects may have a unique pathophysiological basis because of their tendency to persist longer and because the incidence of seizures in this group is much lower than in the group without ocular abnormalities.

It is suggested that the apparent "migration" or "transformation" of foci with the passage of time is an expression of a maturational effect. The site of the focus at a given age is conceived as being largely determined by the readiness, in terms of their developmental level, of the various regions of the brain affected by the causative lesion to express their dysfunction in the form of abnormal electrical discharge.

REFERENCES

BLANC, C., REBUFAT, M. and DREYFUS-BRISAC, C. Le problème des localisations occipitales chez l'enfant. *Rev. Neurol.* *1959*, 101:287–289.

CLARK, W. E. L. and PENMAN, G. G. Projection of retina in lateral geniculate body. *Proc. Roy. Soc. Lond.*, *1934*, 114:291–313.

COHEN, J., BOSHES, L. D. and SNIDER, R. S. Electroencephalographic changes following retrolental fibroplasia. *Electroenceph. clin. Neurophysiol.*, *1961*, 13:914–922.

CONEL, J. L. *Postnatal Development of the Human Cerebral Cortex. I.* Harvard University Press, Cambridge, Mass., *1939*.

COOK, W. H., WALKER, J. H. and BARR, M. L. A cytological study of transneuronal atrophy in the cat and rabbit. *J. comp. Neurol.*, *1951*, 94:267–291.

ECHLIN, F. A. The supersensitivity of chronically "isolated" cerebral cortex as a mechanism in focal epilepsy. *Electroenceph. clin. Neurophysiol.*, *1959*, 11:697–722.

GASTAUT, H. Reported in lecture given at World Course in Electroencephalography. Marseille. August, *1961*.

GIBBS, E. L., FOIS, A. and GIBBS, F. A. The electroencephalogram in retrolental fibroplasia. *New Engl. J. Med.*, *1955*, 253:1102–1106.

GIBBS, E. L. and GIBBS, F. A. *Atlas of Electroencephalography.* Addison- Wesley Press, Inc., Cambridge, Mass., *1952*, p. 162.

GIBBS, E. L., GILLEN, H. W. and GIBBS, F. A. Disappearance and migration of epileptic foci in childhood. *AMA J. Dis. Child.*, *1954*, 88:596–603.

HESS, A. Optic centers and pathways after eye removal in fetal guinea pigs. *J. comp. Neurol.*, *1958*, 109:91–115.

HOLOWACH, J., THURSTON, D. L. and O'LEARY, J. L. Jacksonian seizures in infancy and childhood. *J. Pediat.*, *1958*, 52: 670–686.

HUBEL, D. H. and WIESEL, T. N. Receptive fields of cells in striate cortex of very young visually inexperienced kittens. *J. Neurophysiol.*, *1963*, 26:994–1002.

JASPER, H. H. E.E.G. and thalamocortical relations. Congres Latinoamer. Neurochir. VI, Montevideo, *1955*, p. 794.

JIM, V. K. S. and KRAUS, A. C. Electroencephalography in retrolental fibroplasia. *Amer. J. Ophthal.*, *1954*, 38:337–341.

KELLAWAY, P., BLOXSOM, A. and MAC GREGOR, M. Occipital foci associated with retrolental fibroplasia and other forms of retinal loss in children. *Electroenceph. clin. Neurophysiol.*, *1955*, 7:469–470.

LEVINSON, J. D., GIBBS, E. L., STILLERMAN, M. L. and PERLSTEIN, M. A. Electroencephalogram and eye disorders. Clinical correlation. *Pediatrics*, *1951*, 7:422–427.

LEVINSON, J. D. and STILLERMAN, M. The correlation between electroencephalographic findings and eye disorders in children. *Electroenceph. clin. Neurophysiol.*, *1950*, 2:226.

MORRELL, F. Lasting changes in synaptic organization produced by continuous neuronal bombardment. Conf. on Brain Mechanisms and Learning, Montevideo, August, *1959*. Blackwell, Oxford, *1962*.

PARMELEE, A. H., JR., FISKE, C. E. and WRIGHT, R. H. The development of ten children with blindness as a result of retrolental fibroplasia. *AMA J. Dis. Child.*, *1959*, 98:198–220.

PENFIELD, W. and JASPER, H. *Epilepsy and the Functional Anatomy of the Human Brain.* Little, Brown & Co., Boston, *1954*, pp. 302–322.

PURPURA, D. P. and HOUSEPIAN, H. Morphological and physiological properties of chronically isolated immature neocortex.

Exp. Neurol., 1961, 4:366–401.

SCOTT, J. S. and KELLAWAY, P. Epilepsy of focal origin in childhood. In: *Medical Clinics of North America*, Saunders, Philadelphia, March, *1958*, pp. 415–433.

STILLERMAN, M., GIBBS, E. L. and PERLSTEIN, M. A. Electroencephalographic changes in strabismus. *Amer. J. Ophth.*, 1950, 35:54–63.

THESLEFF, S. Effects of motor innervation in the chemical sensitivity of skeletal muscle. *Physiol. Rev.*, 1960, 40:734–752.

WIESEL, T. N. and HUBEL, D. H. Single cell responses in striate cortex of kittens deprived of vision in one eye. *J. Neurophysiol.*, 1963a, 26:1002–1017.

WIESEL, T. N. and HUBEL, D. H. Effects of visual deprivation on the morphology and physiology of cells in the cat's lateral geniculate body. *J. Neurophysiol.*, 1963b, 26:978–993.

DISCUSSION

DR. PURPURA: This report touches upon several problems which have been discussed in other contexts during this symposium. The authors point out that in over 50 per cent of the cases studied no obvious causes could be found to account for the occipital foci. They cautiously add, however, that perhaps analytical methods have not been developed, as yet, to define the pathophysiological processes responsible for the EEG abnormalities in the absence of overt causative factors. I believe this point cannot be emphasized sufficiently. It is of particular interest that attention has been directed to the relationship of ocular abnormalities and EEG occipital spike foci and findings on the development of structural and functional defects in the normal pathways of light deprived kittens.

The notion that ocular abnormalities result in a reduction in input to striate cortex and that this may occasion a hyperexcitability of cortical neurons secondary to their "functional isolation" is a most provocative suggestion. As a matter of fact it would seem to me that such an hypothesis ought to be readily susceptible to experimental attack and it is to be hoped that Dr. Kellaway and his associates will provide us with additional information on this question at future meetings. It might be pointed out in passing that in their studies of monocular visual deprivation in kittens, Wiesel and Hubel recorded electrocortical activity in only one preparation. Although they noted marked depression of evoked potentials to visual stimulation of the previously occluded eye, no mention was made of any sign of epileptogenic activity or other electrocortical abnormalities. Perhaps it might be possible to induce several types of visual deprivations in young kittens and further define the development of electrographic abnormalities in the immature striate cortex.

DR. KELLAWAY: Several years ago my associates, Dr. Ralph Druckman and Dr. F. J. Moore, and I attempted to induce occipital spike foci in the rabbit and later the kitten by surgical enucleation of the eyes in the newborn period. Recordings were made from chronically implanted cortical electrodes for periods up to eight months after enucleation but in no instance did any evidence of occipital focal spike discharge appear. In some animals intravenous Metrazol was administered in an attempt to demonstrate focal hyperexcitability but without success. As a species difference may account for the failure to reproduce the foci we intend to repeat the experiments in infant Rhesus monkeys.

ELECTROCLINICAL STUDIES OF STATUS EPILEPTICUS AND CONVULSIONS IN THE NEWBORN*

C. DREYFUS-BRISAC AND N. MONOD

*Clinique Baudelocque, Maternity of Hôpital Saint Antoine, and
EEG Department of the Hôpital de la Pitié, Paris, France*

Since the electroencephalogram of the newborn infant was first studied, many investigators have taken up the problem of convulsions of newborn infants and their electrical correlates.

As early as 1953, some observations on the electrical activity of the brain recorded during seizures were reported (Fischgold and Berthault, 1953; Mai and Schaper, 1953; Saint-Anne-Dargassies *et al.*, 1953). More recently, detailed studies of these electrographic patterns have been reported by Aicardi (1955), Fois (1956), Ribstein and Walter (1958), Harris and Tizard (1960) and Engel (1961). Simultaneously, Craig (1960) reported on the clinical aspects of seizures in full-term and premature infants. Studies of clinical and electrical patterns during seizures at different stages of maturation (Gibbs, 1957; Passouant *et al.*, 1959, 1960; Dreyfus-Brisac and Monod, 1960; Passouant and Cadilhac, 1962), and in different species (Bureš, 1953; Servit, 1959; Cadilhac *et al.*, 1960; Bernhard *et al.*, 1962; Caveness *et al.*, 1962; Servit, 1962; Vernadakis, 1962), have stimulated interest in this problem. More recently, anatomical and biochemical data have been added (Millichap, 1957; Larroche, 1962; Yakovlev, 1962).

Convulsions and *status epilepticus* in the human newborn present peculiarities which must be stressed both from a clinical as well as a neurophysiologic point of view. They are, at times, very difficult to recognize and their clinical and electrical polymorphism requires detailed description.

During the previous ten years, 91 cases of *status epilepticus* have been studied. Of these, the electroencephalogram was recorded during seizures in 40 cases (65 records). The clinical material consists of: 88 full-term newborns, two 32-week gestation premature infants, one 28-week gestation premature infant, and one infant born at 28 weeks gestation with *status epilepticus* occurring at 40 days after birth. The small number of prematures is salient.†

I. ELECTROCLINICAL PATTERNS OF STATUS EPILEPTICUS AND CONVULSIONS IN FULL-TERM AND NEWBORN INFANTS

(a) Clinical Patterns

The recognition of *status epilepticus* in a newborn infant is sometimes a

---

*This work has been fulfilled with the aid of the Institut National d'Hygiène and of the Délégation Générale à la Recherche Scientifique.

†These infants were born in the Maternity of Hôpital Saint Antoine (Pr. M. Mayer and Dr. Ducas) and in the Clinique Baudeloque (Pr. Lacomme, Pr. Ag. Minkovski).

difficult problem because the seizures are very often quite anarchic, poly-morphic, and poorly organized. Any method which would help in the recogni-tion of seizures, and even subclinical attacks, should be considered important. Combined use of cinematography and electroencephalography has been of great help in the analysis of the clinical and electrographic manifestations of seizures. It is to be noted that photography of both the infant and the EEG presents special problems because, in these cases, it is necessary to obtain a field wide enough to be able to observe both the infant and the electroenceph-alogram. In addition, the motion picture must be taken without traumatiz-ing the infant, especially without excessively warming him with lights. Three cases of infants studied in this manner are presented:

Case 1. This 15-day-old infant with staphylococcal meningitis had seizures manifested by clonic movement on the right side, spreading sometimes to the left. Radiation and even lateralization of the clonic discharges appeared to be inconstant. For long periods, they were more marked on the right side, but later they began on the left side of the body (Fig. 1–4). Following the institution of anticonvulsive therapy, subclinical seizures were noted (Fig. 2). Only with simultaneous recordings of respiration and the electroencephalo-gram was it noted that, at times, the only behavioral manifestation of the seizure dis-charges appeared to be a short period of apnea.

Case 2. This 5-day-old infant suffered from seizures consisting of paroxysmal episodes of tonic muscular contractions, during which time a diffuse hypertonia predominated on the right side. The electroencephalogram was extremely useful in this case since during the seizures the infant was absolutely quiet, as if completely frozen, the upper limbs flexed and the lower half of the body extended (Fig. 3). The electrographic discharges in this case consisted of slow, monorhythmic delta waves in left rolandic region of several minutes duration. Following cessation of these discharges, there appeared low voltage spikes, be-tween which were noted paroxysmal bursts, some of which persisted over the right hemi-sphere while electrical discharges were occurring over the left hemisphere.

Case 3. This premature 30-week gestation infant, who had previously been discharged from the nursery 40 days postnatally, returned to the hospital 3 days after discharge in critical condition, with respiratory difficulty, diffuse hypertonia and vomiting. Electro-encephalography revealed seizure discharges, sometimes composed of very regular, moder-ate amplitude 2 cycle-per-second activity. At times, the seizures began with low voltage spikes originating either in the left frontal or right occipital region, followed by high voltage slow waves. Following the seizures, rhythmic alpha-like activity was noted. No clinical signs were noted during the discharges, and the infant seemed to be asleep. After prolonged analysis of the combined cinematographic and electrographic data, the relation-ship between the movements of the infant and electrographic seizure discharges re-mained unclear. It appears that these discharges were actually subclinical, since there was no difference between the behavior of the baby during and between them.

These three cases illustrate some of the main features to be discussed.
Generalized tonic-clonic convulsions are very rare in the newborn, as has already been pointed out by many investigators (Sainte-Anne-Dargassies et al., 1953; Minkovski et al., 1955; Minkovski and Sainte-Anne-Dargassies, 1956; Courjon and Cotte, 1958; Ribstein and Walter, 1958; Craig, 1960), although some cases have been reported (Harris and Tizard, 1960). Generally, the tonic and clonic periods are partial or mixed. The clonic discharges, some-

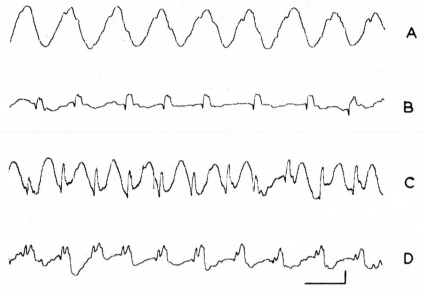

Fig. 1. Different electrical patterns recorded during clonic seizures (case 1).
(A) Rhythmic slow waves. (B) Low voltage negative spikes. (C) Slow spike and waves. (D) Complex pattern.
Calibration: 1 sec.–50 microvolts (the same for the following illustrations).

times limited to small twitches, begin in any part of the body (a limb, face, feet, hand, finger, toe, eye) and move from one region to another without regularity. Homolateral diffusion is often encountered, but the hemiconvulsive seizure is absent at this period of life.

At times, there is no radiation of the clonic movements over the body and they remain localized during the entire episode.

The tonic seizure, with opisthotonos, extension and elevation of a limb, and very often rotation of the head and eyes, is also often encountered in full-term newborn infants. At times, the tonic patterns are localized or very minimal. The resolution of the seizure is generally marked by a more or less complete hypotonia.

Opening of the eyes, paroxysmal blinking, nystagmus, abnormal cry, vasomotor changes, and sudden chewing can also be isolated signs of a clinical seizure, as already pointed out by Minkowski and Sainte-Anne-Dargassies (1956).

Curious movements of the limbs have also been noted. These motions, which involve especially the upper limbs, consist either of pendular movements or of rhythmic and complicated motions resembling swimming or rowing. In the lower limb, they resemble pedaling. All these phenomena can be isolated or associated with other manifestations. Apnea or paroxysmal dyspnea present difficulties as to their identification as clinical seizures (Craig *et al.*, 1960). In all these difficult cases, prolonged observation of the infant, naked if possible, should facilitate the recognition of convulsions or *status epilepticus*. The repetition of isolated phenomena at short intervals, or, better, the identi-

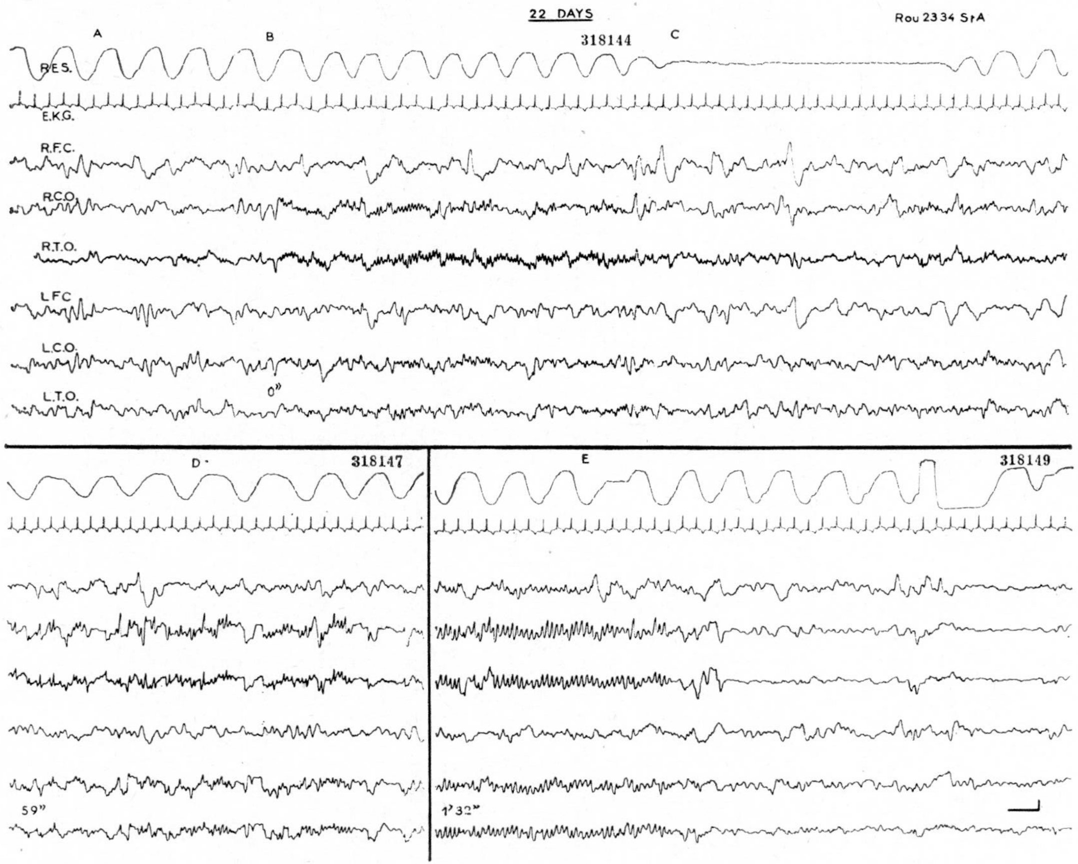

Fig. 2. A subclinical seizure recorded for 1 minute 50 seconds (case 1). The only clinical phenomenon is a long apnea in C. (A) Interseizure record. (B) Beginning of the electrical discharge: right occipital alpha-like rhythm (10 cycles/second). (C) Occipital spikes appear. (D) Acceleration and diffusion of the occipital spikes. (E) End of the discharge: biooccipital alpha-like rhythm (8 cycles/second).

RES: respiration. E.K.G.: Electrocardiogram. R: Right. L: Left. F: Frontal. C: Central. T: Temporal. O: Occipital (the same for the following illustrations).

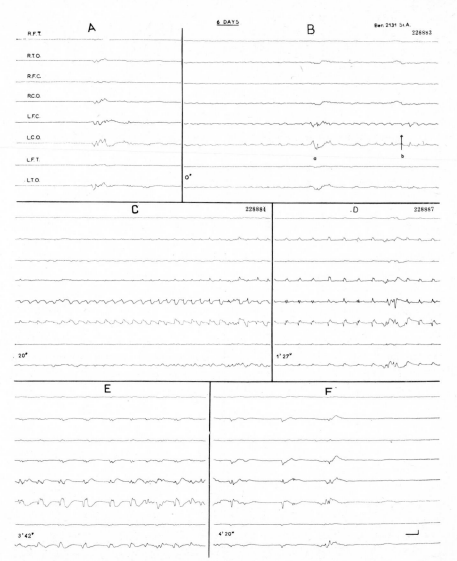

Fig. 3. Electrical patterns during a right tonic seizure (case 2). (A) Interseizure record: paroxysmal activity. (B) Beginning of the electrical discharge. In *B*, beginning of the tonic spasm. In *A*, persistence of the paroxysmal activity at the beginning of the electrical discharge. (C) Rolandic delta waves. (D) Positive rolandic spikes and their right occipital diffusion. (E, F) Progressive slowing and end of the discharge.

fication of a succession of atypical events can help to make the diagnosis. For example, in one case, the successive appearance of dyspnea, opening of the eyes, chewing and salivation permitted the identification of seizures in a case where a respiratory complication seemed to be one of the prominent features because of the seriousness of the dyspnea. (Table 1 demonstrates the symptoms observed during the various EEG recordings). The EEG in

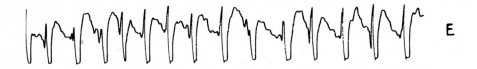

E

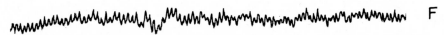

F

Fig. 4. Electrical patterns recorded simultaneously on the right (E) and left (F) hemispheres during a clonic seizure (case 1). (E) High voltage diphasic spikes. The first component is positive. (F) 10 cycles/second activity (alpha-like rhythm).

such cases and in subclinical *status epilepticus* is very helpful. Repeated convulsions can develop into *status epilepticus*. The exact limit between individual convulsions and *status epilepticus* is often difficult to appreciate. In adults, loss of consciousness between seizures is required for the diagnosis of *status epilepticus*. This phenomenon sometimes exists in comatose babies. However, in our series, there was repetition of seizures without loss of consciouness in many cases. It appears that *status epilepticus* in the infant is characterized essentially by the repetition of clinical or even subclinical seizures which occur for at least a few hours. This definition would help the pediatrician to institute adequate therapy without waiting for loss of consciousness and irreversible vegetative phenomena.

(b) Electroencephalographic Patterns

Electroencephalographic patterns associated with *status epilepticus* in our laboratory are in agreement with previous descriptions (Hughes *et al.*, 1948; Sainte-Anne-Dargassies *et al.*, 1953; Ribstein and Walter, 1958; Harris and Tizard, 1960; Dreyfus-Brisac *et al.*, 1961). The critical electrographic wave forms are very variable and, at times, complex (Table 3). Monomorphic rhythmic delta waves with a frequency of 1–4 cycles per second and positive or negative slow spikes appear, with variable amplitude and a frequency generally between 2 and 6 cycles per second. The spikes associated with slow waves may appear as slow "spike and wave" complexes. The importance of the slow components and of the positive activity must be emphasized (Fig. 1, 4 and 9).

A peculiar pattern consisting of an alpha-like rhythm (Fig. 2 and 4), with a frequency between 6 and 10 cycles per second and an amplitude of 25–30 microvolts, can last for 10 to 30 seconds and can appear in rolandic and occipital leads. This activity has not been found in the frontal or temporal leads to this time.

The electrographic pattern sequence is variable. Discharges may be composed of the repetition of the same basic wave form (Fig. 8), with or without variation of its frequency (acceleration, increase in frequency at the beginning, slowing at the end) or amplitude (progressive increase and de-

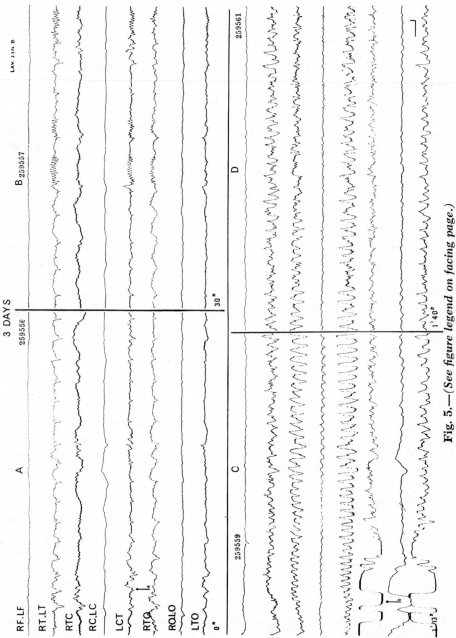

Fig. 5.—(See figure legend on facing page.)

crease) (Fig. 6). One discharge may also consist of a succession of different patterns (Fig. 3 and 5). The alpha-like activity is found more often at the end than at the beginning of a seizure discharge, although it is sometimes found in the first few seconds (Fig. 5). Its frequency also may vary, being lower at the end than at the beginning (Fig. 2). The sequence of wave forms may be variable from one seizure to another in the same infant, as are the clinical patterns as well.

The end of the seizure discharge is sudden (Fig. 6) or gradual (Fig. 3), occurring sometimes as isolated patterns, each lasting 2–3 seconds in duration.

Location of the seizure discharge in the newborn is one of its most important characteristics. They are nearly always limited to one region of the hemisphere (Fig. 3, 6 and 8). Occipital and central leads are more often involved than are frontal and temporal regions (Fig. 3, 5 and 6). In the 40 cases of our series, the following distribution of the initial focus has been shown to exist (Table 2); occipital 23; rolandic, 12; temporal, 6; frontal, 5. In 17 cases, the discharging focus was constant, while in 14 cases, multiple foci were present, an occipital focus always being included (two foci in 11 cases, three foci in 3 cases—Fig. 6).

Propagation of the seizure discharge in an infant is very different from that of the adult. In the newborn, the discharge generally remains localized to its side of initial occurrence (Fig. 6). It may diffuse progressively and slowly to the entire hemisphere, or to the contralateral hemisphere, preferentially to the homolateral region of the opposite side, this diffusion being of low amplitude (Fig. 2, 3 and 8). Occasionally, quite different electrographic patterns may be recorded simultaneously over the right and left hemispheres (Fig. 4).

Bilaterally synchronous electrical discharges are also quite rare (Fig. 5), this having been found in only four cases.

The duration of these discharges can be exceedingly variable, even in the same record of the same infant (varying from a few seconds to 3–4 minutes). At times, continuous discharges appear and these have been noted even in a one-day-old newborn (Fig. 9). In one case, the discharge was uninterrupted for 35 minutes.

(c) Electroclinical Correlations

Electroclinical correlations are variable. It has already been stated that the same electrical discharges may be found in both clinical and subclinical seizures. Passouant states that clonic discharges correspond often to spikes, and tonic phenomena correspond more often to the delta wave discharges (Passouant et al., 1960; Passouant and Cadilhac, 1962). This

---

Fig. 5. Synchronous electrical patterns recorded in the temporal and rolandic area of the right and left hemispheres in a case of left subdural hematoma. (A) Beginning of the temporal and central spikes in A. (B) Alpha-like discharge. (C) Delta waves and beginning in B of the clinical seizure. (D) End of the seizure. The isosynchronism between the left and right central areas is illustrated by the low voltage of the discharge on the 4th channel (RC–LC).

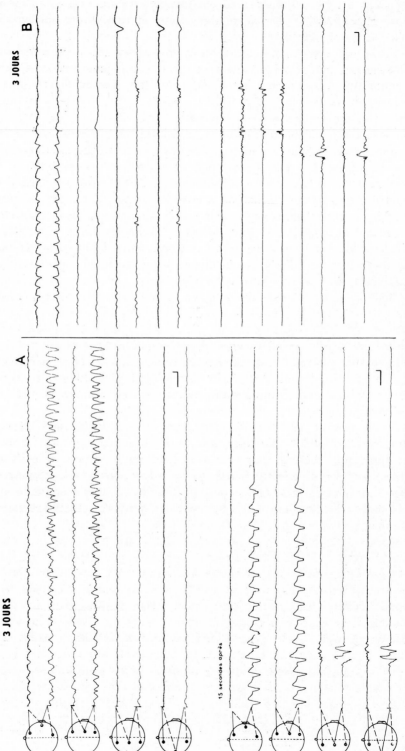

Fig. 6.—(*See figure legend on facing page.*)

latter finding has been confirmed in our own experience (Fig. 3–7; Tables 3 and 4); in addition, alpha-like rhythms have, at times, been observed in relation with apnea (Fig. 2).

The age at which the various wave forms appear does not seem to be very precise (Table 5). Rapid high voltage spikes, as represented in Fig. 4, have been found twice during the first ten days of life. The frequency of the spikes seems to be less during the first week than later. Alpha-like rhythms have been found from three days to four weeks.

An atypical kind of electrical pattern, consisting of disappearance of the interseizure activity simultaneous with the appearance in the electroencephalogram of myographic activity and movement artifact, has been found in six cases, and may occur with unusual behavior of the infant, consisting of swimming or rowing movements, or with a tonic spasm (Fig. 4). Seizures of this type are recorded in very serious cases which are, at times, associated with interseizure paroxysmal electrographic findings. Harris and Tizard (1960) interpret this flattening as a possible result of an acute cerebral anoxia, the paroxysmal discharges being the consequence of a previous episode of anoxia. This possible absence of electrographic discharge occasionally makes the diagnosis very tentative in cases of atypical clinical seizures.

(d) Interseizure Records

Interseizure records, which at times appear normal in cases of isolated convulsions, are rarely normal in *status epilepticus*. The absence of significant abnormalities and the presence of good reactivity and good differentiation between the wakeful and sleeping states indicate a better prognosis than do very abnormal records. It has already been emphasized by our group (Dreyfus-Brisac *et al.*, 1961; Monod and Dreyfus-Brisac, 1962) and by Tizard (Harris and Tizard, 1960) that a very serious prognosis accompanies the interseizure paroxysmal records. This type of activity has been present in 23 out of 88 cases of *status epilepticus* in full-term infants. This bad prognosis is also true for electrograms with very poor activity, lasting more than one week (8 cases). Electrograms with slow continuous diffuse activity (16 cases) were not always followed by such a dramatic evolution (Table 6).

Other abnormal patterns may be quite variable and have been described in previous works (Hughes *et al.*, 1948; Schroeder and Heckel, 1951; Mai and Schaper, 1953; Minkovski *et al.*, 1955; Samson-Dollfus, 1955; Fois, 1956; Minkovski and Sainte-Anne-Dargassies, 1956; Courjon and Cotte, 1958; Ribstein and Walter, 1958; Harris and Tizard, 1960; Passouant *et al.*, 1960; Dreyfus-Brisac *et al.*, 1961; Engel, 1961; Ducas *et al.*, 1962; Monod and Dreyfus-Brisac, 1962). Slow spikes which are localized or diffuse, or bilateral alterations at this period, do not seem to be associated with a very bad prognosis. A low voltage electrogram during sleep has been found in a few cases,

---

Fig. 6. Status epilepticus—3 days. Pluri-focal discharges. (A) Right occipital discharge. (B) End of a right temporal discharge. Between the discharges, paroxysmal record, asynergic bursts on the two hemispheres. These bursts appear on the left hemisphere during a right electrical discharge.

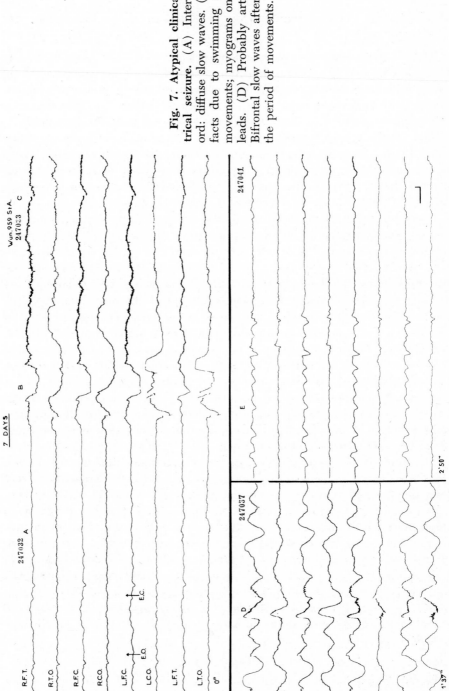

Fig. 7. Atypical clinical and electrical seizure. (A) Interseizure record: diffuse slow waves. (B, C) Artefacts due to swimming and rowing movements; myograms on the frontal leads. (D) Probably artefacts. (E) Bifrontal slow waves after the end of the period of movements.

and this has been in contrast to a high voltage electrogram during the wakeful state. It must be stated that reactivity between and during electrographic seizures has not been studied systematically by our group. We dare not study it for fear of provoking reappearance or accentuation of the seizures.

II. ELECTROCLINICAL PATTERN OF STATUS EPILEPTICUS AND CONVULSIONS IN PREMATURE INFANTS

The occurrence of convulsions among premature infants seems to be less frequent than that of full-term newborn infants. Thus, in our studies we have recognized only three cases of *status epilepticus* among premature infants. One reason for their apparently low incidence is, perhaps, the fact that they are still more difficult to recognize, clinically as well as electrographically.

The electroencephalographic pattern of a fetus of 4½ months gestation (Fig. 10) has been described, and the inconstant relationship between clonic movements and electrographic discharges has been noted (Dreyfus-Brisac and Monod, 1960). This finding has been confirmed in many cases where the observed clinical features of the convulsions were clonic movements.

It was originally thought by our group that localized electrographic discharges could not be recorded in premature infants whose seizures were essentially clonic in nature (Dreyfus-Brisac *et al.*, 1958). More recently, however, we have had opportunity to study a 28-week-old premature infant who had tonic seizures. These seizures would begin with a cry, followed by a prolonged period of apnea with tonic extension of the arms and legs. The entire clinical seizure lasted approximately 40 seconds. During the stage of apnea, there was noted a bitemporal theta rhythm which consisted of slow spikes with a frequency of ½ cycle per second appearing after a short period of theta activity which persisted after the termination of the clinical seizure.

Thus, it seems possible to record electrographic self-sustained discharges as early as 28 weeks of conceptual age. However, the electrographic discharge recorded in this case differed from the discharges described in full-term newborn infants. The fact that rapid bilateralization of seizure activity can occur at such an early age should be noted.

The interseizure electrographic patterns of premature infants with convulsions are difficult to interpret. Abnormal paroxysmal electrograms with very long silent periods have been noted, especially at around 33 weeks of conceptual age. These paroxysmal records do not indicate as bad a prognosis in this early period of development as they would in full-term newborn infants. A disturbance of normal electrographic development has been noted in association with *status epilepticus* of a premature infant, as described elsewhere (Dreyfus-Brisac *et al.*, 1962). Only two cases of fetal epilepsy have been noted in the literature (Badr-Eldin, 1960; Ozan and Gonzalez, 1963).

It is possible that many convulsions of the premature infant cannot be recognized because it is impossible to distinguish them from physiologic movements.

Discussion

Electroclinical studies of status epilepticus and convulsions in the newborn period have demonstrated the peculiar nature of these phenomena, un-

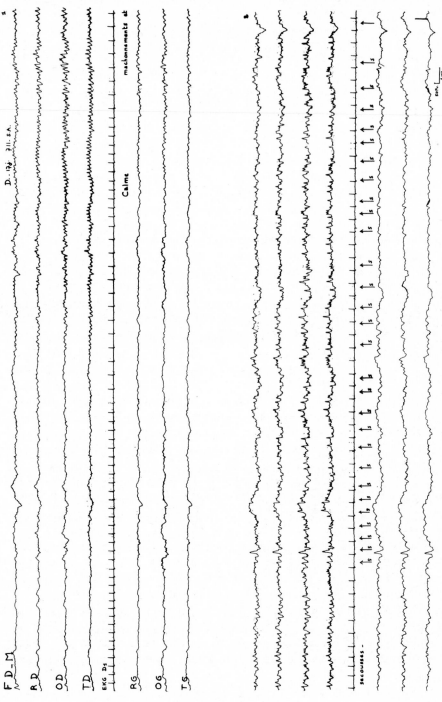

Fig. 8.—(See figure legend on facing page.)

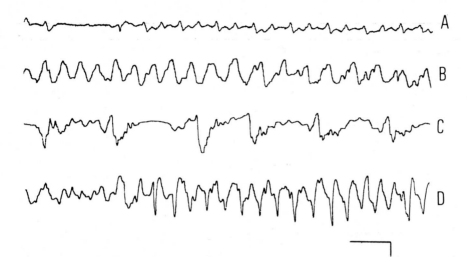

Fig. 9. Different electrical patterns recorded in a one day old newborn.

doubtedly related to the immaturity of the central nervous system. The main characteristics of seizures in this age group appear to be: a) polymorphism, b) atypical clinical manifestations, and c) unusual localization and slow spread of the electrographic discharges. Characteristics of this type can be discussed from an ontogenetic as well as from a phylogenetic point of view.

From a clinical point of view, Servit's observations of seizures in lower animals are indeed of interest (Servit, 1959, 1962). This investigator has found that epileptic seizures in the lower phylogenetic scale are manifested by paroxysmal primitive locomotor elements, mixed with tonic and clonic components, or by abnormal and inadequate behavior. He has noted that such seizures resemble patterns of rowing or swimming which are present in newborns.

The importance of the tonic phase, which decreases as the brain develops phylogenetically, is reminiscent of the importance of tonic seizures in the newborn period, especially as observed in the early premature infant as has been recently recorded.

Nevertheless, clonic discharges have been noted to be often present in the premature infant, thus demonstrating that ontogenetic and phylogenetic development have only a partial parallelism, probably due to the complexity of the developing structures in the immature human brain.

Servit (1959) and Bureš (1953) also note that the threshold of seizure susceptibility decreases with higher phylogenetic development. These findings are consistent with the observation that there is a greater frequency of seizures in full-term infants as compared with premature newborn infants. Interesting-

Fig. 8. Status epilepticus—17 days. Clonic seizure (arrows indicate cloni). Prolonged discharge of right spikes; progressive slowing and amplification; slow propagation on the left hemisphere.

Table 1

Clinical Symptoms during EEG Recording		Number	
Clonic	localized	13)	
	diffuse	10)	23
Hypertonia	limbs	17)	
	axial	12)	29
Rotation of head and eyes		8	
Rowing, swimming, pedaling		7	
Blinking		6	
Ocular symptoms: nystagmus		6)	
	other symptoms	5)	11
Respiratory symptoms		6	
Chewing		10	
Salivation		4	
Vasomotor symptoms		5	

Table 2

Initial Localization of the Electrical Seizure	Number of Cases
Occipital	24
Rolandic	12
Temporal	6
Frontal	5

Some children have been counted twice, if they had one localization in one record and another in the second one.

Table 3.—*Association of Electrical Patterns During the Seizure*

EEG patterns during the seizures	Predominance of tonic symptoms 14 cases	Predominance of clonic symptoms 19 cases	Subclinical seizures 7 cases	Total
theta or delta	4	2	1	7
spikes		4	1	5
alpha-like			1	1
theta or delta + spikes	1	4	3	8
delta + alpha	1		1	2
spikes + alpha	1	1		2
delta + spikes + alpha	1	4		5
flattening or no modification	4	2		6

ly, sensitivity to therapy also seems to increase with ontogenetic as well as phylogenetic development if it is kept in mind that it requires relatively larger dosages than in adults in order to treat *status epilepticus* in premature infants and even in newborn infants.

Electrographic patterns of convulsions in the neonatal period are characterized by a great variety of wave forms and frequencies, the absence of general diffusion, slowness of diffusion and a great number of subclinical seizures. The dominant electrographic activity is low, with rapid spikes ap-

Table 4.—*Presence of Electrical Patterns in the Different Clinical Seizures*

EEG patterns	Predominance of tonic symptoms	Predominance of clonic symptoms	Subclinical seizures	Total
delta	6	6	5	17
spikes	3	13	4	20
alpha	3	5	2	10
flattening or no modification	4	2		6

Table 5.—*EEG Electrical Patterns Recorded during the Seizures*

Age	Number of cases	Delta or theta	Spikes	Alpha	Flattening
1 day	7	4	2	1	3
2–4 days	22	17	11	8	3
5–8 days	9	7	4	1	2
9–15 days	10	5	3	2	1
15 days–1 month	7	6	7	8	
1–2 months	8	3	3	2	

Table 6.—*Electrical Patterns between Seizures*

Interseizure EEG	Number	Death during first year	Encephalo-pathy	Subnormal or normal	Unknown or too recent
Paroxysmal	23	16	3	1	3
Inactive	8	7		1	
Diffuse slow waves	16	15	3	2	6

pearing only rarely. In this regard, phylogenesis provides little information which can be related to these characteristics of the neonate's electrographic seizures. Servit's observations of electroshock-induced seizures in the frog have been that these episodes consist electrographically of a succession of slow and sharp waves and spikes occurring bilaterally during a tonic seizure without any typical pattern.

Studies of ontogenesis in animals provide much data which will aid in the understanding of the development of seizures in the human. Thus, Garcia-Austt (1957) has noted the early appearance of electrographic seizures in the 14-day-old chick embryo, these episodes consisting of rhythmic discharges of several seconds duration. In mammals, experimental studies of the kitten (Grossman, 1955, 1957, 1961; Cadilhac *et al.*, 1960; Passouant *et al.*, 1960), young monkeys (Caveness, 1962) and sheep (Bernhard, 1962) have shown that self-sustained epileptic discharges induced by direct electrical stimulation appear later and are more difficult to evoke in immature cortex than in more mature structures. Passouant (Passouant *et al.*, 1960) has shown that in the kitten electrically or drug-induced discharges are different in the hippocampal gyrus than in the cortex, where they begin and remain focal during the first two days.

In the same manner, Grossman (1955, 1957, 1961) has demonstrated the existence of four degrees of self-sustained afterdischarges in the cortex of the kitten; he has shown that afterdischarges appear later than evoked cortical responses and consist, in their earlier stages, of spike and wave complexes

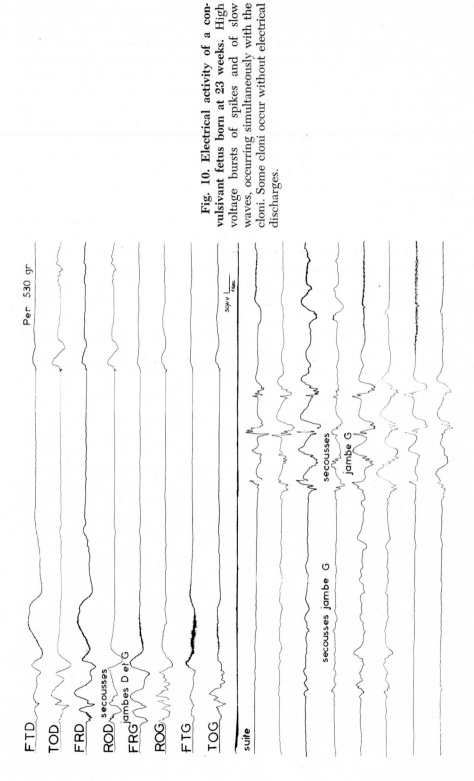

Fig. 10. Electrical activity of a convulsivant fetus born at 23 weeks. High voltage bursts of spikes and of slow waves, occurring simultaneously with the cloni. Some cloni occur without electrical discharges.

without any fast spike components. These fast spikes would probably be due to a more recent ontogenetic system than the slow waves, and the absence of long sustained discharge is probably related to the lack of cortical inter-neuronal connections. The close resemblance of electrographic discharges in the young infant with epileptic "afterdischarges" in cases of gross lesions of the cortex could possibly be explained by persistence of the most resistant, ontogenetically older neurons in damaged cortex (Grossman, 1957). The role of fatigability of the neuronal systems of immature cortex may be demonstrated by the rather low frequencies of the discharges. In this regard, the role of the anatomical structure of the immature cortex is pointed out by Purpura (1961). In addition, Bishop (1950) has shown that strychnine spikes of newborn rabbits are of a lower frequency and amplitude when compared with those of adult rabbits.

Tonic convulsions can be elicited in one-day-old rats by direct stimulation of the spinal cord, but direct electrical stimulation of the brain produces no reaction until the animals are 21 days of age (Vernadakis, 1962). It is concluded from this study that the inability of intact rats to exhibit flexor-extensor convulsions with brain stimulation before 21 days of age is due to lack of maturation of the brain rather than of the spinal cord. It may be noted that audiogenic seizures in rats appear between 15 and 20 days (Bureš, 1953; Servit, 1959), slightly before the possibilty of evoking electrically-induced seizures.

It appears that slow propagation of electrical discharge is a characteristic noted in all young mammals. Thus, in young kittens cortical propagation is very similar to that observed in the newborn human infant (Passouant et al., 1960). Cortical seizures are temporarily restricted to one hemisphere but then spread to the contralateral side without precise organization. However, in newborn monkeys (Caveness et al., 1962) the spread of the discharge is more rapid than in kittens, and there is already synchronization between the two hemispheres. This interhemispheric synchronization is generally absent in human and kitten newborns. In contrast to the slow propagation of cortical discharges to the contralateral hemisphere, immediate propagation of hippocampal seizures to the contralateral hippocampal gyrus appears in the kitten on the first day of life (Passouant et al., 1960).

Slow spread to the opposite hemisphere in the human infant is possibly related to incomplete myelinization of the corpus callosum at birth. Callosal myelinization is much more advanced in newborn monkeys (Larroche, 1962; Yakovlev, 1962), and this may be responsible for the rapid contralateral diffusion in this species. Bremer has called attention to the role of the interhemispheric callosal connections in the spread of electrical discharges, in all probability in association with the bilateral ascending projections of subcortical structures of the brain stem, both structures influencing the spread and interhemispheric synchronization of these discharges (Bremer et al., 1956). Experimental work on the opossum has demonstrated that multiple commissural sections are necessary to prevent the contralateral spread of electrical discharges (Morin and Goldring, 1950). The complexity of the mechanisms of electrographic propagation is apparent from the literature (Green and Naquet, 1957).

Millichap's experiments (1957) on the development of seizure patterns in newborn rats and guinea pigs have demonstrated a correlation between the developmental pattern of the seizures, the threshold of induced seizures, and the level of carbonic anhydrase in the brain, the carbonic anhydrase appearing to act mainly on the generalization of the seizures. Unfortunately, chemical studies of this type have not been performed in humans.

The existence of a primitive cortical or subcortical neural substratum for electrical discharge in full-term newborn infants is questionable. The importance of the positive electrographic components and the experimental work of Passouant would provide evidence in favor of the existence of subcortical firing. The seizure discharges recorded in one human premature of 28 weeks gestation seemed to be of subcortical origin, its rapid bilateralization being suggestive of the rapid propagation of hippocampal discharges in kittens.

The frequency of prolonged subclinical electrographic seizure discharges in *status epilepticus* of the newborn has been noted. It is interesting to observe that in newborn monkeys (Caveness *et al.*, 1962) subclinical electrographic seizure discharges may last as long as 45 minutes, in contrast to subclinical discharges in adult monkeys lasting 3 minutes. Bernhard *et al.* (1962) have noted the absence of motor manifestations during electrographic seizure discharges in fetal sheep. The long duration and the frequency of such subclinical discharges in human newborns is an argument in favor of routinely recording the electroencephalograms of all abnormal infants. This would aid in the early recognition of *status epilepticus,* even when atypical. The importance of the early recognition and treatment of *status epilepticus* has already been emphasized (Minkowski *et al.*, 1955).

Follow-up studies demonstrate the grave prognosis of *status epilepticus.* In our series, 34 cases are presently too young or are not followed. Of 57 cases which have been followed, 30 have died during the first year of life; 15 presently have severe neurologic and behavioral sequelae; 5 are nearly normal; and only 7 are completely normal. It must be noted that in this series there is one 7-month premature infant who is now normal and another similar infant who is presently subnormal.

The etiology of *status epilepticus* is variable, definite lesions of the brain having been found in only 10% of our cases (these being hemorrhage, meningitis, severe anoxia). This is in contrast with the observations of other investigators (Ribstein and Walter, 1958). In 75% of our cases there was a definite history of abnormal pregnancy, sometimes associated with severe anoxia or cerebral hemorrhage. It appears that postnatal complications may be responsible for isolated convulsions (Wood, 1959; Minkowski, 1962). In our studies, tetany and hypoglycemia have not been found to be causes of convulsions in the newborn.

Conclusions

Clinical and electrographic studies of *status epilepticus* and convulsions in newborn infants have revealed their polymorphic and atypical character in comparison with those of adults.

Phylogenetic and ontogenetic studies reveal clinical and electrographic patterns at low stages of phylogenesis and in early phases of mammalian development that are comparable to those noted in the human newborn. The helpfulness of simultaneous electrographic and motion picture recording in the recognition of atypical or subclinical seizures is emphasized.

ACKNOWLEDGMENT

We are indebted to Mrs. E. Plassart, Miss N. Pajot and F. Morel-Kahn for their assistance in recording and analyzing the data.

REFERENCES

AICARDI, J. Etudes sur 200 observations de convulsions dans la première année de la vie. Thèse, Paris, 1955.

BADR-ELDIN, M. K. Convulsive familial disease beginning during intra-uterine life. Pediat., 1960, 56:655–657.

BERNHARD, C. G., KAISER, I. H. and KOLMODIN, G. M. On the epileptogenic properties of the fetal brain. An electrophysiological study on the electrically and chemically induced convulsive brain activity in sheep fetuses. Acta Pediat., 1962, 51:81–87.

BISHOP, E. J. The strychnine spike as a physiological indicator of cortical maturity in the postnatal rabbit. Electroenceph. clin. Neurophysiol., 1950, 2:309–315.

BREMER, E., BRIHAYE, J. and ANDRE-BALISAUX, G. Physiologie et pathogénie du corps calleux. Arch. Suiss. Neuropsych., 1956, 78:31–87.

BURES, J. Susceptibility to convulsions in reflex epilepsy in the ontogenesis of rats and mice. Cs. Fysiologie, 1955, 2:263–273.

CADILHAC, J., PASSOUANT-FONTAINE, TH., MIHAILOVIC, L. and PASSOUANT, P. L'épilepsie expérimentale du chaton en fonction de l'âge. Etude corticale et sous-corticale. Path. Biol. (Paris), 1960, 8:1571–1581.

CAVENESS, W. F., NIELSEN, K. C., YAKOVLEV, P. I. and ADAMS, R. D. Electroencephalographic and clinical studies of epilepsy during the maturation of the monkey. Epilepsia, 1962, 3:137–150.

COURJON, J. and COTTE (Mme.). L'épilepsie avant 3 ans. Rev. Neurol., 1958, 99:68–76.

CRAIG, W. S. Convulsive movements oc-

curring in the first ten days of life. Arch. Dis. Child., 1960, 35:336–344.

DREYFUS-BRISAC, C., SAMSON, D., BLANC, C., and MONOD, N. L'EEG chez l'enfant normal de moins de 3 ans. Aspect fonctionnel bio-électrique de la maturation nerveuse. Et. Neonat., 1958, 7:143–175.

DREYFUS-BRISAC, C. and MONOD, N. Bases biologiques de la maturation. Aspect évolutif de l'électrogénèse cérébrale chez l'enfant. Ier Congr. Européen Pedopsychiatrie, S.P.E.I. ed., Paris, 1960, 39–51.

DREYFUS-BRISAC, C., MONOD, N., SALAMA, P., DUCAS, P. and MAYER, M. L'EEG dans les six premiers mois de la vie, après réanimation prolongée et état de mal néonatal. Vth Int. Congr. Electroenceph. clin. Neurophysiol., Rome. Excerpta Med. Int. Congr. Series, 1961, 37:228–229.

DREYFUS-BRISAC, C., FLESCHER, J. and PLASSART, E. L'électro-encéphalogramme. Critère d'âge conceptionnel du nouveau-né à terme et prématuré. Bio. Neonat., 1962, 4:154–173.

DUCAS, P., MONOD, N., DREYFUS-BRISAC, C., PAJOT, N. and MAYER, M. Etude électro-encéphalographique de 185 enfants réanimés à la naissance. Arch. Franc. Pediat., 1962, 19:1057–1085.

ENGEL, R. Evaluation of electro-encephalographic tracings of newborns. J. Lancet (Minneapolis), 1961, 81:523–532.

FISCHGOLD, H. and BERTHAULT, F. EEG de l'épilepsie du nouveau-né et du nourrisson. Et. Neonat., 1953, 2:59–77.

FOIS, A. Le epilessie focali corticali dell'infanzia. Pediat. Internaz., 1956, 6:109–140.

GARCIA-AUSTT, J. R. Ontogenetic evolution

of the EEG in human and animals. IVe Congr. Int. Electroenceph. clin. Neurophysiol., Bruxelles. *Acta Med. Belg.*, *1957*, 173–177.

GIBBS, F. A. Changes in generalized and focal seizure activity with age. IVe Congr. Int. Electroenceph. clin. Neurophysiol., Bruxelles. *Acta Med. Belg.*, *1957*, 9–10.

GREEN, T. D. and NAQUET, R. Etude de la propagation locale et à distance des décharges épileptiques. IVe Congr. Int. Electroenceph. clin. Neurophysiol., Bruxelles. *Acta Med. Belg.*, *1957*, 225–249.

GROSSMAN, G. C. Electro-ontogenesis of cerebral activity. Forms of neonatal responses and their recurrence in epileptic discharges. *Arch. Neurol. Psych.*, *1955*, 74:186–202.

GROSSMAN, G. C. Topic ontogenetic evolution of the EEG in human and animals. IVe Congr. Int. Electroenceph. clin. Neurophysiol., Bruxelles. *Acta Med. Belg.*, *1957*, 157–162.

GROSSMAN, G. C. Electrophysiological mapping of brain maturation. Vth Int. Congr. Electroenceph. clin. Neurophysiol., Rome. *Excerpta Med. Int. Congr. Series*, *1961*, 37:32–33.

HARRIS, R. and TIZARD, J. P. M. EEG in neonatal convulsions. *J. Pediat.*, *1960*, 57:501–520.

HUGHES, J. G., EHEMANN, B., and BROWN, U. A. EEG of new-born. IV. Abnormal EEG of neonate. *Amer. J. Dis. Child.*, *1948*, 76:634–647.

KELLAWAY, P. Ontogenic evolution of the electrical activity of the brain in man and animals. IVe Congr. Int. Electroenceph. clin. Neurophysiol., Bruxelles. *Acta Med. Belg.*, *1957*, 140–152.

LARROCHE, J. C. Quelques aspects anatomique du développement cérébral. *Biol. Neonat·*, *1962*, 4:126–153.

LINDSLEY, D. B. Electrical potentials of the brain in children and adults. *J. Gen. Psych.*, *1938*, 21:285–306.

LINDSLEY, D. B. Heart and brain potentials of human fetuses in utero. *Amer. J. Psychol.*, *1942*, 55:412–416.

LILIENFELD, A. M. and PASAMANICK, B. Association of maternal and fetal factors with the development of epilepsy. 1. Abnormalities in the prenatal and perinatal periods. *J.A.M.A.*, *1955*, 155:719–724.

LOISEAU, P., VERGER, P. and FAURE, J. Remarques sur les convulsions du premature. *Rev. Neurol.*, *1958*, 99:143–149.

LOOMIS, A. L., NEWTON-HARVEY, E. and GARRET-HOBART. Electrical potentials of the human brain. *J. Exp. Psychol.*, *1936*, 19:249–279.

MAI, H. and SCHAPER, G. Electroencephalographische Untersuchungen an Frühgeborenen. *Ann. Pediat.*, *1953*, 180: 345–365.

MILLICHAP, J. G. Development of seizure patterns in newborn animals. Significance of brain carbonic anhydrase. *Proc. Soc. Exp. Biol. Med.*, *1957*, 96:125–129.

MINKOVSKI, A., SAINTE-ANNE-DARGASSIES, S., DREYFUS-BRISAC, C. and SAMSON, D. L'état du mal convulsif du nouveau-né. *Arch. Franc. Pediat.*, *1955*, 12:271–284.

MINKOVSKI, A. and SAINTE-ANNE-DARGASSIES, S. Les convulsions du nouveau-né. *L'Evolution Psych.*, *1956*, 1:279–289.

MINKOWSKI, A. Le ralentissement cardiaque de la polycythemie néo-natale (jumeaux) et post-natale (enfant unique). *Biol. Neonat.*, *1962*, 4:61–74.

MONOD, N. and DREYFUS-BRISAC, C. Le tracé paroxystique chez le nouveau-né. *Rev. Neurol.*, *1962*, 106:129–130.

MORIN, F. and GOLDRING, S. Roles of anterior commissure and thalamus in interhemispheric spread of after-discharge in the opossum. *J. comp. Neurol.*, *1950*, 93: 229–240.

OZAN, H. A. and GONZALEZ, A. A. Post-traumatic fetal epilepsy. *Neurol.*, *1963*, 13:541–542.

PASSOUANT, P., CADILHAC, J. and RIBSTEIN, M. L'électro-encéphalographie au cours de la maturation cérébrale. *Montpellier Med.*, *1960*, 57:138–154.

PASSOUANT, P. CADILHAC, J. and RIBSTEIN, M. L'électro-encéphalographie au cours de la maturation cérébrale (Aspect pathologique: la décharge épileptique). *17e Congr. de l'Assoc. Pédiat. de langue Franc.* Dehan ed., *1959*, 67–168.

PASSOUANT, P. and CADILHAC, J. EEG and clinical study of epilepsy during maturation in man. *Epilepsia*, *1962*, 3:14–43.

PURPURA, D. P. Developmental electroclinical physiology and the EEG. Vth Int. Congr. Electroenceph. clin. Neurophysiol. *Excerpta Med. Int. Congr. Series*, *1961*, 37:28–29.

RIBSTEIN, M. and WALTER, M. Convulsions du premier mois. *Rev. Neurol.*, *1958*, 99: 91–99.

ROSSIER, A. Convulsions du nouveau-né. *Enc. Méd. Chir. Pédiat.*, 1, 4002, R70 1–3.

SAINTE-ANNE-DARGASSIES, S., BERTHAULT, F., DREYFUS-BRISAC, C. and FISCHGOLD, H. La convulsion du tout jeune nourisson; aspects électroencéphalographiques du probleme. *Presse Med.*, *1953*, 46:965–966.

SAMSON-DOLLFUS, D. L'EEG du prématuré jusqu'à l'âge de 3 mois et du nouveau-né à terme. Thèse, Paris, *1955*. Foulon ed.

SCHROEDER, G. and HECKEL, H. Zur diagnose des Geburtstraumes bein Neugeborenen. *Klin. Wschn.*, *1951*, 31:808–813.

SCHROEDER, G. and HECKEL, H. Zur trage der Hirntaligkeit bein Neugeborenen. *Geburtsh. Frauenkeik.*, *1952*, 12:992–999.

SERVIT, Z. Phylogenetic development of susceptibility to, and symptomatology of epileptic seizures. *Epilepsia*, *1959*, 1:95–104.

SERVIT, Z. Phylogenesis and ontogenesis of epileptic seizures. A comparative study. *World Neurol.*, *1962*, 3:259–274.

SMITH, J. R. EEG during infancy and childhood. *J. Gen. Psych.*, *1938*, 53:431–482.

VERNADAKIS, A. Spinal cord convulsions in developing rats. *Science*, *1962*, 137:532.

WOOD, J. L. Plethora in the newborn infant associated with cyanosis and convulsions. A review of postnatal erythropoiesis. *J. Pediat.*, *1959*, 54:143–151.

YAKOVLEV, P. I. Maturation of cortical substrata of epileptic events. *World Neurol.*, *1962*, 3:299–315.

DISCUSSION

DR. LOMBROSO: In our studies of the prognostic value of the electroencephalogram in neonatal convulsions we found that newborn infants who develop seizures tend to fall into two groups: (1) a majority, whose convulsions cease after days or weeks and whose development proceeds normally, and (2) a minority who either die early or survive with severe neurological deficits. Examinations and tests are often unhelpful in predicting early to which group a given infant will belong.

We were able to demonstrate that the morphological features of early electroencephalograms correlated well with the clinical outcome. We studied 75 infants with convulsions in the neonatal period and followed them for an average of 2 to 3 weeks. Serial electroencephalograms were obtained and classified as: (1) normal, (2) unifocal (with normal background patterns), (3) multifocal, (4) hypsarhythmic, and (5) flat. Borderline tracings were classified as normal. Thirty-three of the initial electroencephalograms were normal. Hypocalcemia and hypoglycemia were present in 30 per cent of the cases in this group. Twenty-eight of these patients did quite well. The most frequent abnormality in the electroencephalogram were localized diphasic blunt spikes. In 12 out of 24 cases it was situated in the right rolandic area. In 9 there was definite hypocalcemia. In the great majority, these patients also did quite well. The multifocal group, although only 11 cases, appeared to show severe prognostic clues: all in this group either died early or had gross deficits on follow-up. Two developed classic hypsarhythmic electroencephalograms. A relatively large group of neonatal electroencephalograms could be classified as hypsarhythmic. It is important to realize that many hypsarhythmic features may appear only in sleep and are not necessarily correlated clinically with infantile spasms. Most of these early cases of hypsarhythmia in sleep progressed to fully developed picture of hypsarhythmia in waking. In some, however, it was a transient phenomenon, still constituting a grave prognostic sign. Similarly, poor prognosis is offered by a "flat" electroencephalogram of which we had four.

Thus, relating the clinical outcome to the *initial and early electroencephalogram*, it appears that in the 70 per cent of the patients who were doing well, the initial electroencephalogram was either normal or unifocal with normal background. In contrast, in the 30 per cent of the infants who died or survived with severe deficits, the initial electroencephalogram was either multifocal, hypsarhythmic or flat. We realize that longer follow-up will be necessary to recognize minor neurological defects and to rule out the possibility of recurrent convulsions later.

THE CHARACTER AND SIGNIFICANCE OF EPILEPTIC SEIZURES IN INFANCY*

JOHN STOBO PRICHARD

Department of Pediatrics, Hospital for Sick Children, Toronto, Canada

The symptom of cerebral seizures in the newborn period presents many problems of diagnosis and prognosis and management.

When one considers the maturational state of the brain this is not surprising. At this age a child's cerebral hemispheres are grossly immature and he probably does not use them at all under normal circumstances. Conel (1959) has pointed out that the nerve cells are different in shape, size and constitution to the mature pattern. The arrangement of nerve cells within the cortex is grossly oversimplified. Myelination above the tentorium is almost completely absent. It is not possible to determine from the behavior of a child at this age whether he has a cerebral hemisphere deficit or not. For instance, a congenital hemiparesis is not clinically apparent until about the age of two months and even an astute mother will not usually notice it until about three months. Hydranencephalic children who have little or no cerebral tissue above the thalamus have behaviour that is indistinguishable from normal at the age of one month. We had one such child assessed by our psychological department at the age of three months and he was reported to have an I.Q. of 75. On the other hand, under certain abnormal circumstances, the cortical nerve cells can undoubtedly produce symptoms. One has only to watch the focal twitching of a newborn with the beautiful discrete spike foci over the appropriate area of cortex to realize that this is the case.

In an attempt to resolve some of these difficulties a clinical survey of neonatal seizures was undertaken. It was hoped that it would be possible to lay down criteria for diagnosis and prognosis that would be of practical help.

During the six years between 1954 and 1959, 287 newborns were admitted to our hospital with the symptom of twitching during the first four weeks of life and all these children were included in a retrospective study.

However these children represent a selected group. We are a children's hospital and have no maternity ward. Other hospitals transfer their infants to us only if they feel they are sufficiently sick to require the rather specialized care that our neonatal unit can provide. In another respect they are not a homogenous group because they may be admitted to the public ward or as private patients. Thus several pediatricians are involved in their care resulting in differences of method and completeness of investigation. For in-

---

*The investigation was undertaken with funds provided by the Rani Ghar Grotto of Toronto.

stance, in this particular group only 70 electroencephalograms were carried out.

Eighty-four of the patients were seen by myself or one of my fellows, usually several times daily during their hospital stay. The data about the rest were collected from the hospital records.

The diagnosis of twitching due to cerebral seizure discharges in the neonatal period is not always easy. We recognize the following as being definite convulsive episodes:

1. *Generalized seizure.* This usually begins as a focal seizure and eventually spreads to involve the whole body. Occasionally it is apparently generalized from the outset.

2. *Focal seizure.* Characteristically this last a few seconds or minutes and then stops. It may recur in the same area of the body or elsewhere. The twitching is rhythmic.

In addition there are numerous transient episodes that may or may not be due to cerebral seizure discharges. These include sudden brief attacks of stiffness of the arms and legs with arching of the back into an opisthotonic position, apneic spells, cyanotic spells or spells in which the baby will suddenly stop sucking. If these occur several times and are associated with an apparent change in consciousness or motor phenomena, they may be judged to be due to seizure discharges. The electroencephalogram may be of help in diagnosis. Excessive tremulousness is a problem. It is normal for hypertonic infants to have some tremulous movements when startled. Some very hyper-irritable children have tremulousness with any movement or even at rest and there comes a point when it becomes difficult to distinguish extreme tremulousness from a seizure.

Of the 287 newborns who were admitted to the hospital presenting with this complaint, three could not be traced, six refused to co-operate in the follow-up study and were excluded and two hundred and seventy-eight were followed up for a minimum period of six months (Table 1). One hundred and eighty-three of the patients were seen at the hospital. The remainder were traced by means of a detailed form being sent to the family physician, cerebral palsy clinic or institution for the mentally retarded.

Within three months of life, sixty-three (22.7 per cent) of the infants were dead. Post-mortems were obtained on 53 (Table 2). It is of considerable interest that 26 or approximately one-half of the children who came to post-mortem had gross cerebral hemorrhage. This was characteristically complicated in that there was usually a combination of subarachnoid, subdural and intracerebral hemorrhage. In four there was a subdural hemorrhage alone and in another four massive subarachnoid hemorrhage alone.

The other large group consists of 16 children who died apparently because of cerebral edema. They all died within 10 days after birth. While there are many possible causes of cerebral edema, the probability is that it was caused in these children by cerebral anoxia at or about the time of birth.

These two large groups include 42 of the 53 post-mortems. Of the remainder it is of interest that only three had a gross congenital cerebral

Table 1

Died within Three Months	63
Abnormal on Follow-up	75
Normal on Follow-up	140
TOTAL	278

Table 2.—*P. M.*

Cerebral Hemorrhage	26
Cerebral Edema	16
Congenital Cerebral Abnormality	3
Meningitis	2
Cerebral Thrombophlebitis	1
"Extracerebral"	5
TOTAL	53

Table 3.—*Follow-up*

M.D.	17
M.D. and Convulsive Disorder	14
Convulsive Disorder	5
Organic Behavior Disorder	2
Cerebral Palsy	37
TOTAL	75

abnormality. Four children were thought to have died from "extracerebral" causes. The cause of twitching was probably transient cerebral anoxia, but of this one cannot be certain.

Of the children who survived the first three months of life 75 (27 per cent) had an obvious neurological disability and these are shown in Table 3.

Thirty-seven of the children had "cerebral palsy" of one kind or another of which quadriplegia was the most common. Twenty-five out of the 37 children had cerebral palsy of the spastic type. Only three had pure athetosis. One child is classified "unknown." He has been attending a cerebral palsy clinic but we have been unable to obtain a report about the disability.

Seventeen children were mentally retarded but have no other abnormal neurological signs. Fourteen children were retarded and also had a convulsive disorder and five had a convulsive disorder alone. Two children are classified as having an "organic behaviour disorder." They are listless, hyperactive, distractible children with a very short attention span and intelligence within the lower limits of the normal range.

Of the total group, 20 children had microcephaly and seven had hydrocephalus, which was, in all cases, of the communicating type.

One hundred and forty of the children were considered to be within the limits of normal on follow-up (Table 4), although 21 of these were under one year of age when last seen. But within this group there are some that require qualification.

Five had at least one episode of febrile convulsions. These have all been short and have left no sequelae but the incidence of febrile convulsions is

Table 4.—"*Normal*"

Normal		121
Febrile Convulsions		5
Strabismus		6
Abnormal E.E.G.		8
Temporal spike	1	
Spike and wave	2	
Excess slow	5	
		140

rather greater than one would expect of the normal population (Prichard and McGreal, 1958). Six have strabismus and this also is an abnormally large proportion.

Ninety-six of the 147 children had electroencephalograms done at follow-up and there were eight children who had abnormal tracings although they appeared to be clinically normal. One child had a unilateral temporal lobe spike focus. Two children had short bursts of ragged bilaterally synchronous spike and wave activity. Five children had very poorly organized records with some diffuse excess of slow activity that was considered outside the range of normal.

It can be seen that this symptom, certainly as it presents itself in this group of children admitted to our pediatric hospital, has a very serious prognosis. Approximately a quarter of the patients die within the first three months of life. Approximately one-quarter will be left with gross neurological deficits and only one-half will be normal. These results are not peculiar to ourselves for other similar series have been reported in the past (Capon, 1922; Fleming and Morton, 1930; Craig, 1950; Keith *et al.*, 1953; Burke, 1954).

It is obvious that the symptom of twitching in the newborn period can be caused by a very large number of different conditions. In our cases that came to post-mortem there are examples of cerebral hemorrhage, cerebral edema, congenital abnormalities, infections and extracerebral diseases of several kinds. From a clinical point of view the differential diagnosis is often extremely difficult and consequently one's ability to give an accurate prognosis is very limited. For these reasons we thought it was worthwhile to study the case histories again to see if we could find any correlation between the neonatal clinical picture and the subsequent prognosis. As already mentioned the children were being looked after by several different members of the pediatric staff of the hospital, so the amount and type of investigation varied considerably from case to case. We have included in the study investigations that were done sufficiently frequently to be of significance.

The following charts represent the most interesting and significant findings. (A statistical evaluation is being prepared for publication in more detailed form).

Birth Weight (Table 5). Thirty-eight (13.7 per cent) of the babies were premature by weight (5½ pounds) and of these 17, or almost one-half, died. However among the survivors there was no significant deviation from the expected normal or abnormal groups. Taking the group as a whole, the

Table 5.—*Birth Weight*

	Normal	Abnormal	Deaths	Total
Under 5½ lbs.	12	9	17	38
5½–5 lb. 15 oz.	10	8	6	24
6–6 lb. 15 oz.	33	20	13	66
7–7 lb. 15 oz.	41	22	11	74
8–8 lb. 15 oz.	36	12	12	60
9–9 lb. 15 oz.	8	4	4	16

Table 6.—*Condition at Birth*

	Normal	Abnormal	Deaths	Total
Good	75	26	20	121
Poor	65	49	43	157

Table 7.—*"Asphyxia"*

Time in Minutes	Normal	Abnormal	Deaths	Total
1–5	13	6	6	23
5–10	4	1	0	5
10–15	1	2	0	3
15–20	0	4	3	7
20 or more	6	13	13	32

bigger babies have a better prognosis both from the point of view of death within the first three months and also from the point of view of subsequent neurological abnormality. There were no babies over 10 pounds in weight.

Condition at Birth (Table 6). The condition of the child at birth was classified "good" if he breathed spontaneously, cried vigorously, was active and of good color and tone. If he did not fulfill all these criteria, his condition was described as "poor." It can be seen that if the rating of the baby was "poor," his chances of survival and developing normally were much less good than a baby who was classified as "good". On the other hand, a child whose condition was classified as "poor" and did not die had about an equal chance of growing up normally as abnormally, whereas a child classified as "good" would have a 75 per cent chance of developing normally, if he survived. If the causes of "poor" condition at birth are broken down it is seen that there are some features that are helpful in prognosis. For instance, 70 of the infants took longer than 60 seconds to take their first breath (Table 7). Only 25 per cent of the children who were longer than 10 minutes in taking their first spontaneous breath were considered normal at follow-up.

Bradycardia seemed to carry a particularly bad prognosis (Table 8). In addition the children who developed abnormally (Table 8) had a higher incidence of respiratory distress, cyanosis, paleness, listlessness or limpness.

Various features during the course of the illness also helped in determining the prognosis. Children who were to die within the first three months had a high incidence of cyanosis (Table 9). However if they did not die there was little difference between the normals and the abnormals. The children who had a gray colour were much more likely to develop abnormally. Hyper-

Table 8.—*Condition at Birth*

	Normal	Abnormal	Deaths	Total
Bradycardia	9	25	18	52
Respiratory Distress	14	13	13	40
Cyanosis	26	11	5	42
Pallor	12	11	5	28
Listlessness	31	40	30	102
Hypotonia	19	32	23	74

Table 9.—*Course of Illness*

	Normal	Abnormal	Deaths	Total
Blue	35	21	47	103
Pale	19	19	15	46
Gray	3	9	11	36

Table 10.—*Course of Illness*

	Normal	Abnormal	Deaths	Total
Hyperactivity	20	4	4	28
Hyperirritability	58	12	11	81
Listlessness	40	51	45	136
Poor Feeding	33	55	59	147
Poor Cry	39	51	36	126

Table 11.—*Course of Illness*

	Normal	Abnormal	Deaths	Total
Hypotonic	4	5	4	13
Flaccid	5	15	13	33
Hypertonic	37	21	14	72
Rigid	7	17	9	33
Combination	2	1	12	15

activity (Table 10) or hyperirritability does not seem to be predisposed to a poor prognosis. On the other hand limpness, listlessness, difficulty in feeding or a weak cry are associated with a higher tendency to develop abnormally. A good deal of information can be obtained from the degree of tonus in the child (Table 11). Once the child is over the acute phase of the illness moderate degrees of hyper- or hypotonicity seem to affect the prognosis very little. On the other hand, extreme hypertonicity or hypotonicity, particularly if they are alternating, both predisposed to a poor prognosis.

In our group we did not find the presence or absence of a tense fontanelle of much value (Table 12). While it is true that children with a tense fontanelle were a little more likely to die within the first three months than the rest of the group, if they survive there is no significant difference between the two groups. Likewise we were not impressed with the "anxious starring expression" described by Craig, as being important in the diagnosis of severe cerebral irritation with a poor prognosis.

We did find that ocular manifestations were helpful. The presence of ocular palsies, pupillary dilatation, nystagmus or incoordinate eye move-

Table 12.—*Course of Illness*

	Normal	Abnormal	Deaths	Total
Bulging Fontanelle	14	17	12	43
"Anxious"	9	5	6	20
Eye Movements	11	20	13	44
7th Nerve Palsy	4	9	7	20

Table 13.—*Course of Illness*

	Normal	Abnormal	Deaths	Total
Respiratory Distress	23	28	22	73
Apneic Spells	28	21	14	63
Combination	9	13	22	44
Excess Mucus	0	6	9	15
Bradycardia	7	9	15	31
Shock	0	0	4	4

ments all predisposed toward subsequent abnormality. It is interesting that a unilateral facial nerve palsy was much more common in the children who died or developed abnormally. Of the 13 newborns who presented with this disability in the combined normal/abnormal groups, only four developed as normal children.

Respiratory distress (Table 13) was common in all groups but as a prognostic sign it can only be said that the child who has apneic spells alone has a slightly higher chance of being normal than a child who has apneic spells and respiratory distress.

It is interesting that of the fifteen babies who presented with the symptom of excess mucus all died or developed abnormally. The presence of "shock" was of very bad prognositc significance. All died within a few days.

We did not find vomiting or diarrhea useful in determining the prognosis. Neither did we find the presence of hypothermia or hyperthermia significant.

Characteristically these seizures begin within the first day or two of life although they may sometimes be first seen later. Table 14 shows the time of first observed occurrence in the present series. Almost 75 per cent of the children began to have their convulsive episodes within the first 48 hours of life. While there seems to be no strong tendency in this table, it is perhaps fair to say that infants who begin to convulse in the first 24 hours of life are more likely to die or be abnormal than chlidren who begin to convulse after this time.

When the duration of the convulsive episodes are considered it can be seen that an infant who stops having this symptom quickly is much more likely to survive and develop normally than a child who continues to have it (Table 15). None of the children (12 in all) who were twitching for fourteen days or longer developed normally.

The duration of the total illness (Table 16)—that is, the time until the child is considered to be behaving normally—is also of considerable interest in prognosis. If a child is going to die he was likely to do so within the first 12 days. If he survived this time he has an excellent chance (over 90 per cent)

Table 14.—*Time of Onset*

	Normal	Abnormal	Deaths	Total
Less than 24 hours	48	46	32	126
1–2 days	49	15	13	77
2–3 days	15	7	10	32
3–7 days	15	4	5	24
7–14 days	9	2	3	14
14–28 days	4	1	0	5

Table 15.—*Duration of Seizures*

	Normal	Abnormal	Deaths	Total
Less than 24 hours	54	14	36	109
1–2 days	35	15	14	64
3–4 days	32	22	4	58
5–7 days	10	12	3	15
8–14 days	9	3	3	15
15–28 days	0	2	1	3
28 and more	0	2	1	3

Table 16.—*Duration of Illness*

	Normal	Abnormal	Deaths	Total
Less than 24 hours	14	0	8	22
1–2 days	13	1	14	28
2–4 days	34	5	14	54
5–7 days	36	13	10	59
8–14 days	34	23	7	64
15–21 days	9	14	1	24
22–28 days	0	6	1	7
28 and more	0	13	8	21

of being normal if the total illness lasted five days or less. He has a reasonable good chance of normal development if he becomes well within 14 days.

The only biochemical investigations to be done consistently, and which might seem to be of value, were the serum calcium and phosphorus and the examination of the cerebrospinal fluid for blood (Table 17). While the calcium and phosphorus levels had a wide range there seemed to be no important trend. However a child with a normal calcium level, irrespective of the phosphorus level, has a rather more favorable chance of normal development than if his calcium is abnormal. One hundred and sixty-one of the newborns had lumbar punctures (Table 18). There seems to be no doubt that xanthrochromic fluid is of poor prognostic significance.

Electroencephalograms were performed on only 70 of this group in the neonatal period. Thirty-eight of the 40 children who had normal electroencephalograms proved to be normal at follow-up, whereas 24 of the 30 children with abnormal electroencephalograms developed abnormally. The numbers were small and we had doubt about the significance of these figures. We did not believe that the electroencephalogram was likely to be as effective as this in prognosis. Consequently a further study of the electroenceph-

Table 17.—*Biochemistry*

Normal CA. 8.0–11.5   P. 4.5–7.5

	Normal	Abnormal	Deaths	Total
Normal CA and P	60	35	18	113
Decreased CA and P	0	0	2	2
Decreased CA Normal P	25	17	7	49
Decreased CA Abnormal P	10	6	5	21
Normal CA Abnormal P	23	8	7	38
TOTAL	118	66	39	223

Table 18.—*Cerebrospinal Fluid*

	Normal	Abnormal	Deaths	Total
Clear	34	19	12	65
Xanthochromic	21	23	10	54
Bloody	19	12	11	42

alograms of a larger group of children presenting in a similar way was undertaken.

All the children over a 10-year period who presented with the symptom of seizures during the first month of life and who also had an electroencephalogram were included. There were 135 such patients. The electroencephalograms were reviewed without knowledge of the diagnosis or prognosis. The children were followed up clinically either by being seen in the hospital or by a detailed form from their physician.

The standards of normality in the neonatal period are, I think, those generally accepted. The waking electroencephalogram is flat and featureless with little or no rhythmic activity. There is a very little irregular slow activity. As the child becomes drowsy, more slow waves are seen. In light sleep much more slow activity is seen. It tends to occur in bursts, giving the record a periodic quality. There may be brief runs of fast activity occurring independently in either hemisphere and probably representing the beginning of sleep spindles. Random sharp wave forms are also seen. At the age of three or four weeks fairly well formed spindles are seen in sleep and the periodicity has almost disappeared.

The records were classified as normal, abnormal or borderline. Electroencephalographic interpretation at this age, when organized rhythms are the exception rather than the rule, is often so subjective that we thought it would be more informative if we called abnormal only those records which were abnormal beyond any shadow of doubt. The rather large number in which there was any element of doubt we put in the borderline category.

In the series (Table 19) there were 33 abnormal records, 45 borderline records and 57 normal records.

Table 19.—*Clinical State at Follow-up in Relation to E.E.G.'s*

Normal E.E.G.'s Initially in 57/135

At follow-up:		
	Normal Intellect and No Handicaps	40
	Borderline Attainments	3
	Died	4
	Intellectual and/or Neurological Deficits	5
	No Follow-Up	5
	TOTAL	57

Abnormal E.E.G.'s Initially in 33/135

At follow-up:		
	Normal Intellect and No Handicaps	11
	Borderline Attainments	1
	Died	9
	Intellectual and/or Neurological Deficits	12
	TOTAL	33

Borderline E.E.G.'s Initially in 45/135

At follow-up:		
	Normal Intellect and No Handicaps	19
	Borderline Attainments	5
	Died	7
	Intellectual and /or Neurological Deficits	10
	No Follow-Up	4
	TOTAL	45

In the abnormal group, 26 patients showed abnormalities that were apparent in both hemispheres and seven had a lateralized abnormality.

Of the generalized abnormalities, 24 had bursts of spikes or sharp waves, one child had no apparent cerebral electrical activity either when awake or asleep, and one showed gross periodicity. When these children were followed clinically it was found that seven were normal in every way, seven died in the first four weeks of life of cerebral pathology and 12 were neurologically abnormal. Of the children who only had a lateralized electroencephalogram abnormality, five were normal on follow-up, one died and one had borderline intellectual attainments. Thus if a newborn has an unequivocally abnormal electroencephalogram associated with the symptom of twitching he has a 65 per cent chance of either dying or developing abnormally.

Fifty-seven electroencephalograms were unequivocally normal. At clinical follow-up 40 of these 57 children seemed to be completely normal in every way. Four had died and five had obvious intellectual or neurological deficits. Three had borderline intellectual attainments. Five could not be followed up. Thus, if a baby who is twitching in the newborn period has a normal electroencephalogram, he would appear to have a 75 per cent chance of being normal on follow-up.

Forty-five children had neonatal electroencephalograms that were classified as "borderline." The main problem in interpretation is an assessment of slow activity. None of the records that presented in this way were put in the definitely abnormal group. Another problem was the assessment of periodicity. Some periodicity is normal in light sleep. There comes a point when the degree of periodicity is abnormal and in one instance that was so striking that the record was considered definitely abnormal. However in several instances it was difficult to determine whether the periodicity was within normal limits and these too were put in the borderline group. An assessment of sharp wave activity can also be difficult. If they appeared to be excessive the record was still put in the borderline group unless there was a persistent rhythmic focus. In five cases it was not possible to be certain whether abnormal wave forms were due to artifact or true cerebral activity and these were put in the borderline group. When this group of 45 children were followed up it was found that their clinical state lay intermediate between the definitely abnormal and the definitely normal group. Nineteen were apparently quite normal, five had borderline attainments, seven had died, and 10 had definite intellectual and/or neurological deficits. No follow-up could be obtained on four.

Because of these findings we went over the borderline electroencephalograms again to see if we could find some factor or factors which would put them in one or other group, beyond any reasonable doubt. In 14 children the periodicity was thought to be excessive. There seemed to be no definite increase in incidents of sequelae in these children although the numbers are, of course, small. A possible excess of sharp wave activity was seen in 14 patients. In these too there seemed to be no more increase in sequelae than in the borderline group as a whole. Brief runs of fast activity in the occipital, parietal and frontal regions were seen in 13 cases. These too were not associated with any increase in sequelae. A number of records were thought to have a generalized increase of slow activity. This group also showed no deviation from the borderline group as a whole with regard to subsequent neurological deficits.

So it appears that further analysis of our borderline records does not reveal any obvious remedial errors of interpretation, which is disappointing.

Thus, according to our figures, this symptom of twitching rather broadly interpreted among babies under the age of one month admitted to our newborn nursery is of very grave prognostic significance. Approximately 25 per cent of them will die within the first few months of life. Approximately 25 per cent will be left with severe neurological sequelae. About 50 per cent will grow up as normal children. It must be emphasized again, however, that this is a highly select group. These babies have been considered by their physician to be so ill that they were transferred from the infant wards of the maternity hospitals to our pediatric hospital.

When we review the clinical picture presented by these children in the acute stages of the disease, we find that there seems to be no single symptom or sign or laboratory test which, by itself, will give a good indication of the prognosis. But some clues can be obtained.

As might be expected, the children who have a long delay before they take their first breath are less likely to develop normally than the others. In particular it can be said that if a child takes longer than 10 minutes to take his first breath then there is a high probability that he will not do well. Similarly, lethargy and limpness within the first few minutes of life are important, and this is particularly true if it is associated with bradycardia.

During the course of the child's illness, when he is having episodes of twitching, there are other clues. If there is a very striking change in tone, either great hypertonicity or hypotonicity, and particularly if this symptom alternates, then the prognosis is poor. Listlessness and feeding difficulties, particularly if the child has difficulty in handling his mucus, are bad signs. Opthalmoplegia or pupillary abnormalities are also, as one might expect, sinister. On the other hand hyperirritability or hypoirritability, if not associated with a gross tonal abnormality, is often associated with a good prognosis.

It is interesting that the presence or absence of respiratory distress except in extreme degrees and the presence or absence of a bulging fontanelle do not, in our series, prejudice to any considerable extent the eventual prognosis.

The laboratory data is likely to be equally inconclusive. The finding of a normal calcium level irrespective of the phosphorus level is of good prognostic significance. On the other hand the presence of xanthrochromic fluid in the cerebral spinal fluid is sinister.

At the present time, using standard techniques, the electroencephalogram is disappointing. According to our figures if a child has an unequivocally abnormal electroencephalogram then he has a 65 per cent chance of being abnormal.

Probably the most important single factor is the rate of recovery of the child. If a child is going to die he will do so within the first 12 days of life, in most instances. If he makes a complete recovery by five days then the chances of normal development are very good. If he has still not recovered after 14 days, his chances of normal development are poor.

We have to say then that the symptom of seizures in the neonatal period is highly significant and usually, but not always, related to cerebral hemorrhage or cerebral anoxia. There is no single symptom or sign or laboratory investigation which will provide an answer to whether the child will do well or badly. I think it should be possible to draw up a score for a child with this symptom in the same way as an "Apgar" index can be given to an infant immediately after birth. But the only one I have been able to invent is too clumsy to be of practical value.

I think it is probable that we will have to develop some newer techniques for investigating the cerebral function of the newborn. The whole problem is certainly one of more than academic interest. For instance, our colleagues in the respiratory field are now able to keep children alive during the acute stages of the respiratory distress syndrome by means of artificial aids to respiration and very precise electrolyte control. After a while these children settle down from a respiratory point of view but by this time they may have had gross irreparable cerebral damage from anoxia. At the present time we are unable to tell them at what point this cerebral anoxia is becoming critical. For the well being of everybody, we should be able to do so.

ACKNOWLEDGMENT

I wish to thank my colleagues, Dr. Mathew Edward Graham and Dr. John Tibbles, for their great help with this communication.

REFERENCES

BURKE, J. B. Prognostic significance of neonatal convulsions. *Arch. Dis. Child.*, 1954, 29:342–345.

CAPON, N. B. Intracranial traumata in newborn. *J. Obst. Gyn. Brit. Emp.*, 1922, 29: 572–590.

CONEL, J. LEROY. *The postnatal development of the human cerebral cortex.* Harvard University Press, Cambridge, Mass., 1959.

CRAIG, W. S. Intracranial irritation in newborn: immediate and long term prognosis.

Arch. Dis. Child., 1950, 25:325–350.

FLEMING, G. B. and MORTON, E. D. Meningeal haemorrhage in newborn. *Arch. Dis. Child.*, 1930, 5:361–368.

KEITH, H. M., NORVAL, M. A. and HUNT, A. B. Neurologic lesions in relation to the sequelae of birth injury. *Neurol.*, 1953, 3:139–147.

PRICHARD, J. S. and McGREAL, D. A. Febrile Convulsions. *Med. Clinics N. Amer.*, 1958, 42:379–387.

DISCUSSION

DR. PETERSÉN: It appears that the central problem is that of evaluation of a child with convulsions in the newborn period. How are we going to determine or what methods are there for determining how abnormal this baby's brain is? In this regard I wonder if Dr. Ellingson would perhaps tell us not only what he has done but what possibly might be done?

DR. ELLINGSON: We have followed children from four to eight years, and we have been unable even retrospectively to identify those who were to develop abnormally by examination of their neonatal EEG's. Nor could we have identified them through their evoked responses. Further, even now we find no differences in evoked response latencies between the abnormal and the normal groups at ages four to eight years. This is not to say that EEG abnormalities are not seen in newborns who display clinical abnormalities at the time of recording.

DR. PRICHARD: What kind of abnormalities are there?

DR. ELLINGSON: It is quite a varied group: seizures of various types, multiple congenital abnormalities, one subject with spastic quadriplegia and severe mental retardation, one with phenylketonuria, several with borderline low I. Q.'s and so forth.

DR. ALVORD: Is it fair to say that this evoked potential method is a more useful estimate of age than of abnormality?

DR. ELLINGSON: I don't think it's useful as an estimate of age beyond three months. In infants less than three months of age it is useful, but even in this group there is a standard deviation of 20 milliseconds, which means that about 35 per cent of the cases fall beyond ± 20 milliseconds. So, although evoked response latency does correlate significantly with age, it is not so high that you could predict age with any confidence from it. It might be used together with other criteria.

DR. ENGEL: In my evoked potential study, among 600 cases I singled out two groups, one with abnormal EEG's and one with low Apgar rating (below five), and there was no significant difference between the two groups. On the other hand, in the follow-up studies including 300 infants up to eight months of age there was a correlation between mental score and shorter latency, but no correlation between motor performance and latency up to eight months of age.

DR. GLASER: I think it's very interesting that the comment that Dr. Ellingson and Dr. Engel made represents the conclusion that Dr. Levy and I have come to recently in going over our case material. We found that there was not a good correlation between the ability to elicit an evoked potential and Apgar score. To get a disturbance in the ability to evoke a potential a gross lesion in the pathways involved or some kind of metabolic depressant probably is needed.

DR. KELLAWAY: I would like to comment about the problem of normality and abnormality in the infant as far as the EEG is concerned. We identify what we call the "triphasic change" in the EEG in the infant. If you study serially a group of brain damaged infants from birth you often find that the first EEG taken in the neonatal period is abnormal, the second EEG in later infancy is normal, and a third taken in young childhood is abnormal again. This is to say that there appears to be a cryptic period dating sometime between early infancy and say one year in which existing brain abnormality is electrographically hidden—is not expressed in electrical terms.

Thus the time at which the initial EEG is made will determine its clinical usefulness. For example, an EEG recorded in the first four days of life may show focal seizure activity but a subsequent record at two months may be normal and then later at the age of three years a dramatically abnormal record showing, for instance, multiple foci of spike discharge may be demonstrated.

DR. GLASER: I have wondered, however, in an attempt to think of how the EEG can be more useful, that maybe there is another period in the first year of life that may be more productive than the neonatal period. Is there another time in the first twelve months? Could it not be that evaluating the child and his EEG at age eight months or nine months might be more significant?

DR. DREYFUS-BRISAC: What we can say is that if we have a very abnormal EEG during the first week the prognosis should be very bad. This is the case when we have paroxysmal activity in the first weeks of a full-term baby or a very low voltage or inactive record for more than the first ten days.

DR. PRICHARD: But it often isn't.

DR. DREYFUS-BRISAC: I hope that perhaps the study of a long period of sleep and of the cyclic organization of sleep patterns will allow us to find disturbances of the organization of vegetative, motor and EEG patterns of sleep. This would perhaps be more significant for the prognosis. But, in fact, I think that there are many levels of organization of the brain, so that one cannot ask of the EEG in infancy what will take place at five years. The level of cortical development is still too poor at birth. That is why it is so difficult.

ELECTROENCEPHALOGRAPHIC ASPECTS OF SUBDURAL FLUID ACCUMULATION IN INFANCY*

I. PETERSEN, H. ANDERSSON, INGRID HAGNE AND
BARBRO JOHANSSON

*Departments of Clinical Neurophysiology, Neurology and Neurosurgery,
Sahlgrenska Sjukhuset, and Departments of Medicine and Surgery,
the Children's Hospital, Göteborg, Sweden*

That subdural accumulation of fluid occurs even in children, and that it is amenable to treatment, was pointed out by Sherwood (1930) and Peet and Kahn (1932). A number of series have since been reported, notably by Dowman and Kahn (1942), Ingraham and Matson (1949), Elvidge and Jackson (1949), Lowrey (1952), Guthkelch (1953), Rougerie (1958), Crosby (1957) and Boissiere (1960). Ingraham and Matson (1954) outlined a plan of treatment which has since been followed by the majority of neurosurgeons. Some authors—Scheppe (1954), Herzberger, Rotem and Braham (1956) and Shulman and Ransohoff (1961)—consider, however, that a conservative approach may yield results equally as good as those of conventional surgical treatment.

Purely clinical aspects of subdural fluid accumulation in infants have received little attention. We have recently systematically investigated a series of 20 cases with special reference to roentgenology, morbid anatomy and pre- and post-operative electroencephalographic pattern.

Etiology

Subdural accumulation of fluid is seldom observed in adults unless preceded by trauma. In infants, birth trauma is implicated in only 25–50 per cent of the cases (Ingraham and Matson, 1949). According to Gröntoft (1954), subdural hematomas are responsible for 12 per cent of perinatal deaths. A similar figure was reported by Sulamaa and Vara (1952), who also called attention to the significantly higher incidence in cases of instrument delivery and of premature birth. McKay, Morissette, Ingraham and Matson (1950) pointed out that subdural accumulation of fluid may develop as a complication of meningitis. According to Dressler and Albrecht (1957) and Girard (1956), among others, it may also stem from a pathologic general reaction of the brain or from a reduced intracranial pressure secondary to infections or toxic conditions.

Eight of our 20 cases had records of possible brain damage attributable to

*This investigation has been supported by a grant from the Swedish Medical Research Council and the Medical Society of Gothenburg, Sweden.

Table 1.—*Total Series, Tabulated with Respect to Signs and Known Etiology. The Initial Symptom Is Circled*

Case number	1	2	3	4	5	6	7	8	9	10	11	12	13	14	15	16	17	18	19	20	Total
Seizures	⊕			⊕	⊕	⊕	⊕	⊕		⊕		⊕	⊕	⊕	⊕	⊕	⊕	⊕	⊕		13
Retarded development		+	+		+	⊕		+	⊕		+	+	+				+				10
Hyperpyrexia, vomiting and irritability							⊕		+		⊕			+							4
Enlargement of head and/or bulging fontanelle	⊕		⊕					+		+	+		+			+	+	+		⊕	9
Caput Quadratum			+		+	+	+	+	+	+	+	+		+	+	+					11
Abnormal fundi			+		+	+	+	+					+								6
Postmeningitic															+	+	+				3
Pathologic partus	+			+	+	+		+	+	+				+	+						8
Postoperative retarded development	+	+	+			+	+	+		+			+				+				7
Postoperative normal				+	+	+	+	+	+	+	+	+	+	+	+	+	+	+	+	+	13
Sex	M	M	M	M	M	M	M	M	F	M	F	M	F	F	M	M	M	M	F	F	14 M 6 F

Table 2

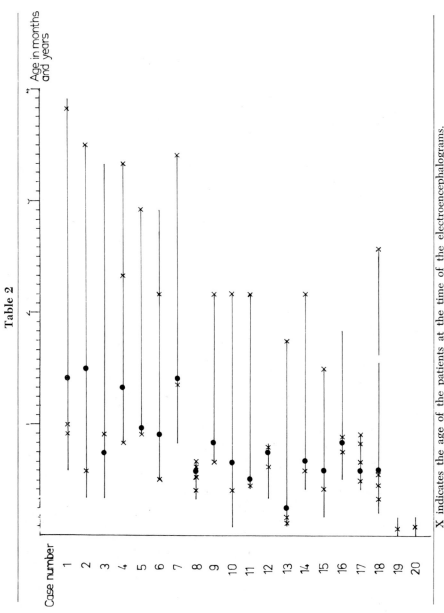

X indicates the age of the patients at the time of the electroencephalograms.
● indicates the age of the patients at the time of the surgery.

intra- or extrauterine asphyxia, prematurity, or twin birth with manual extraction. The subdural accumulation of fluid was diagnosed in the neonatal period in two of the cases (No. 19 and 20) and, in the entire series, the time of diagnosis ranged from four days to sixteen months. In three cases (No. 16, 17 and 18), there was a history of meningitis. Fourteen of the patients were male and 6 female. A similar sex disparity has been observed by other investigators.

Clinical Picture

Statistical study (Mabon, 1959) of clinical data presented by several authors showed the following incidence of the principal symptoms: vomiting, 58 per cent; hyperreflexia, 56 per cent; fever, 48 per cent; irritability, 33 per cent; enlargement of head and/or fontanel tension, 30 per cent; convulsions, 27 per cent; eyeground lesions, 21 per cent; retardation, 15 per cent.

In our series (see Tables 1 and 2), convulsions were the most common symptom, being noted in 13 cases. The seizures were predominantly generalized or focal motor in type. Next in order were retarded development (ten cases) and enlarged head (nine cases). Most of the infants had multiple symptoms and signs. The initial symptoms are indicated in Table 1. *Caput quadratum* (see Fig. 5, Case 5) was observed in 11 cases. This head shape, as has been pointed out (Andersson and Rådberg, 1962), is due to widening of the cranium across the frontal eminences, which presents a characteristically square appearance. It frequently afforded diagnostic guidance, particularly when the disease was ushered in by nonspecific symptoms, such as hyperthermia, irritability, or psychomotor retardation. All except one of the other 9 cases (No. 4) showed head enlargement or fontanel tension.

Diagnosis

The diagnosis was based on cranial roentgenography, carotid angiography, pneumoencephalography (PEG) and electroencephalography.

Cranial roentgenograms served, in several cases, to confirm a suspected increase in cranial breadth and in cases with head enlargement or fontanel tension, they revealed widely separated sutures.

In most cases, the clinical diagnosis was verified by subdural puncture prior to neuroradiologic examination. For carotid angiography—which was performed via percutaneous puncture without complications—lateral views and oblique projections were chiefly employed (see Fig. 2). Infantile accumulations of fluid, as pointed out by Andersson and Rådberg (1962), tend to be situated in the frontal region and toward the midline. For this reason, they are not identifiable on anteroposterior views to the same extent as in adults, in whom such hematomas are usually situated, in the main, over the lateral aspect of the hemisphere. Fig. 1 illustrates normal angiograms from an infant, taken in lateral and frontal projection. Fig. 2, 3 and 4 show subdural accumulation of fluid as visualized by carotid angiography (Cases 7, 3 and 6). Carotid angiography enabled us to make a positive diagnosis in 19

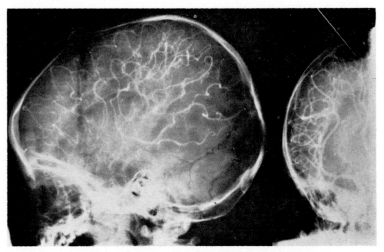

Fig. 1. Normal carotid angiography in a child aged 14 months. Lateral and frontal projection.

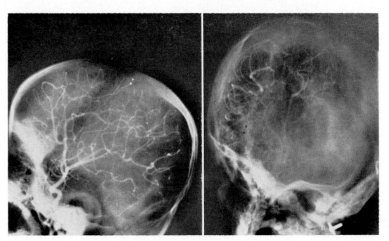

Fig. 2. Carotid angiography. Extracerebral accumulation of fluid (5–10 mm.) with a maximum in the frontotemporal region. (Case 7).

cases and, in the other case, was not completed because of complications of anesthesia (Case 13).

Pneumoencephalography was carried out in eight cases and was unsuccessful in one because of complications of anesthesia (Case 13). With this single exception, it invariably afforded grounds for a positive diagnosis. Examples of the abnormalities disclosed by PEG are given in Fig. 3 and 4 (Cases 3 and 6).

The diagnosis was confirmed in 14 cases by membrane biopsy. In each instance, the specimens were found to have the character of hygroma or hematoma membranes. In four cases, no membrane was demonstrable at operation (Cases 4, 9, 19 and 15) and, in two cases, subdural puncture only was

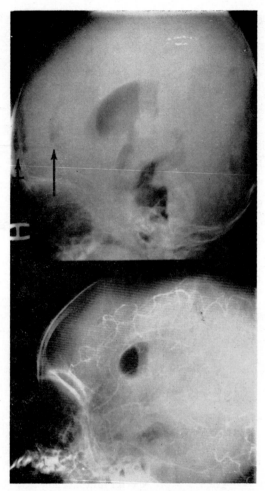

Fig. 3. **Pneumoencephalography: Somewhat dilated lateral ventricles.** Subarachnoid gas (↑) in wide sulci, and subdural gas (⤡) delimiting an extracerebral fluid accumulation 20–25 mm. thick. (Case 3)—Carotid angiography, showing extracerebral fluid accumulation in the frontal region (20–25 mm.). Lateral and oblique projection.

performed (Cases 19 and 20). The fluid accumulation was bilateral in all but three cases (No. 4, 15 and 18)—an incidence consistent with that reported by other authors, e.g. Ingraham and Matson.

Treatment and Results

The treatment in this series conformed to the schema described by Ingraham and Matson (1954). Repeated subdural puncture was followed by craniotomy with inspection of any membranes exposed. In refractory cases, as well as those with extensive lesions, this therapy was supplemented by the establishment of an osteoplastic flap with membrane excision. Fig. 6 illustrates the operative findings in one of the infants (Case 6).

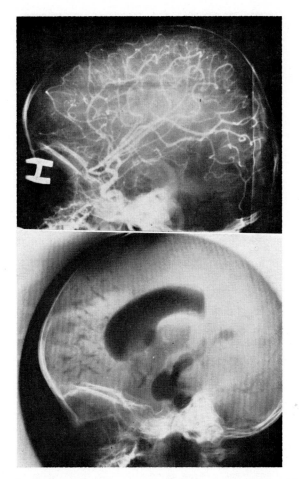

Fig. 4. Carotid angiography: Extracerebral fluid accumulation with its maximum in the frontal region (7–8 mm.). Pneumoencephalography: The gas discernible frontally in the wide sulci does not extend to the inside of the calvaria but terminates 4–5 mm. therefrom. (Case 6).

Over a follow-up period ranging from two months to two and one-half years, seven of the children showed signs of psychomotor retardation (Cases 1, 2, 3, 6, 8, 13 and 17) and two developed hydrocephalus (Cases 1 and 3). The remaining 13 were considered healthy and normally developed. These figures, representing approximately 65 per cent with normal development postoperatively, are in close agreement with the results of Ingraham and Matson (1949).

Electroencephalography

There are several early reports of electroencephalographic studies concerned with, or touching upon, subdural hematomas (Balado, Romero and Noiseaux, 1939; Jasper, Kershman and Elvidge, 1940; Rogers, 1941; Glaser

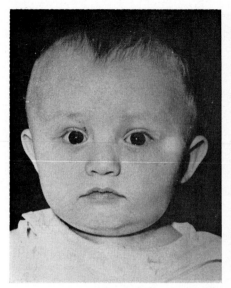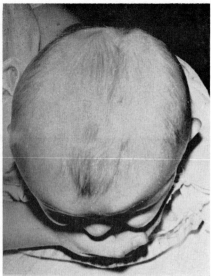

Fig. 5. Case 5. Photograph showing the widened head.

and Sjaardema, 1941; Schwab and Carter, 1942; Sjaardema and Glaser, 1942; Puech, Lerique-Koechlin and Lerique, 1943). Increasingly extensive series have since been published (Heersema and Freeman, 1945; Marsh, Hjartarson and Courville, 1949; Wertheimer, Courjon and Allègre, 1950; Friedlander, 1951; Sullivan, Abbot and Schwab, 1951; Levy et al., 1952; Lundervold and Nordlie, 1953; Nordlie, 1958; Kaplan, Huber and Browder, 1956; Wolf, 1962). These investigations have been concerned mainly with subdural hematomas in adults. Special EEG studies of subdural hematomas in infancy are of interest, however, inasmuch as this condition has certain peculiar features in the infant. Some studies of such cases have in fact been reported but are not as numerous nor as comprehensive as those pertaining to adults (Marinacci, Rand and Marinacci, 1951; Ferrier and Mégevand, 1955; Rodin, Bickford and Svien, 1953; Grützner and Koch, 1955; Freundlich, Beller and Berman, 1956; Streifler, Freundlich and Beller, 1958).

Method

The EEG recordings were made with eight—or sixteen—channel Grass or Kaiser electroencephalographs. Recording was bipolar, with the electrodes positioned in accordance with the international 10–20 system. Evaluation of the electroencephalograms was based on personal experience of a normal series and by observations reported in the literature (Smith, 1937; Bernhard and Skoglund, 1939; Lindsley, 1939; Laplane, Fischgold and Brisac, 1947; Hughes, Ehemann and Brown, 1948; Gibbs and Knott, 1949; Gibbs and Gibbs, 1950; Kellaway and Fox, 1952; Kirchhoff and Fröhlich, 1952; Garsche, 1953; Kellaway, 1957; Rohmer and Isch-Treussard, 1957; Engel, 1961; Fois, 1961; Liberson and Frazier, 1962; Dreyfus-Brisac, 1962; Lesný, 1962).

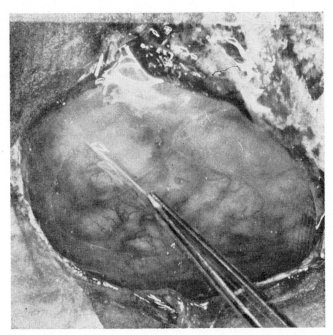

Fig. 6. Photograph from operation on Case 6. Osteoplastic flap. At arrow, the outer membrane is reflected. An incised inner membrane is held in the pincers.

Results

PREOPERATIVE EEG

Two infants with acute subdural accumulation of fluid (Cases 19 and 20, Fig. 25 and 26) were immediately subjected to repeated subdural puncture. After two to three weeks of treatment (at the age of approximately one month), when these patients were considered clinically cured, cerebral angiography revealed no subdural fluid and the electroencephalograms were within the normal range for that age.

In one of the early cases (No. 3), no electroencephalograms were taken preoperatively. In each of the remaining 17 cases, the preoperative electroencephalograms showed pathologic features.

Asymmetry of delta and theta activity was noted in ten cases, usually in association with abnormal amounts of low-frequency activity over both hemispheres. In one case (No. 6, Fig. 12A), it was largely evidenced during sleep. In another (No. 1, Fig. 7A), there appeared, in addition, rhythmic theta activity over one hemisphere.

Suppression of basic activity was observed in three cases (No. 1, 7 and 12; Fig. 7, 13 and 18), in one of which (No. 7, Fig. 13A) it was the only pathologic finding. The basic activity in this case was localized to the side on which subdural puncture had been done two days before.

Depressed activity over one hemisphere was equivocal in three cases. In Case 8, delta activity was more pronounced on the left side (Fig. 14A), but

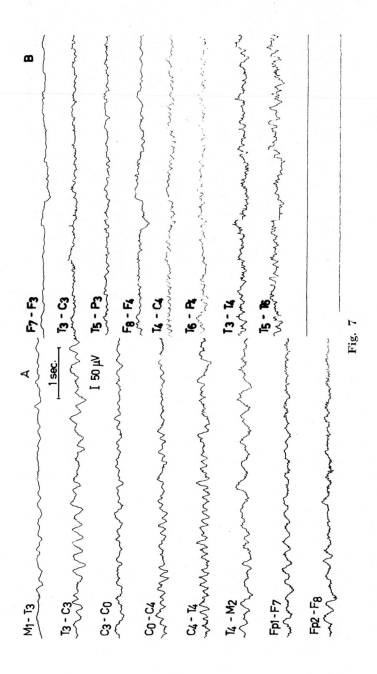

Fig. 7

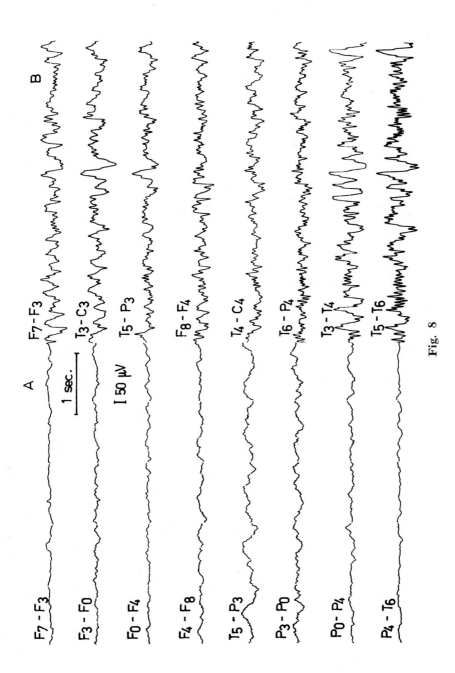

Fig. 8

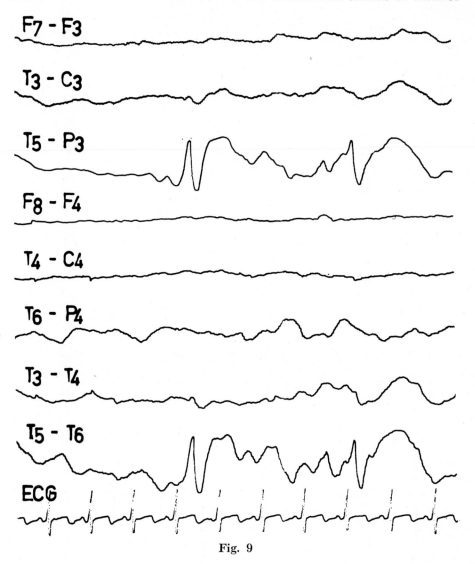

Fig. 9

focal sharp wave activity subsequently appeared over the right hemisphere (B). The activity of lower amplitude on the right side in Fig. 14A could possibly be regarded, therefore, as depressed activity. (Similar circumstances may have been present in Case 10, Fig. 16A). In the second of these three cases (No. 12, Fig. 18), the sleeping EEG (B) showed normal sleep activity on the left side, but the sleep pattern was poorly defined on the right. The basic waking activity also was poorly expressed on this side (A). The third case (No. 15, Fig. 21) is of particular interest. Here the angiographic picture was typical of right frontal subdural accumulation of fluid, and the EEG showed considerably decreased voltage in the frontal and temporal leads on the right side. Puncture yielded negative results, but this circumstance does not, as Koch and Grützner and Koch have pointed out, preclude sub-

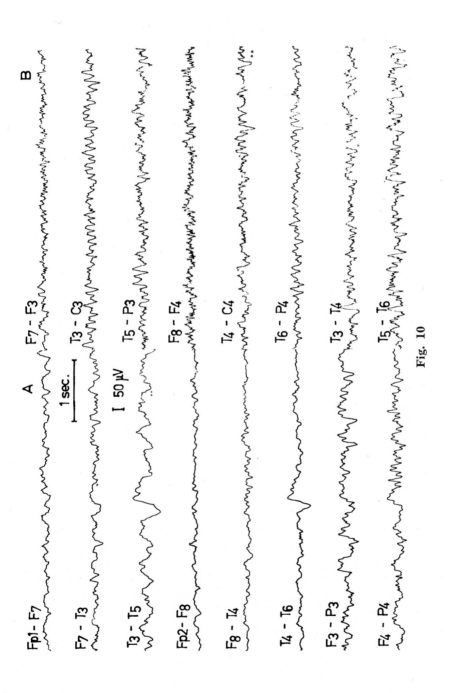

Fig. 10

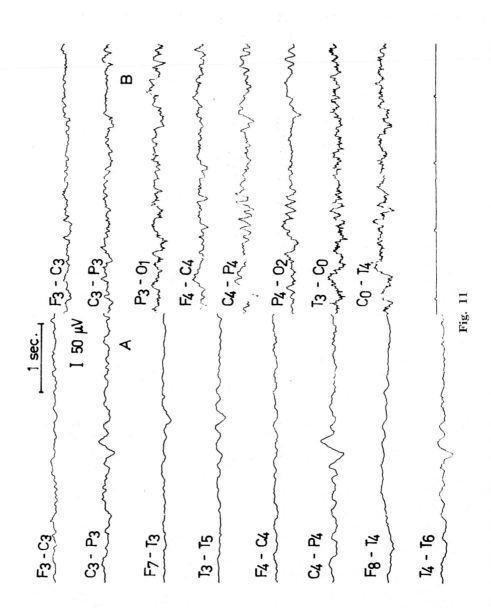

Fig. 11

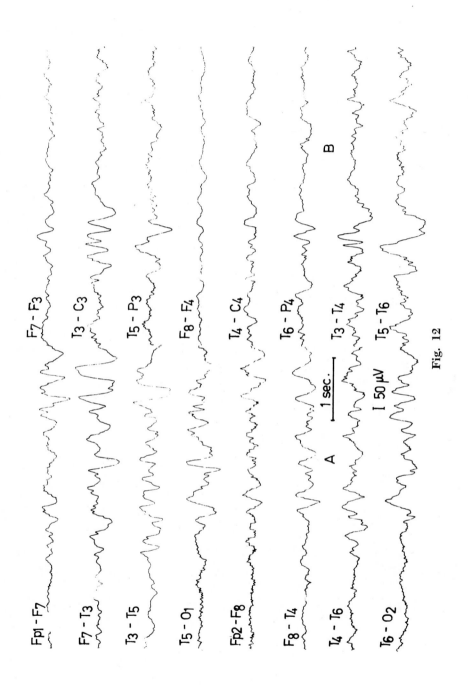

Fig. 12

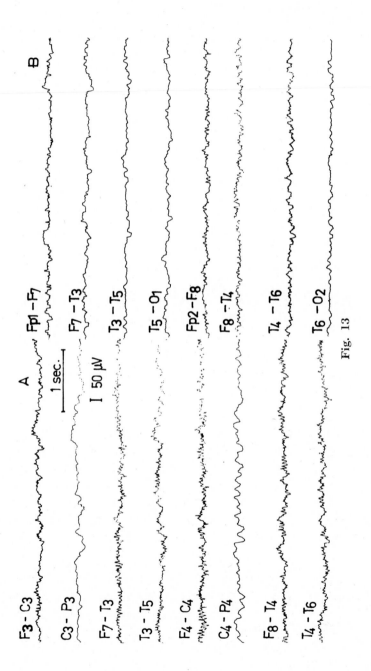

Fig. 13

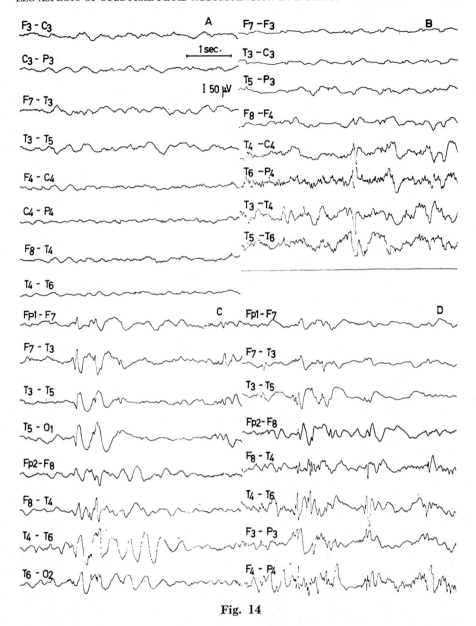

Fig. 14

dural accumulation of fluid. (Depression over the left hemisphere may have been present in Cases 5 and 16, Fig. 11 and 12, although it was impossible to determine whether such was the case or whether there was a right hemispheric preponderance of low-frequency activity.)

Paroxysmal sharp and slow wave activity was observed in three cases (No. 6, 8 and 17)—in one of them during sleep. Case 17 (Fig. 23A) first showed unilateral epileptiform activity and then, at the last few preoperative examinations, hypsarhythmia (Fig. 23B).

Electrical silence was noted in one case (No. 13, Fig. 19).

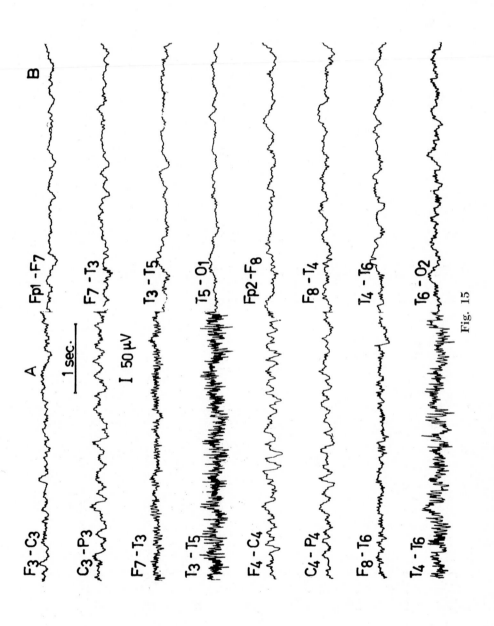

Fig. 15

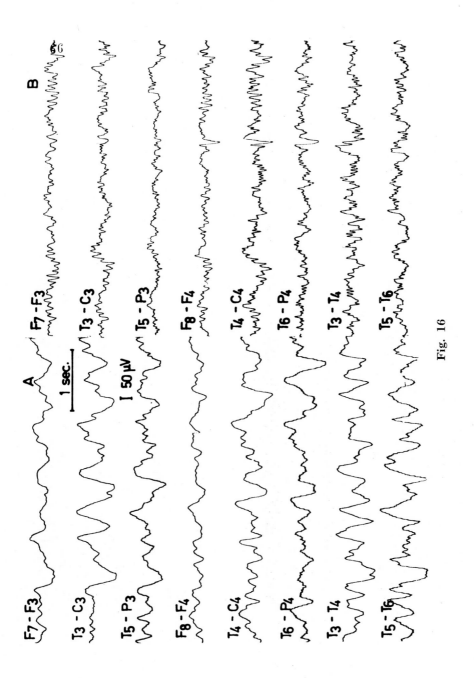

Fig. 16

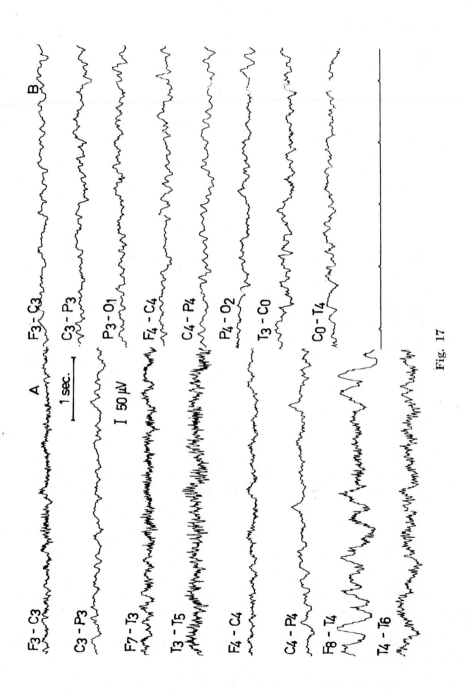

Fig. 17

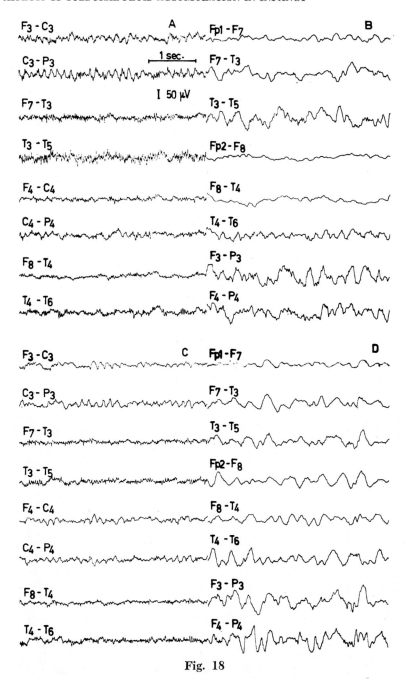

Fig. 18

LOCATION OF EEG ABNORMALITY IN RELATION TO THAT OF SUBDURAL FLUID IN SEVENTEEN CASES

In three cases with unilateral fluid accumulation, the EEG abnormalities implicated the affected side. In two others with bilateral effusion chiefly involving one side, the EEG findings were similarly indicative. In another patient with bilateral fluid accumulation chiefly affecting the right side, no alpha

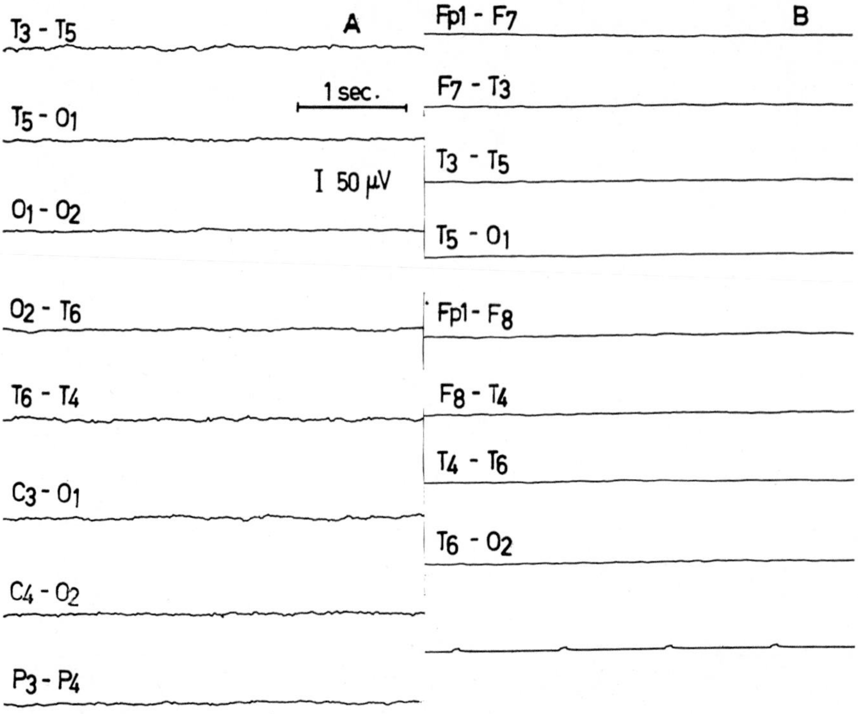

Fig. 19

activity was noted on the left side. Eleven other cases had bilateral effusion with no appreciable difference, either roentgenologically or at operation, in the volume of the hematomas on the two sides. Electroencephalographic asymmetry of one type or another was manifest in all of these except one which had an isolectric record.

Correct lateralization of the subdural fluid by EEG was made in certain cases, but more precise localization was possible only in one patient (Case 15) whose electroencephalograms implicated the anterior portion of the right hemisphere. In the majority of cases, the EEG abnormalities were most pronounced posterior to the extension of the hematoma as determined angiographically and as observed at operation.

DIAGNOSTIC SIGNIFICANCE OF SLEEP ACTIVATION

Numerous authors have called attention to the importance of sleep activation in electroencephalographic diagnosis, with emphasis on the age factor (Smith, 1937; Gibbs and Gibbs, 1941; Gibbs and Gibbs, 1947; Kellaway, 1950; Pampiglione, 1952; and others). Three of the children in our series showed preoperatively, during sleep, abnormal EEG activity that was absent in the waking record. Paroxysmal sharp and slow abnormalities were also recorded during sleep in three cases post-operatively.

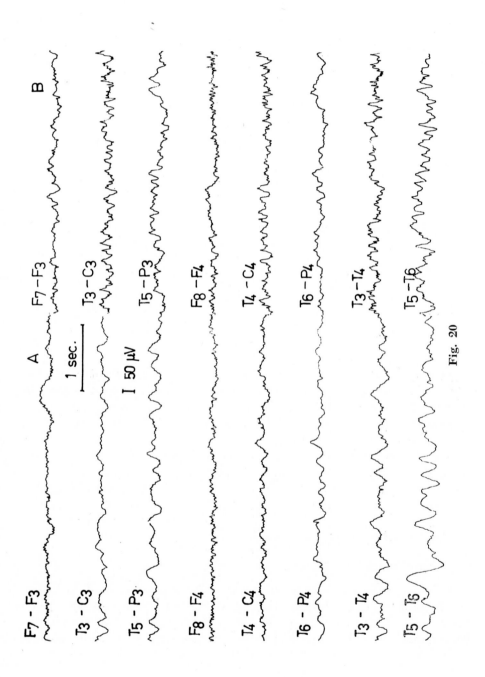

Fig. 20

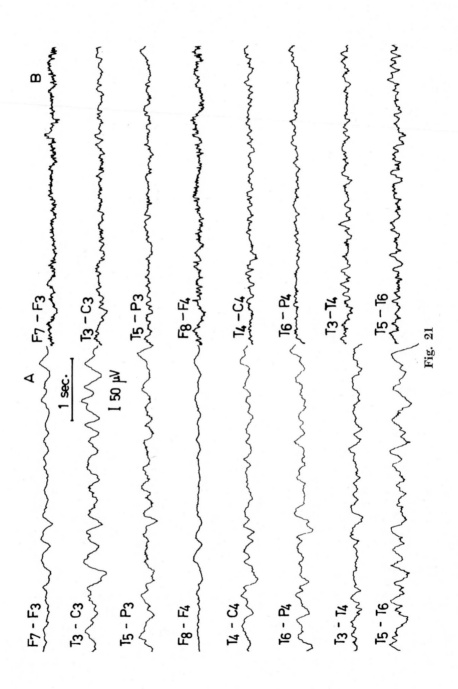

Fig. 21

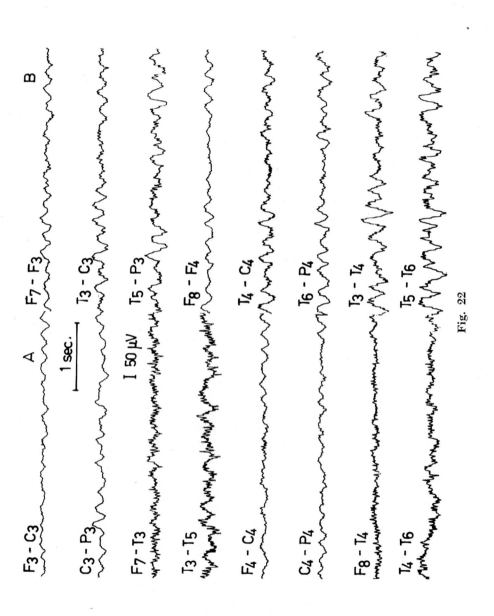

Fig. 22

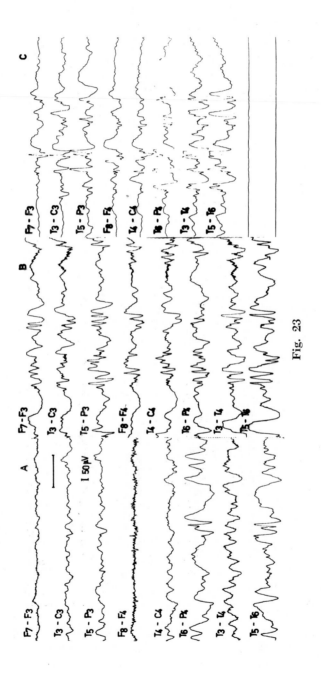

Fig. 23

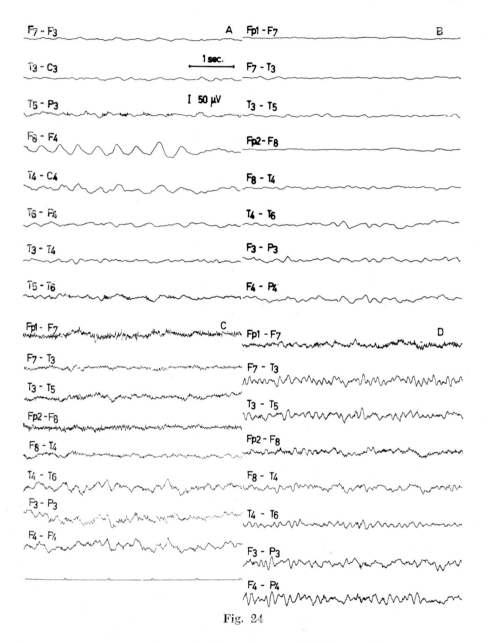

Fig. 24

Interrelationship of Pre- and Postoperative EEG with Respect to Clinical Results

One patient (Case 3) was not examined electroencephalographically prior to operation. This case was complicated postoperatively by subdural empyema and hydrocephalus. The child remained seriously retarded and showed highly pathologic electroencephalograms with focal epileptogenic activity and virtual extinction of activity over all other areas (Fig. 9).

Of 17 cases with both pre- and postoperative electroencephalograms, ten

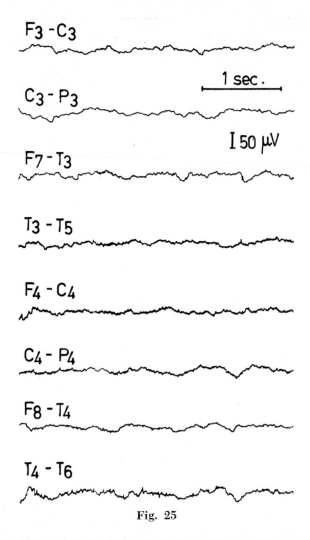

Fig. 25

exhibited normal electroencephalograms postoperatively (Cases 4, 5, 7, 9, 12, 14, 15, 16 and 18). It is interesting to note that all of these patients were clinically asymptomatic after operation and that the preoperative electroencephalograms had revealed abnormalities of delta-theta asymmetry, alpha asymmetry, and depressed activity. Another surgically treated patient who became clinically asymptomatic had shown abnormalities of this type prior to operation, but subsequently manifested focal sharp wave activity during sleep (Case 10, Fig. 16B).

Six patients showed no clinical improvement after operation. Three of them (Cases 6, 8 and 17) had paroxysmal activity both pre- and postoperatively, and one (Case 13) showed isoelectric EEG records before and after operation. Delta asymmetry and alpha asymmetry were noted pre- and postoperatively in Case 1; delta asymmetry preoperatively, and paroxysmal slow activity during sleep postoperatively in Case 2.

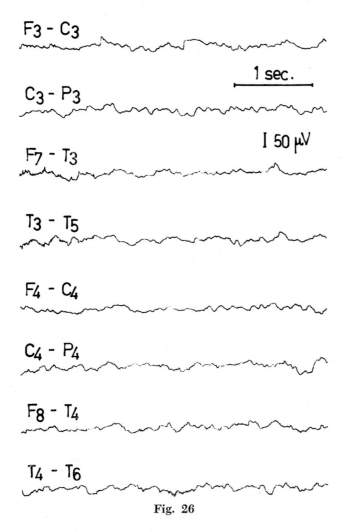

Fig. 26

In the group with chronic subdural accumulation of fluid, we recorded the approximate interval between diagnosis and operation in those who recovered and in those who did not show improvement. The first subgroup comprised 11 patients, the second, seven. For both subgroups, the interval averaged four months.

Comment

In the 17 of our 18 infants with subdural fluid accumulation who underwent preoperative EEG examination, the tracings invariably showed pathologic features. The abnormalities are illustrated by EEG tracings for each case history. Those shown in Cases 5, 7, 9 and 16 (Fig. 11, 13, 15 and 22) are, it is true, no more pronounced than those which may be observed in certain sectors of electroencephalograms from normal children of the same age; but since they appeared fairly consistently throughout the tracings, they were considered abnormal. This result is consonant with the few investigations of infant series that are available for comparison—e. g., those of Freundlich, Beller and Berman (1956), Rodin, Bickford and Svien (1953), Marinacci, Rand and Marinacci (1951), Streifler, Freundlich and Beller (1958)—as well as with observations reported by Grützner and Koch (1955) who found normal preoperative electroencephalograms in only two of 23 cases. In reports of adults series, the data range from pathologic findings on all preoperative electroencephalograms to normal findings in 10–12 per cent (Heersema and Freeman, 1945; Wertheimer, Courjon and Allègre, 1950; Paillas and Naquet, 1950; Gerlach and Steinmann, 1953; Nordlie, 1958; Schwab, 1951; and Abbot and Schwab, 1951).

As to the type of abnormal activity, the literature on subdural hematomas in adults alludes particularly to ipsilateral supression of alpha activity* and to slow activity over the hematoma or the hemisphere to which it is localized. In addition, there are records of general dysrhythmia; also occasional mention of "inversion" of alpha distribution and fast basic activity for acute or subacute subdural hematomas (Dawson, Webster and Gurdjian, 1951), and of delta activity plus high-amplitude beta activity both for subdural hematomas and for other cerebral lesions as well as subdural hematomas experimentally produced in animals (Glaser and Sjaardema, 1941; Sjaardema and Glaser, 1942). (In 1955, Steinmann and Jost described a case with unilateral subdural hematoma and unilateral arousal reaction). In the case of infants also, the reported findings are chiefly of alpha suppression as well as low-frequency activity, focal or diffuse. Paroxysmal activity is seldom mentioned in studies on adult series (Marsh, 1944; Sullivan, Abbot and Schwab, 1951); it is probably more common in infant series such as ours and that communicated by Grützner and Koch (1955). Hypsarhythmia was noted in one of our cases before operation, and persisted thereafter. Like Marinacci, Rand and Marinacci (1951) and Streifler, Freundlich and Beller (1958), we occasionally found diffusely isoelectric records.

The diagnostic usefulness of electroencephalography in subdural hematoma is a question with several facets. One immediate problem concerns localization: Is it a case of subdural hematoma or not? Sullivan, Abbot and Schwab (1951), in a series of adults, reported correct lateralization in 75 per cent and specific localization in 47 per cent. Nordlie (1958) recorded "positive results" in 87 per cent. In our series of infants, we had correct lateralization in the three cases of unilateral subdural fluid accumulation. Rodin, Bickford and Svien (1953) observed that EEG was "less helpful in diagnosis in the child group than in the adolescent and adult group". A very useful investigation in this respect is that of Levy et al. (1952) who studied 60 cases of severe head injuries in adults. In each of these cases, there was a clinical suspicion of subdural hematoma and indication for operation by virtue of "an ictal period of coma following the injury, bloody cerebrospinal fluid, a subsequent period of mental depression and/or increasing abnormal focal

---

*Which is by no means specific for subdural accumulation of fluid (vide e.g. Case and Bucy, 1938; Jasper, Fitzpatrick and Solomon, 1939; Williams and Reynell, 1945; Courville, 1949; Rohmer, Gastaut and Dell, 1952; Friedlander, 1954).

neurological signs. Thirty of the 60 patients had unilateral subdural hematomas. The remainder had neither subdural nor epidural hematomas. The findings indicate that the initial EEG is identical in these two groups. It would seem that the initial EEG is of no value in the differentiation of the 'operative' from the 'nonoperative' type of head injury."[*]

The great majority of subdural effusion cases in infants, both in our series and in others, are of chronic type, usually with nonspecific clinical symptoms, particularly in the form of retarded development and spasms that are often of nonfocal type. Electroencephalographic examination is warranted because it can be easily carried out without danger or discomfort and the results may confirm the suspicion of subdural fluid accumulation or indicate the necessity for diagnostic puncture or for neurological or neurosurgical consultation.

Neither we nor Rodin, Bickford and Svien (1953) have found that suppression of the alpha activity is dependent upon posterior location of the hematoma, as assumed by Williams and Reynell (1945) and surmised by Marsh, Hjartarson and Courville (1949), for, in our series, we noted purely frontal localization in association with alpha suppression.

With respect to the correlation between the clinical result of surgery and the changed EEG pattern after operation, we found—as did Sullivan, Abbot and Schwab (1951) and Nordlie (1958) in their series of adults—that with recovery of the patient, the EEG became normalized.

It is possible that the preoperative EEG findings may afford some prognostic guidance. The patients whose retardation persisted after operation included all of those with abnormal paroxysmal activity in the preoperative electroencephalograms as well as the single case with an isolectric record. Each of the patients who showed full recovery and normal development after operation had preoperative electroencephalograms with asymmetry for delta-theta activity and/or suppression of the basic activity.

To sum up, electroencephalography is not, in our judgment, adequate for diagnosis or exact localization of subdural accumulations of fluid; for this purpose, the neuroradiologic methods are superior. The EEG findings may, however, corroborate a clinical suspicion of subdural hematoma and thus strengthen the indication for diagnostic puncture and neuroradiologic examination. They may, moreover, afford prognostic information as well as some measure of guidance regarding the need of anticonvulsive therapy in the subsequent course.

Summary

Twenty cases of subdural fluid accumulation in infants—14 males and six females—were studied electroencephalographically. Two were acute cases;

---

[*]Levy, Abbot and Schwab, in common with Schmidt et al. (1950) before them, as well as Lundervold and Nordlie (1953) and Turrel et al. (1956) later on, noted yet another aspect of EEG as used for localization of subdural hematomas in adults. The presence of ipsilateral paresis and contralateral mydriasis is a not uncommon clinical source of error in diagnostic determination of the involved side. In such cases, EEG correctly indicated the side on which the subdural hematoma was located.

of the remaining 18, three were unilateral and 15 bilateral. Three cases followed meningitis, and birth trauma was probable in eight. Convulsions were noted in 13 cases, retarded development in ten, and enlargement of the head in nine.

The clinical diagnosis was verified by subdural puncture, carotid angiography, pneumoencephalography, operation and histopathologic examination of membranes. Treatment conformed to the schema described by Ingraham and Matson (1949).

The two acute cases were treated immediately by repeated subdural puncture. At age one month, by which time these infants were considered clinically healthy, cerebral angiography and EEG showed no evidence of abnormality.

Preoperative electroencephalograms were made in 17 of the 18 cases of chronic subdural hematoma. Considerable asymmetry for delta and theta activity was noted in ten cases; suppression of the basic activity in three. Equivocal depression of activity over one hemisphere was present in three cases. One patient showed no evidence of electrical activity over either hemisphere. Paroxysmal slow and sharp wave activity was observed in three cases, including one with hypsarhythmia.

Correct lateralization by EEG was possible in the three cases of unilateral subdural hematoma.

With clinical recovery after operation, there was a concomitant normalization of the EEG findings.

All the patients who had shown very pronounced EEG abnormalities preoperatively showed unsatisfactory postoperative development.

Case Histories

Case 1. B. G. Male. Only child. Mother aged 24. Parturition uneventful. At age 7½ months, mother thought his head was too large. Admitted to Children's Hospital and Neurosurgery Department.

Psychomotor development apparently normal. Head circumference at age 1 year, 51 cm.

Cranial roentgenography: *Caput quadratum.*

PEG: Bilateral subdural accumulation of fluid.

Bilateral common carotid angiography: Frontotemporal extracerebral fluid accumulation of 2 cm. on left and 1 cm. on right side.

Operation at age 17 months: Bilateral frontoparietal subdural fluid accumulation with membranes.

Pathologist's report: Hygroma membranes.

EEG I at age 11 months, 6 months before operation (Fig. 7A): 7 c/sec. basic activity on the right side, absent on the left. Bilateral frontotemporal delta activity and, on the left side, partially rhythmic theta activity.

EEG II, 5 months before operation: Unchanged pattern.

EEG III, 2½ years after operation (Fig. 7B): Slight asymmetry; basic activity less conspicuous on left than on right side.

Clinical follow-ups over 2½-year period postoperatively: Slight mental retardation and development of hydrocephalus; head circumference 56.5 cm.

Case 2. M. E. Male. First of two children. Mother aged 32. Labor of 40 hours duration; intrauterine asphyxia. At age 4 months, onset of right-sided seizures of focal motor type, unresponsive to therapy. At age 16 months, in Children's Hospital: *Caput quadratum;* fontanel closed. Head circumference 48 cm. Slight psychomotor retardation.

PEG: Bilateral subdural fluid accumulation.

Bilateral internal carotid angiography: Frontal extracerebral fluid accumulation, 4–5 mm. in depth.

Operation at age 17 months: Bilateral frontal subdural fluid accumulation with membranes.

Pathologist's report: Hygroma membranes.

EEG I, 11 months before operation (Fig. 8A): Delta activity mainly in left parietal leads. At four further preoperative examinations, this pattern was unchanged.

EEG II, 2 years after operation (nine examinations) (Fig. 8B): Diffuse nonspecific abnormality during consciousness. Paroxysmal slow activity on the left side during sleep.

Clinical follow-ups over 2-year period postoperatively: Persistence of right-sided focal motor seizures; psychomotor retardation.

Case 3. Z. R. Male. Third of three children. Mother aged 31. Parturition uneventful. Development normal until age 4 months; subsequently, retardation, increasing head circumference, impairment of vision, exophthalmus. Admitted to Neurosurgery Department at age 9 months. Dull and unresponsive. Head circumference, 53 cm. Fontanel tension, 4.6 cm.

Cranial roentgenography: Separation of sutures; *caput quadratum.*

PEG: Bilateral subdural fluid accumulation in frontal region.

Right common carotid angiography: Extracerebral fluid accumulation, probably bilateral, 2 cm. in depth.

Operation at age 9 months: Extensive bilateral subdural fluid accumulation.

Pathologist's report: Hygroma membranes.

Subdural empyema and spasms of decerebration type occurred postoperatively.

EEG, 2 months after operation (Fig. 9): Low voltage slow waves and left epileptogenic focus.

Clinical follow-ups over 2½-year period postoperatively: Idiocy, hydrocephalus.

Case 4. L. C. Male. Second of two children. Mother aged 30. Parturition uneventful. Birth weight 2.750 grams. Twin birth, the other twin stillborn. Attacks of cyanosis in neonatal period. Normal somatic and psychomotor development. At age 11 months, three generalized convulsive seizures, onset of which alternated between right and left sides. At age 13 months, status epilepticus, abolished by chloral.

Condition at age 16 months: Physical and neurologic examinations: N.A.D. Head circumference 49 cm.

Cranial roentgenography: Normal findings.

PEG: Bilateral subdural fluid accumulation.

Left internal carotid angiography: Extracerebral fluid accumulation, 3–4 mm. in depth, with location corresponding to middle and posterior portions of frontal lobe.

Right internal carotid angiography: Normal findings.

Operation at age 16 months: Subdural fluid accumulation, with no membranes, over left frontal lobe.

EEG I, 6 months before operation (Fig. 10A): Pathologic, with delta activity on the left side.

EEG II, 1 year after operation: Normal.

EEG III, 2 years after operation (Fig. 10B): Normal.

Clinical follow-ups over 2-year period postoperatively: Normal psychomotor development, but two convulsive seizures during first year.

Case 5. K. E. Male. Only child. Mother aged 20. Labor uncomplicated but of short duration (6 hours). Moderate cephalic hematoma. At age 11 months, akinetic attacks. Periretinal hemorrhages and *caput quadratum* were observed during hospitalization.

Admitted to Neurosurgery Department at age 11 months. Slight psychomotor retardation. Head circumference, 47 cm. Fontanel normal.

Cranial roentgenography: Normal findings.

PEG: Bilateral subdural fluid accumulation.

Bilateral internal carotid angiography: Bilateral frontoparietal fluid accumulation, 5–10 mm. in depth.

Operation at age 11 months: Bilateral subdural fluid accumulation with membranes, location corresponding to posterior portions of frontal lobes.

Pathologist's report: Granulation membrane.

EEG I, 2 weeks before operation (Fig. 11A): Theta and delta activity bilaterally, more pronounced on the right side.

EEG II, 2 years after operation (Fig. 11B): Normal.

Clinical follow-ups over 2-year period postoperatively: Healthy; normal development.

Case 6. J. M. Male. Second of two children. Mother aged 23. Parturition normal. Examined at Children's Hospital at age 6 months for psychomotor retardation. PEG warranted suspicion of bilateral subdural fluid accumulation. Transferred, at age 11 months, to Neurosurgery Department. Head circumference, 48 cm. Fontanels normal.

Cranial roentgenography: N. A. D.

Right common carotid angiography: Frontal extracerebral fluid accumulation, 5–6 mm. in depth.

Operation at age 11 months: Bilateral frontoparietal subdural fluid accumulation.

Pathologist's report: Hygroma membranes.

EEG I, 5 months before operation (Fig. 12A): Paroxysmal slow activity, more pronounced on the left side, most evident when infant was somnolent.

EEG II, 15 months after operation (Fig. 12B): Essentially unchanged pattern.

Clinical follow-up 2 years after operation showed persistent grave psychomotor retardation.

Case 7. K. F. Male. Second of four children. Mother aged 25. Parturition uneventful. As from age 10 months, periodic fever and vomiting. Fontanel tension and periretinal hemorrhages observed during hospitalization. Subdural fluid at repeated puncture.

Admitted to Neurosurgery Department at age 12 months. Normal psychomotor development.

Periretinal hemorrhages. Fontanel, 4.3 cm. Head circumference, 47 cm.

Cranial roentgenography: *Caput quadratum.*

PEG: Bilateral frontal subdural fluid accumulation, somewhat heavier on right.

Bilateral internal carotid angiography: Bilateral extradural fluid accumulation, heavier on left.

Operation at age 17 months: Bilateral subdural fluid accumulation with membranes.

Pathologist's report: Hygroma membranes.

EEG I, 2 weeks before operation, 2 days after right subdural puncture, showed 7 c/sec. basic activity on right, not evident on left (Fig. 13A).

EEG II, 2 years after operation (Fig. 13B): Normal findings.

Clinical follow-up 2 years after operation: Healthy; normal development.

Case 8. M. L. Female. Only child. Mother aged 21. Parturition uneventful. At age 4 months, generalized convulsive seizure. Admitted to hospital where somewhat tense fontanel and peripapillary hemorrhages in the eyegrounds were observed. At age 5 months, admitted to Children's Hospital for further examination. Some psychomotor retardation. Eyegrounds now normal. Head circumference, 41 cm.

Cranial roentgenography: N. A. D.

Right common carotid angiography: Frontoparietal extracerebral fluid accumulation, 8 mm. in depth.

Left common carotid angiography: Parietotemporal fluid accumulation, 1½ cm. in depth.

Repeated subdural puncture failed to improve patient's condition. She had series of brief convulsive attacks with rotation of the eyes and head to the left.

Operation at age 7 months: Bilateral subdural fluid accumulation with membranes.

Pathologist's report: Hygroma membranes.

EEG I, 2 months before operation (Fig. 14A): Substantial delta activity with left hemispheric preponderance.

EEG II, 1 week before operation (Fig. 14B): Following a series of convulsive attacks and repeated subdural puncture, the record was now flatter for the left than for the right hemisphere and showed focal sharp wave activity—mostly on the right.

EEG III, 1 week after operation (Fig. 14C): Paroxysmal sharp and slow wave activity, more pronounced on the right and intensified during somnolence.

EEG IV, 2 weeks after operation (Fig. 14D) Unchanged pattern.

Clinical follow-up 10 months after operation: Spasms.

Case 9. M. M. Male. Third of four children. Mother aged 23. Twin birth. Birth weight 2,840 grams. At age 8 months, admitted to Children's Hospital because of fever. Psychomotor retardation and *caput quadratum* were observed. Head circumference, 47 cm. Fontanels normal.

Cranial roentgenography: N. A. D.

Bilateral common carotid angiography: Bilateral frontoparietal extracerebral fluid accumulation, 4–7 mm. in depth.

Operation at age 10 months: Bilateral frontoparietal subdural fluid accumulation.

EEG I, 2 months before operation (Fig. 15A): Asymmetry with left preponderance of low-frequency activity.

EEG II, 16 months after operation (Fig. 15B) Normal pattern.

Clinical follow-up 16 months after operation: Normal development. Healthy.

Case 10. M. E. Female. First of two children. Mother aged 27. Intrauterine asphyxia. Twin birth. Birth weight 2,500 grams. At age 1 month, otitis, left peripheral facial palsy and convulsions of nonfocal type. Admitted to Children's Hospital at age 5 months for investigation of convulsive attacks. *Caput quadratum.* Diagnostic subdural puncture positive. Further examinations were delayed through various infections.

At age 8 months, normal psychomotor development. Head circumference, 43 cm. Fontanels normal.

Bilateral common carotid angiography: Extracerebral fluid accumulation 3–4 mm. in depth.

Operation at age 8 months: Bilateral frontoparietal subdural fluid accumulation.

EEG I, 3 months before operation (Fig. 16A): Left preponderance of low-frequency activity during sleep.

EEG II, 1½ years after operation (Fig. 16B): Focal sharp wave activity occurring sporadically over right hemisphere.

Clinical follow-ups over 1½-year period postoperatively: Normal development; no convulsions.

Case 11. E. H. Female. Second of two children. Mother aged 28. Parturition normal. Development somewhat retarded. Hospitalized at age 5 months for upper respiratory infection. Routine examination disclosed fontanel tension. Diagnostic puncture showed subdural fluid accumulation. Admitted to Children's Hospital at age 5½ months. Slight psychomotor retardation and mild general hypertension. Head circumference, 46 cm.

Cranial roentgenography: Normal findings. Fontanel bulging, 3, 5.4 cm.

Right common carotid angiography: Frontoparietal extracerebral fluid accumulation, 3–4 mm. in depth.

Operation at age 6 months: Bilateral subdural fluid accumulation with location corresponding to lateral portions of frontal lobes.

Pathologist's report: Hygroma membranes.

EEG I, 3 weeks before operation (Fig. 17A): Delta activity in right frontal region.

EEG II, 1½ years after operation (Fig. 17B): Normal pattern.

Clinical follow-ups over 1½-year period postoperatively: Normal development. Healthy.

Case 12. E. L. G. Male. Only child. Mother aged 19. Parturition uneventful. At age 4 months, onset of generalized convulsions which, during the ensuing month, showed some right preponderance. Admitted to Children's Hospital at age 7 months. Slightly retarded psychomotor development. Head circumference, 46 cm. Fontanels normal. Preretinal hemorrhages. Subdural puncture positive.

Bilateral common carotid angiography: Frontal extracerebral fluid accumulation with membranes.

Pathologist's report: Hygroma membranes.

EEG I, 6 weeks before operation (Fig. 18A): During consciousness 7 c/sec. activity in parietal leads was less pronounced on right than on left side (Fig. 18A). During sleep, substantial asymmetry with depression of the activity on the right side (Fig. 18B).

EEG II, 1 week after operation: Symmetrical electroencephalogram, within the normal range both during consciousness and during sleep. (Fig. 18C and D).

This patient was followed up for only one month after operation. Uneventful postoperative course. Clinical follow-up 1 month after operation: No spasms.

Case 13. S. A. Female. Third of three children. Mother aged 27. Parturition uneventful. At age 2 weeks, meningitis following upper respiratory infection treated with antibiotics. Repeated spasms in left arm as well as generalized convulsions. Admitted to Children's Hospital at age 1 month in poor condition; monotonous cry. Fontanel tension. Head circumference, 36.5 cm.

Cranial roentgenography: Separation of sutures.

PEG and angiography technically unsuccessful.

Subdural puncture positive bilaterally.

Operation at age 3 months: Bilateral subdural fluid accumulation, somewhat heavier on right. No positively identifiable membranes.

EEG 6 weeks and 4 weeks before operation (Fig. 19A): Almost isoelectric tracings on both occasions.

EEG 1½ years after operation (Fig. 19B): Unchanged isoelectric record.

Clinical follow-up 1½ years after operation: Frequent convulsive seizures with no focal signs. Mentally isolated from environment.

Case 14. B. F. Female. Second of two children. Mother aged 20. Premature delivery. Birth weight 1,230 grams. Poor weight gain. At age 5 months, vomiting and tonic convulsions. Admitted to Children's Hospital at age 7 months. Head circumference, 43 cm. Increased fontanel tension.

Cranial roentgenography: Separation of sutures.

Ophthalmologic findings: Papilledema with preretinal hemorrhage.

Right common carotid angiography: Frontoparietal extracerebral fluid accumulation, 1 cm. in depth.

Operation at age 8 months: Bilateral fluid accumulation with membranes.

Pathologist's report: Hygroma membranes.

EEG I, 1 month before operation (Fig. 20A): Diffuse nonspecific abnormality with distinct preponderance of delta activity over left hemisphere.

EEG II, 1½ years after operation (Fig. 20B): Normal pattern.

Clinical follow-ups over 1½-year period postoperatively: Normal development. Healthy.

Case 15. E. T. Male. Only child. Mother aged 23. Parturition 1 month before estimated term. Birth weight 2,480 grams. At age 2 months and at age 5 months, convulsions with clonic spasms in the arms. During examination at Children's Hospital when patient was 5 months old, *caput quadratum* was observed. Subdural puncture yielded small quantity of yellow fluid on the right side. Psychomotor development normal. No appreciable abnormality of fontanels.

Cranial roentgenography: Normal findings.

Right common carotid angiography: Fluid accumulation, 1 cm. in depth, with location corresponding to right frontal lobe.

Operation at age 7 months: Exploratory craniotomy failed to verify the angiographic findings.

EEG I, 2 months before operation (Fig. 21A): Considerable flattening in anterior leads on the right.

EEG II, 11 months after operation (Fig. 21B): Normal findings.

Clinical follow-ups over 11-month period after operation: Normal development. Healthy.

Case 16. B. P. O. Male. Only child. Mother aged 22. Parturition uneventful. At age 6 months, pneumococcal meningitis. Admitted to Children's Hospital where he was tracheotomized for apnea. Convulsions with right preponderance. In the subsequent course, fontanel tension pointed to subdural effusion, which was verified by subdural puncture.

Bilateral common carotid angiography: Bilateral frontal extradural fluid accumulation, more extensive on right.

Operation at age 10 months: Bilateral frontotemporal subdural fluid accumulation with membranes.

Pathologist's report: Granulation membranes.

EEG I, 1 month before operation (Fig. 22A): Distinct asymmetry with low-frequency activity of lower amplitude over the right hemisphere.

EEG II, 2 weeks after operation (Fig. 22B): Preoperatively observed asymmetry no longer present.

Clinical follow-ups over 1-year period postoperatively: Normal development. Healthy.

Case 17. J. T. Male. Second of two children. Mother aged 35. Parturition uneventful. Admitted to Children's Hospital at age 5 months for pneumococcal meningitis. Severe convulsions. Tracheotomy and respirator treatment resorted to. Psychomotor retardation. In the subsequent course, bilateral subdural fluid accumulation—treated by repeated puncture.

Bilateral common carotid angiography: Extradural fluid accumulation.

Operation at age 7 months: Bilateral subdural fluid accumulation with membranes.

EEG I, 1 month before operation (Fig. 23A): Nonspecific abnormality over both hemispheres and focal sharp wave activity in right temporal leads.

EEG II, 1 month after operation (Fig. 23B): Multiple epileptogenic foci; here and there, hypsarhythmia-like pattern.

EEG III, 3 months after operation: Essentially unchanged picture.

EEG IV, 4 months after operation (Fig. 23C): No change.

Postoperatively, the patient was free from spasms but, when followed up 3 months later, still showed conspicuous psychomotor retardation.

Clinical follow-ups over 4-month period postoperatively: Supervenient infantile spasm. Distinct psychomotor retardation.

Case 18. L. U. M. Male. Second of two children. Mother aged 26. Parturition uneventful. Normal psychomotor development. At age 2½ months, acute pneumococcal meningitis, allayed by antibiotics. Increased fontanel tension and concomitant spasms raised the suspicion of subdural effusion, which was confirmed by subdural puncture at Children's Hospital.

At age 6 months: Normal psychomotor development. Fontanel, 4.4 cm; no tension. Head circumference, 44 cm.

Cranial roentgenography: Right frontal protrusion.

PEG: Subdural fluid accumulation, right side.

Right common carotid angiography: Extradural fluid, 5 mm. in depth, over anterior portion of frontal lobe.

Operation at age 7 months: Right frontal subdural fluid accumulation with membranes. Pathologist's report: Subchronic inflammation of membrane.

EEG I, 3 months before operation, following nine subdural punctures and subsidence of the meningitis (Fig. 24A): Episodic delta activity in anterior and middle leads on right side.

EEG II, 6 weeks before operation, following continued punctures (Fig. 24B): Lesser degree of abnormality.

EEG III, 2 days before operation (Fig. 24C): Some further regression.

EEG IV, 2 years after operation (Fig. 24D): Normal pattern.

Clinical follow-ups over 2-year period postoperatively: Normal development. Healthy.

Case 19. H-P. T. Male. Second of two children. Mother aged 32. Parturition in 43rd. week uneventful. When only 1 day old, frequent spasms. Fontanel tension. Head circumference 32.5 cm. at birth and 35.5 cm. at age two weeks. Bilateral puncture at age 3 weeks; Positive findings. Under subsequent treatment with repeated puncture, the fluid accumulation subsided. At the end of 3 weeks, patient had recovered and bilateral angiography showed normal conditions.

EEG at time of angiographic examination (Fig. 25): Normal pattern.

Case 20. M. C. Female. Fifth of five children. Mother aged 32. Parturition uneventful. Transferred to Children's Hospital at age 4 days because of fontanel tension and hypertonia of lower extremities. Bilateral subdural puncture was positive, the fluid consisting of blood. During the ensuing month, repeated subdural puncture yielded decreasing amounts of fluid. Patient meanwhile showed normal development. At age 1 month, left common carotid angiography revealed no appreciable subdural hematoma and the EEG was normal (Fig. 26). Patient was discharged as healthy.

ACKNOWLEDGMENT

We are indebted to the Department of Roentgenology II (Head: Ingemar Wickbom, M.D.) for the kind cooperation in this study.

REFERENCES

ANDERSON, H. and RADBERG, C. Infantilt subduralt hematom. *Nord. Med., 1962,* 67:791.

BALADO, M., ROMERO, L. F. and NOISEAUX, P. J. Electroencefalograma humano. *Arch. Argent. Neurol., 1939,* 20:215–380.

BERNHARD, C. G. and SKOGLUND, C. R. On the alpha frequency of human brain potentials as a function of age. *Skand. Arch. Physiol., 1939,* 82:178–184.

BOISSIERE, H. Hématome sous-dural chronique du nourrisson. (H.S.D.) *Concours Med., 1960,* 82:801–805.

CASE, T. J. and BUCY, P. C. Localization of cerebral lesions by electroencephalography. *J. Neurophysiol., 1938,* 1:245–261.

COURJON, J., BONNET, H. and ALLEGRE, G. Étude électroencéphalographique de 17 hématomes sous-duraux. *Rev. Neurol.,* 1950, 83:609–612.

COURVILLE, C. B. The effect of certain lesions of the brain on electroencephalographic wave patterns. *Bull. Los Angeles Neurol. Soc.,* 1949, 14:119–148.

CROSBY, R. M. N. Subdural collections of fluid in infants and children. III The chronic membrane. *Clin. Neurosurg.,* 1957, 5:66–72.

DAWSON, R. E., WEBSTER, J. E. and GURDJIAN, E. S. Serial electroencephalography in acute head injuries. *J. Neurosurg.,* 1951, 8:613–630.

DOWMAN, C. E. and KAHN, E. A. Subdural hematoma in infants. *South. Surgeon,* 1942, 11:164–172.

DRESSLER, W. and ALBRECHT, K. Klinische Betrachtungen zur Pathogenese des subduralen Hämatoms. *Acta Neurochir.,* 1957, 5:46–67.

DREYFUS-BRISAC, C. The electroencephalogram of the premature infant. *World Neurol.,* 1962, 3:5–15.

ELVIDGE, A. R. and JACKSON, I. J. Subdural hematoma and effusion in infants. *AMA J. Dis. Child.,* 1949, 78:635–658.

ENGEL, R. Evaluation of electroencephalographic tracings of newborns. *J. -Lancet, Minneapolis,* 1961, 81:523–532.

FERRIER, S. and MÉGEVAND, A. L'hématome sous-dural chez l'enfant. *Rev. Méd. Suisse Rom,* 1955, 75:77–94.

FOIS, A. *The Electroencephalogram of the Normal Child.* C. C. Thomas, Springfield, Ill., 1961, 123 pp.

FREUNDLICH, E., BELLER, A. J. and BERMAN, S. Subdural hematoma in infancy. *AMA J. Dis. Child.,* 1956, 91:608–613.

FRIEDLANDER, W. J. Clinical evaluation of focal depression of voltage in electroencephalography. *Neurology,* 1954, 4: 752–761.

FRIEDLANDER, W. J. The electroencephalographic findings in 39 surgically proven subdural hematomas. *Electroenceph. clin. Neurophysiol.,* 1951, 3:59–62.

GARSCHE, R. Grundzuge des normalen Elektroencephalogramms im Kindesalter. *Klin. Wschr.,* 1953, 31:118–123.

GERLACH, G. and STEINMANN, H. Hirnelektrische Befunde bei subduralen Hämato-

men. *Zbl. Neurochir.,* 1953, 13:107–113.

GIBBS, F. A. and GIBBS, E. L. *Atlas of Electroencephalography.* Lew. A. Cummings Co., Cambridge, Mass., 1941.

GIBBS, E. L. and GIBBS, F. A. Diagnostic and localizing value of electroencephalographic studies in sleep. *Res. Publ. Ass. nerv. ment. Dis.,* 1947, 26:366–376.

GIBBS, F. A. and GIBBS, E. L. *Atlas of Electroencephalography.* 2 ed. Addison-Wesly, Cambridge, Mass., 1950.

GIBBS, F. A. and KNOTT, J. R. Growth of the electrical activity of the cortex. *Electroenceph. clin. Neurophysiol.,* 1949, 1: 223–229.

GIRARD, F. Les hématomes sous-duraux; étude expérimentale. *Acta Paediat. (Upps),* 1956, 45:618–632.

GLASER, G. H. The neurological status of the newborn: neuromuscular and electroencephalographic activity. *Yale J. Biol. Med.,* 1959, 32:173–191.

GLASER, M. A. and SJAARDEMA, H. Electroencephalographic diagnosis of extradural and subdural hemorrhage. *Proc. Soc. Exp. Med.,* 1941, 47:138–140.

GRÖNTOFT, O. Intracranial haemorrhage and blood-brain barrier problems in the new-born. *Acta Path. Microbiol. Scand.,* 1954, Suppl. 100:1–109.

GRUTZNER, A. and KOCH, F. Elektrencephalographische Befunde bei subduralen Ergüssem im Säuglings- und Kleinkindesalter. *Z. Kinderheilk.,* 1955, 76:148–166.

GUTHKELCH, A. N. Subdural effusions in infancy: 24 cases. *Brit. Med. J.,* 1953, 1: 233–239.

HEERSEMA, P. H. and FREEMAN, J. G. The importance of diagnosing chronic subdural hematoma. *Med. Clin. N. Amer.,* 1945, 29:1042–1053.

HERZBERGER, E., ROTEM, Y. and BRAHAM, J. Remarks on thirty-three cases of subdural effusion in infancy. *Arch. Dis. Child.,* 1956, 31:44–50.

HUGHES, J. G., EHEMANN, B. and BROWN, U. A. Electroencephalography of the newborn: I. Studies on normal, full term, sleeping infants. *Am. J. Dis. Child.,* 1948, 76:503–512.

HUGHES, R. R. *An Introduction to Clinical Electroencephalography.* John Wright and Sons LTD, Bristol, 1961, 118 pp.

INGRAHAM, F. D. and MATSON, D. D. Subdural hematoma in infancy. *Advance Pediat.*, *1949*, 4:231–263.

INGRAHAM, F. D. and MATSON, D. D. *Neurosurgery of Infancy and Childhood.* C. C. Thomas, Springfield, Ill., *1954*, 456 pp.

JASPER, H. H. FITZPATRICK, C. P. and SOLOMON, P. Analogies and opposites in schizophrenia and epilepsy. *Amer. J. Psychiat.*, *1939*, 95:835–851.

JASPER, H. H., KERSHMAN, J. and ELVIDGE, A. Electroencephalographic studies of injury to the head. *Arch. Neurol. Psychiat.*, *1940*, 44:328–350.

KAPLAN, H. A., HUBER, W. and BROWDER, J. Electroencephalogram in subdural hematoma. *J. Neuropath. Exp. Neurol.*, *1956*, 15:65–78.

KELLAWAY, P. The use of sedative-induced sleep as an aid to electroencephalographic diagnosis in children. *J. Pediat.*, *1950*, 37:862–877.

KELLAWAY, P. Ontogenetic evolution of the cerebral activity of the brain in man and in animals. In IVᵉ congrès d'EEG et de neurophys. clin. *Ed. Acta Med. Belg.*, Bruxelles, *1957*, 141–154.

KELLAWAY, P. and FOX, B. J. Electroencephalographic diagnosis of cerebral pathology in infants during sleep. *J. Pediat.*, *1952*, 41:262–287.

KIRCHHOFF, H. W. und FRÖHLICH, B. Elektrencephalographische Untersuchungen über den Schlaf des Säuglings. *Arch. Psychiat.*, *1952*, 189:341–354.

KOCH, F. Beitrag zur Therapie der Pachymeningitis hämorrhagica interna (Hämatoma Durae matris). *Arch. Kinderheilk.*, *1953*, 147:213–225.

LAPLANE, R., FISCHGOLD, H. et BRISAC, C. L'électroencéphalographie chez l'enfant. *Nourrisson*, *1947*, 35:59–63.

LESNY, I. *Elektroenzephalographie im Kindesalter.* VEB Verlag Volk und Gesundheit, Berlin, *1962*, 171 pp.

LEVY, L. L., SEGERBERG, L. H., SCHMIDT, R. P., TURRELL, R. C. and ROSEMAN, E. The electroencephalogram in subdural hematoma. *J. Neurosurg.*, *1952*, 9:588–598.

LIBERSON, W. T. and FRAZIER, W. H. Evaluation of EEG patterns of newborn babies. *Am. J. Psychiat.*, *1962*, 118:1125–1131.

LINDSLEY, D. B. A longitudinal study of the occipital alpha rhythm in normal children: frequency and amplitude standards. *J. Genet. Psychol.*, *1939*, 55:197–213.

LOWREY, J. J. Subdural hematoma in infants. *Hawaii Med. J.*, *1952*, 11:145–148.

LUNDERVOLD, A. and NORDLIE, R. The electroencephalograms in chronic subdural hematoma. *Vth International Neurological Congress*, Lisbon, *1953*.

MABON, R. F. Trauma—Subdural effusions and hematomas in infants. *In:* I. J. JACKSON and R. K. THOMPSON (Editors), *Paediatric neurosurgery.* Oxford, *1959*.

MARINACCI, A. A., RAND, C. W. and MARINACCI, H. K. Electroencephalographic findings in chronic subdural hematoma of infancy and early childhood. *Bull. Los Angeles Neurol. Soc.*, *1951*, 16:255–266.

MARSH, C. Electroencephalographic changes due to cerebral trauma. *Bull. Los Angeles Neurol. Soc.*, *1944*, 9:38–45.

MARSH, C., HJARTARSON, G. D. and COURVILLE, C. B. The electroencephalographic findings in subdural hemorrhage and hematoma. *Bull. Los Angeles Neurol. Soc.*, *1949*, 14:163–181.

McKAY, R. J., MORISSETTE, R. A., INGRAHAM, F. D. and MATSON, D. D. Collections of subdural fluid complicating meningitis due to haemophilus influenzae (type B). *New England J. Med.*, *1950*, 242:20–21.

NORDLIE, R. *Chronic Subdural Hematoma.* Diss. Johan Grundt Taunum Forlag, Oslo, *1958*, p. 164.

PAILLAS, J. E. et NAQUET, R. Corrélations électro-anatomoclinques au cours des hématomes sous-duraux. *Rev. Neurol.*, *1950*, 83:602–608.

PAMPIGLIONE, G. Induced fast activity in the EEG as an aid in the location of cerebral lesions. *Electroenceph. clin. Neurophysiol.*, *1952*, 4:79–82.

PEET, M. M. and KAHN, E. A. Subdural hematoma in infants. *JAMA*, *1932*, 98:1851–1856.

POND, D. A. The development of normal rhythm. *In:* D. HILL and G. PARR (Editors), *Electroencephalography.* Macdonald, London, *1963*, 193–206.

PUECH, P., LERIQUE-KOECHLIN, A. et LERIQUE, J. L'électro-encéphalogramme dans les traumatismes cranio-cérébraux. Sa valeur diagnostique, pronostique et médico-légale. *Rev. Neurol.*, *1943*, 75:169–183.

RODIN, E. A., BICKFORD, R. G. and SVIEN, H. J. Electroencephalographic findings associated with subdural hematoma. *Arch. Neurol. Psychiat.*, *1953*, 69:743–755.

ROGERS, L. Electro-encephalography in traumatic intracranial haemorrhage. *Brit. Med. J.*, *1941*, 1:510–511.

ROHMER, F. et ISCH-TREUSSARD, C. L'électroencéphalogramme de l'enfant; ses indications; ses résultats. *Strassbourg Med.*, *1957*, 8:37–59.

ROHMER, F., GASTAUT, Y. et DELL, M. B. L'EEG dans la pathologie vasculaire du cerveau. *Rev. Neurol.*, *1952*, 87:109–144.

ROUGERIE, M. J. L'hématome sous-dural chronique du nourrisson. *Neurochir.*, *Stuttgart*, *1958*, 1:109–112.

SCHEPPE, K. J. Über das Schicksal konservativ behandelter Kinder mit subduralem Hämatom. *Mschr. Kinderheilk.*, *1954*, 102:414–417.

SCHWAB, R. S. *Electroencephalography in Clinical Practice.* W. B. Saunders Co., Philadelphia, *1951*, 195 pp.

SCHWAB, R. S. and CARTER, R. Electroencephalography in relation to otology. *Laryngoscope*, *1942*, 52:757–767.

SHERWOOD, D. Chronic subdural hematoma in infants. *AMA J. Dis. Child.*, *1930*, 39:980–1021.

SHULMAN, K. and RANSOHOFF, J. Subdural hematoma in children. The fate of children with retained membranes. *J. Neurosurg.*, *1961*, 18:175–181.

SJAARDEMA, H. and GLASER, M. A. The electro-encephalographic diagnosis of subdural hemorrhage. *Ann. Surg.*, *1942*, 116:452–460.

SMITH, G. W., MOSBERG, W. H., PFEIL, E. T. and OSTER, R. H. The electroencephalogram in subdural hematoma. *J.*

Neurosurg., *1950*, 7:207–218.

SMITH, J. R. Electroencephalogram during infancy and childhood. *Proc. Soc. Exp. Biol. Med.*, *1937*, 36:384–386.

SMITH, J. R. The electroencephalogram during normal infancy and childhood: III Preliminary observations on the pattern during sleep. *J. Genet. Psychol.*, *1953*, 53:471–482.

STEINMANN, H. und JOST, A. Über einen ungewöhnlichen hirnelektrischen Befund bei einem subduralen Hämatom. *Zbl. Neurochir.*, *1955*, 15:329–332.

STREIFLER, M., FREUNDLICH, E. and BELLER, A. J. Electroencephalography in subdural hematoma and effusion in infants. *AMA J. Dis. Child.*, *1958*, 95:25–29.

SULAMAA, M. and VARA, P. An investigation into the occurrence of perinatal subdural hematoma: Its diagnosis and treatment. *Acta Obst. Gynec. Scand.*, *1952*, 31:400–412.

SULLIVAN, J. F., ABBOT, J. A. and SCHWAB, R. S. The electroencephalogram in cases of subdural hematoma and hydroma. *Electroenceph. clin. Neurophysiol.*, *1951*, 3:131–139.

TURRELL, R. C., LEVY, L. L. and ROSEMAN, E. The value of the electroencephalogram in selected cases of subdural hematoma. *J. Neurosurg.*, *1956*, 13:449–454.

WERTHEIMER, P., COURJON, J. et ALLEGRE, G. E. Étude clinique et électroencéphalographique comparée de 17 hématomes sous-duraux. *Rev. Neurol.*, *1950*, 83:370–373.

WILLIAMS, D. and REYNELL, J. Abnormal suppression of cortical frequencies. *Brain*, *1945*, 68:123–161.

WOLF, G. *Das subdurale Hämatom und die Pachymeningitis haemorrhagica interna.* Springer Verlag., Berlin-Göttingen-Heidelberg, *1962*, 118 pp.

DISCUSSION

DR. PETERSÉN: I would suggest that we divide the considerations concerning diagnosis and prognosis into some categories for purposes of discussion. For instance, diagnostic information provided in the newborn period and diagnostic information in late infancy after the age of three years. Concerning prognostic information we have already discussed seizures to some extent, though we should add encephalitis, toxic infection, anoxia, etc., and also perhaps brain damage of unidentified origin and head injuries.

DR. GLASER: Dr. Petersén, your incidence of seizures in subdurals was 13 out of 20 which is as high as is known in infancy. In adults, clinical seizures in subdural hematoma are quite unusual unless the patients are in the chronic alcoholic group.

DR. PETERSÉN: There are big differences between subdurals in adults and infants. Regarding seizures, Ingraham and Matson point out that seizures are the most common symptom of subdural hematoma in infancy and childhood.

DR. GLASER: It has been said earlier that it may be difficult to elicit seizures from infants' cortex, so these seizures may not be related to the subdural directly but to some other pathologic process in the brain.

DR. PETERSÉN: Yes, in some cases, particularly in the cases which showed paroxysmal EEG abnormalities before operation and who did not improve after surgery.

DR. DREYFUS-BRISAC: Are you doing arteriography in newborns?

DR. PETERSÉN: Yes.

DR. KELLAWAY: I wonder if you have ever noticed that following removal of a subdural fluid accumulation that the EEG may be more depressed in that area than it was prior to surgery.

DR. PETERSÉN: I couldn't answer that question because in our small series there were no patients who had EEG's soon after surgery.

NEUROLOGICAL DEFICITS OF ASPHYXIA AT BIRTH OF RHESUS MONKEYS. PREVENTION AND THERAPY

WILLIAM F. WINDLE

*Laboratory of Perinatal Physiology, National Institute of Neurological Diseases and Blindness, National Institutes of Health, Public Health Service, U. S. Department of Health, Education and Welfare, Bethesda, Md., and the University of Puerto Rico, San Juan, Puerto Rico**

The brain damage of asphyxia during birth is an important factor in the etiology of mental retardation, using the term in its broadest sense. One definition of mental retardation is: "an organic condition of arrested or limited neural development that blocks successful evolution of the capacity of the brain to function, as the result of which, behavior and, at least in man, intellectual ability are impaired" (Windle, 1963b). The monkey (*Macaca Mulatta*) has been used for an experimental model to investigate this condition. Without going into details I shall sketch some of the findings of recent experiments and conclusions that can be drawn from them. A major tenet is that much of mental retardation should, in man, be avoidable and when conditions disposing toward it are unavoidable, mental retardation should be preventable by instituting appropriate therapeutic measures promptly, some of which we are now in position to discuss.

Natural Incidence of Brain Damage

Retardation of the kind to which I referred rarely if ever occurs naturally in rhesus monkeys. There have been over 500 births in freely ranging bands of these animals on islands in Puerto Rico and nearly half as many more have been born spontaneously in caged colonies. Prematurity is practically non-existent in the natural habitat groups, but occasionally a viable premature birth has taken place in the caged colony where spontaneous abortions are fairly common. Incidence of stillbirths has been about 4 per cent on the islands; these offspring were dead when first seen (Koford, 1964). There has been only one instance of retardation among surviving spontaneously born monkeys; this followed a breech delivery that was completed by our intervention to resuscitate the asphyxiated fetus (Hibbard and Windle, 1961). Had human obstetrical assistance been available in other instances some of the 4 per cent designated stillborn might have been resuscitated and likewise brain-damaged. It proved quite easy to induce brain damage experimentally. All rhesus monkeys delivered by cesarean section under local anesthesia and

---

*The author's present address is: Institute of Physical Medicine and Rehabilitation, New York University Medical Center, New York City.

asphyxiated experimentally for 7 minutes or more were found at postmortem to have permanent brain damage although most of them had shown only transient or no clinical signs of retardation (Windle, 1963a).

Characteristics of Asphyxia Neonatorum

When a monkey fetus is delivered by cesarian section under local anesthesia near term and asphyxiated by detaching the placenta or clamping the umbilical cord, being prevented the while from inhaling air, a series of events marks the progress of asphyxiation (Adamsons et al., in press). It begins to make rhythmical respiratory movements within 30 seconds. These cease in less than a minute and are followed briefly by mass movements of a clonic nature. Apnea lasts about a minute before the fetus begins to gasp in a slow rhythm (3 to 8 per minute) which ceases after about 8.5 minutes of asphyxia at 30° C environmental temperature.

During asphyxia the blood pressure rises transiently and then falls to very low levels (e. g. 15 mm Hg). In the brief period during which it rises the heart rate declines to less than half its normal value, continuing on down more slowly to 50 beat/min or even less as the asphyxia progresses. The skin color changes from pink to blue in the first minute or two and then to white as *asphyxia pallida* ensues. The pH of arterial blood drops to 6.8 or lower, the pCO_2 becomes markedly elevated, blood lactate increases, the lactate: pyruvate ratio becomes very high, and a base deficit of more than 20 meq per liter accumulates. Thus the circulation fails rapidly and a severe metabolic acidosis develops during asphyxia neonatorum (Adamsons et al., in press; Adamsons et al., 1964 in press). The oxygen content of the fetal blood is practically zero at this time. How much of the subsequently observed brain damage is attributable to anoxia per se and how much to the acidosis is not yet clear.

These changes are not reversed immediately or completely by correcting the anoxia. After intubating the trachea, artificial ventilation (and cardiac massage, when necessary) bring about a rapid increase in rate of the heart beat and a rise in blood pressure. The arterial pCO_2 declines from its high asphyxial to a normal value and the pH usually rises to about 7.0 within 4 minutes; there is little or no change in blood lactate and 20 minutes or more may elapse before the pH reaches 7.2. Even though artificial ventilation is accompanied by these encouraging signs the rate of oxygen uptake by the neonatal monkey often does not rise promptly, but it may take as long as 2 minutes before any significant increase occurs (Adamsons et al., 1964 in press). Therefore asphyxia may continue in the tissues for some time after air fills the lungs of the newborn. The lag in elevation of oxygen uptake is illustrated in Figure 1.

When asphyxia is permitted to continue beyond 10 or 12 minutes the metabolic acidosis becomes more marked and the chance that resuscitation will be successful diminishes. Monkeys asphyxiated for more than 15 minutes often failed to recover.

Among forty-three animals that were asphyxiated for 10, 12.5 and 15

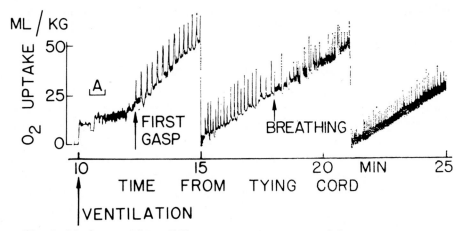

Fig. 1. Monkey weighing 565 g. at cesarien section delivery near term was asphyxiated for 10 minutes. The record shows O_2 uptake during resuscitation. Blood pressure was less than 10 mm. Hg. at start. Cardiac massage through closed chest occurred at A. The fetal lungs began to expand at the first artificial ventilation (upswing at first arrow). No signicant increase in O_2 uptake occurred until after the first gasp 2 minutes later (Adamsons *et al.*, 1964, in press).

minutes, the mean time from onset of asphyxia until the last gasp before terminal apnea was 8.5 minutes. The longer the asphyxia was continued thereafter, the longer it took to establish spontaneous breathing with artificial ventilation. For each 1 minute after the last gasp *in amnio*, 2 minutes were required before the first gasp of air, and 4 minutes before rhythmical breathing was established (Adamsons *et al.*, 1964 in press). This is shown in Figure 2.

The behavior of monkeys that were asphyxiated during birth and resuscitated has been discussed (Ranck and Windle, 1958; Windle, 1962, 1963; Windle *et al.*, 1962, 1961). Acute effects and residual deficits have been illustrated with motion pictures. The neuropathology of *asphyxia neonatorum* likewise has been described (Dekaban and Windle, 1962; Lucey *et al.*, 1964; Ranck and Windle, 1959; Windle, 1963; Windle *et al.*, 1962, 1961).

The least asphyxia that put a mark on the brain of a mature newborn monkey was 7 minutes in duration (Windle, 1963a). That animal required no resuscitation when released from the fetal membranes because it was still making gasps, not having reached the stage of terminal asphyxial apnea. Nevertheless discrete, bilaterally symmetrical lesions were present in the inferior colliculi and in a few other brain stem nuclei. Neonatal monkeys with such small lesions show no lasting clinical signs of retardation although tests may not have been refined enough to detect effects of relatively minor injuries limited to afferent centers in the brain stem.

A more extensive pattern of discrete nonhemorrhagic lesions in the brain stem presented itself in all monkeys asphyxiated for 10 minutes or more; these animals did require artificial ventilation. Besides those of the inferior colliculi,

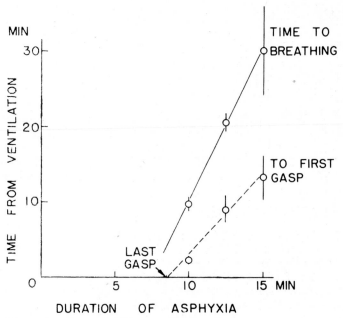

Fig. 2. Mean time from artificial ventilation to first gasp (broken line) and to spontaneous rhythmical respiration (solid line) in groups of five or six monkeys each after standard conditions of asphyxia for 10, 12.5 and 15 minutes without treatment. Last gasp (arrow before ventilation was at 8.54 0.20 minutes (Adamsons *et al.*, 1964, in press).

other nuclei in auditory, vestibular and somesthetic pathways were selectively destroyed. As a rule the losses were confined to the thalamus and brain stem, the most severe lesion being found in the inferior colliculus. An acute focal lesion encountered there is shown in Figure 3. Monkeys that experienced episodes of early postpartum depression, including the respiratory distress syndrome, showed very severe central nervous damage, not infrequently in the vermis of the cerebellum, hippocampus and cerebral cortex (Figure 4) in addition to marked damage of the brain stem centers. Animals in the latter catagory were unequivocally retarded; indeed, they presented many of the signs of neurological disorders of human infancy (Windle *et al.*, 1962, 1961). On the other hand, those monkeys that experienced no postnatal depression and recovered uneventfully after asphyxia of 10 to 15 minutes duration exhibited more subtle or no clinical signs. They were apt to be quiet, hyporeactive and somewhat clumsy. Some of then lacked the emotional outbursts that in test situations characterize normal rhesus monkeys (Saxon and Ponce, 1961). Efforts to evaluate clinically the effects of anatomical lesions have not been rewarded in many monkeys; the animals seemed quite "normal" as they matured. The impression has been that the least effect manifested itself as a docile and rather unperturbable monkey. On the other extreme, the most marked anatomical brain damage was associated with a state of coma. In between lay a wide range of sensory and motor deficits constituting

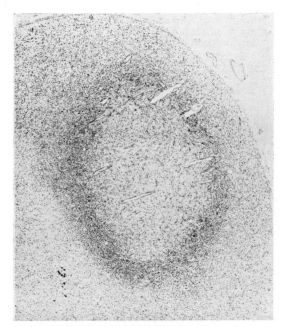

Fig. 3. Photomicrograph showing necrotic lesion in nucleus of inferior colliculus 9 days after asphyxiation for 15+ minutes and no treatment.

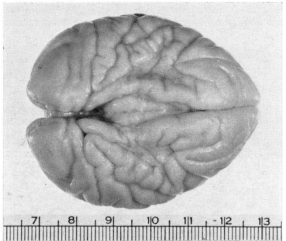

Fig. 4. Cerebral cortical atrophy in the brain of a monkey asphyxiated but not treated. This animal recovered from prolonged respiratory distress after resuscitation at birth.

various degrees of mental retardation, as I have defined the term (Windle, 1963b).

Mitigation of Deficits of Asphyxia

Having established clinical and neuropathological parameters of asphyxia neonatorum in the rhesus monkey, it was proposed by Dr. Geoffry Dawes that attention be directed toward prolonging survival under asphyxia, and if successful, toward instituting therapeutic measures to mitigate or perhaps even to prevent the neural damage, which lies at the heart of the problem of mental retardation.

The ability of a neonate to withstand anoxia is directly related to myo-

Table 1.—*Monkeys Treated with Na$_2$CO$_3$ and Glucose during Asphyxia for 15 Minutes at Birth in 1960–61*

	Total No.	Dead on day 1	Survivors used for histology	Living October 1963
Untreated	11	7	3	1
Treated	11	3*	4	4

*One treated monkey was immature; another had a cardiac infarct at 4 hours.

cardial concentration of glycogen, the circulation being maintained from energy released during anaerobic glycolysis, a process favored by an alkaline environment (Dawes *et al.*, 1960; Shelley, 1960). Experiments were designed to prevent development of the metabolic acidosis of a standard degree of asphyxia at birth (Adamsons *et al.*, in press; Dawes *et al.*, 1963).

A solution of glucose containing anhydrous sodium carbonate was infused slowly into the femoral vein during asphyxiation lasting 15 minutes. This prolonged the survival at birth, assisted recovery and lessened the degree of brain damage. There were twenty-two monkeys in this catagory. These are shown in Table 1. Seven of eleven untreated ones could not be resuscitated or died on day 1; four survived and three of these were sacrificed for histological studies. Three of eleven monkeys infused with sodium carbonate in glucose solution died on day 1 (one with a cardiac infarct and one immature that had been in poor condition before delivery); four of the eight survivors were sacrificed for histological studies.

Severe permanent brain damage was found in two of the three untreated monkeys. Exceptionally slight lesions appeared in the brains of three of the four that had been infused. The lesions were about equal in the remaining monkeys, one treated and one untreated. Five animals of this series are still living. The one untreated animal has an abnormal EEG and marked clinical neurological deficits resembling human cerebral palsy. Two of the four treated monkeys appear normal clinically, a third is borderline, and the fourth is an athetoid individual with an abnormal EEG (unpublished).

It became evident during these studies that 15 minutes of asphyxia was more than optimal for experimental purposes and furthermore that sodium carbonate was too basic and hypertonic. Thirty-three other monkeys were asphyxiated for periods of 12.5 and 10 minutes during cesarian section delivery under local anesthesia as before. Approximately equal numbers were untreated as were given infusions of glucose and an alkali by way of the umbilical vein, some during (Adamsons *et al.*, in press) and other after asphyxiation (Adamsons *et al.*, 1964 in press). In both groups the treated differed from untreated monkeys in that the blood pressure and heart rate were better maintained, gasping was prolonged and spontaneous respiration was established more rapidly.

Of the three bases tested in these experiments, sodium carbonate and sodium bicarbonate were discarded because the former caused severe liver damage, even though it was effective in prolonging survival, and the latter required large volume and give higher pCO$_2$ values than found in controls. The best base was 0.5M THAM (trishydroxymethylaminomethane), 6 ml be-

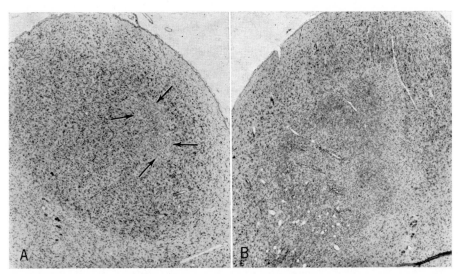

Fig. 5. Photomicrographs of nucleus of inferior colliculus about 2 months after 12.5 min. asphyxia at birth. A. Scar of a small lesion (arrow) in the lateral part of the nucleus; most of the nucleus was unaffected. B. Entire nucleus involved in massive scar. (Dawes *et al.*, 1964, in press).

ing infused with 3.5 per cent glucose solution into the umbilical vein in 2–4 minutes. It was the most satisfactory agent in lowering pCO_2 and maintaining vital signs.

At the time of the Symposium, neurological evaluation of the subjects asphyxiated for 12.5 minutes (Adamsons *et al.*, in press) was incomplete. The brains of thirteen had been sectioned and studied histologically but the identity of infused and noninfused subjects was unknown to me. I reported that two brains had no recognizable lesion; three had a small scar in the lateral part of the nucleus of inferior colliculus but no lesion elsewhere (Figure 5A); and three had a larger though incomplete inferior collicular lesion and no other pathological findings. Brain damage of such limited extent is less than encountered previously in untreated asphyxiated monkeys. Five other brains displayed nearly complete destruction of the inferior colliculi (Figure 5B) and a number of other brain stem nuclei were involved; two had cerebellar lesions.

Following the Symposium Dr. Dawes and I decoded the data. As seen in Table 2, administration of alkali and glucose during asphyxia of 12.5 minutes duration reduced the incidence and extent of brain lesions. There was a good correlation between physiological observations and pH changes in the blood during asphyxia and resuscitation, and the histological evidence of permanent brain damage. Thus it appears that neurological damage of *asphyxia neonatorum* can be mitigated therapeutically (Dawes *et al.*, 1964 in press).

Respiratory Distress

Respiratory distress remarkably like that in human infants was encountered after spontaneous respiration had been established in some of the asphyxiated

Table 2.—*Permanent Brain Damage in Rhesus Monkeys Asphyxiated for 12.5 Minutes at Birth, With or Without Infusion of Alkali and Glucose*[*]

	Infusion	Duration of gasping during asphyxia mins.	Time from beginning resuscitation to establish breathing mins.	Lesions in	
				Inferior Colliculus	Other brain-stem nuclei
1	+	12.3	7.2	0	0
2	+	12.5	3.8	0	0
3	+	12.3	5.1	+	0
4	+	10.0	10.6	+	0
5	+	12.2	12.1	+	0
6	+	10.9	8.8	++	0
7	+	12.5	7.2	++	0
8	+	11.2	8.5	++	0
9	0	9.3	16.0	++++	+
10	0	7.2	20.5	++++	+
11	0	8.5	22.5	++++	++
12	0	7.5	22.3	++++	+
13	0	7.9	47.5	++++	++

[*]Infusion into the umbilical vein of either sodium carbonate, sodium bicarbonate or Tris, each with glucose, from 6.5 minutes after the onset of asphyxia for 4 minutes.

neonatal monkeys (Adamsons *et al.*, 1964 in press). The syndrome is characterized by labored respiration lasting more than an hour, with deep sternal recession during inspiration, grunting expiration, pallor, increased respiratory rate, periodic breathing and cyanotic attacks. Oxygen must be given. Pulmonary edema was encountered in some, especially those of lighter body weights. Monkeys in respiratory distress usually had lower rates of oxygen utilization that those resuscitated uneventfully. Administration of oxygen improved the condition, but recovery of others took as long as 2 or 3 days. Death frequently occured during respiratory distress. Animals recovering and later sacrificed exhibited marked neuropathological defects. Lesions of the cerebral cortex (Figure 3) have been encountered only in animals which had experienced respiratory distress on the first day or two of life. Monkeys born normally or delivered by cesarean section without asphyxiation have not shown respiratory distress. In recent experiments involving forty-three monkeys asphyxiated for 10 to 15 minutes, there were twenty-one in respiratory distress (Table 3). The incidence was significantly higher among those of lower birth weights. Data on the relation between infusion of alkali and glucose solution and occurrence of respiratory distress are too few to be significant. However, some of the infused monkeys did develop the syndrome. It is noteworthy that respiratory distress did not develop in two whose hearts had stopped beating (one for more than 4–5 minutes). Asphyxia during

Table 3.—*Incidence of Respiratory Distress in Monkeys Asphyxiated for 10–15 Minutes at Birth*

Weight	No.	No. with pulmonary complications	No. dying in 24 hours
>500	13	5	0
400–500	17	7	2
<400	13	9	7

birth appears to be a causal factor in the respiratory distress syndrome of the monkey, but the precise relationship has not been determined.

ACKNOWLEDGMENT

The research summarized in this communication was carried out by various members of our staff collaborating with a number of guests from other institutions in this and foreign countries during the last five years. The names of participants, too numerous to include on the title page, will be found in the list of references cited.

REFERENCES

ADAMSONS, K. JR., BEHRMAN, R. E., DAWES, G. S., DAWKINS, M. J. R., JAMES, L. S. and Ross, B. B. The treatment of acidosis with alkali and glucose during asphyxia in foetal rhesus monkeys. *J. Physiol. (London)*, in press.

ADAMSONS, K. JR., BEHRMAN, R. E., DAWES, G. S., JAMES, L. S. and KOFORD, C. B. Asphyxia and metabolic acidosis in foetal rhesus monkeys. *J. Pediat., 1964,* in press.

DAWES, G. S., HIBBARD, E. and WINDLE, W. F. The effect of alkali and glucose infusion on permanent brain damage in rhesus monkeys asphyxiated at birth. *J. Pediat., 1964,* in press.

DAWES, G. S., JACOBSON, H. N., MOTT, J. C. and SHELLEY, H. J. Some observations on foetal and newborn rhesus monkeys. *J. Physiol. (London), 1960,* 152:271–298.

DAWES, G. S., JACOBSON, H. N., MOTT, J. C., SHELLEY, H. J. and STAFFORD, H. The treatment of asphyxiated, mature foetal lambs and rhesus monkeys with intravenous glucose and sodium carbonate. *J. Physiol. (London), 1963,* 169:167–184.

DEKABAN, A. and WINDLE, W. F. Hemorrhagic lesions in acute birth injuries. *J. Neuropathol. Exp. Neurol., 1962,* 21: 305–307.

HIBBARD, E. and WINDLE, W. F. Neurological consequences of a spontaneous breech delivery with head-retention in a monkey. *Anat. Rec., 1961,* 140:239.

KOFORD, C. B. Population dynamics of rhesus monkeys on Cayo Santiago. *In: Primate Behavior: Field Studies of Monkeys and Apes.* Holt, Rinehart and Winston, *1964,* in press.

LUCEY, J. F., BEHRMAN, R. E., ESQUIVEL DE GALLARDO, F. O., HIBBARD, E. and WINDLE, W. F. Kernicterus in asphyx-

iated newborn rhesus monkeys. *Exp. Neurol., 1964,* 9:43–58.

RANCK, J. B. JR. and WINDLE, W. F. Asphyxia neonatorum in Macaca mulatta. *Physiologist, 1958,* 1:63.

RANCK, J. B. JR., and WINDLE, W. F. Brain damage in the monkey Macaca mulatta, by asphyxia neonatorum. *Exp. Neurol., 1959,* 1:130–154.

SAXON, S. V. and PONCE, C. G. Behavioral defects in monkeys asphyxiated during birth. *Exp. Neurol., 1961,* 4:460–469.

SHELLEY, H. J. Blood sugars and tissue carbohydrate in foetal and infant lambs and rhesus monkeys. *J. Physiol. (London), 1960,* 153:527–552.

WINDLE, W. F. Deficiencias neurologicas en monos recien nacidos. *Inter. J. Neurol., 1962,* 3:428–432.

WINDLE, W. F. Selective vulnerability of the central nervous system of rhesus monkeys to asphyxia during birth. *In:* J. P. Schade and McMenemey (editors) *Selective Vulnerability of the Brain in Hypoxaemia.* Blackwell Sci. Publ., London, *1963(a),* pp. 251–255.

WINDLE, W. F. Neuropathology of certain forms of mental retardation. *Science, 1963(b),* 140:1186–1189.

WINDLE, W. F., JACOBSON, H. N., ROBERT DE RAMIREZ DE ARELLANO, M. I. and COMBS, C. M. Structural and functional sequelae of asphyxia neonatorum in monkeys *(Macaca mulatta). Res. Publ. Assoc. Res. Nerv. Men. Dis., 1962,* 39:169–182.

WINDLE, W. F., ROBERT DE RAMIREZ DE ARELLANO, M. I. and HIBBARD, E. Role de l'asphyxia pendant la naissance dans la génése des troubles du jeune singe. *Rev. Neurol., 1961,* 105:142–152.

DISCUSSION

DR. PETERSÉN: Have neuropathologic studies been conducted on these neonatal monkeys subjected to asphyxia?

DR. WINDEL: Yes, it appears that all monkeys that are carried beyond the point of intraamniotic gasping have more severe neuropathology. Essentially this is limited to brain stem and thalamus, the diencephalon and parts caudal to that. These lesions are nonhemorrhagic, selective, bilateral and well circumscribed. They involve predominantly nuclei of the afferent systems such as the auditory, which is the most sensitive. The nucleus of the inferior colliculus is invariably damaged bilaterally, and next in order the other nuclei of the auditory system. There is no cerebral cortical injury that we can detect and no cerebellar injury, as a rule, except in the nuclei of the cerebellum, and that isn't usually pronounced. But if these animals undergo a period of respiratory difficulty after birth, including the respiratory distress syndrome, they may then show damage to the cerebral cortex which may be very severe. The cerebellum, hippocampus, and corpus striatum may be involved also.

DR. GOLDRING: Could you please clarify the conditions under which the cortex is damaged?

DR. WINDLE: We encountered damage to cerebral cortex only in monkeys in which the "respiratory distress syndrome" had been noted. This syndrome was characterized by retraction of the chest, depression of the sternum, deep inspiration and grunting expiration, the animals often appearing cyanotic at intervals and requiring oxygen.

DR. PARMELEE: In corroboration of your observations of the "lack of emotionality" in brain-damaged monkeys, Prechtl has noticed a somewhat similar situation in children with neonatal hypoxia. It appears that these children demonstrate various types of choreiform movements, and have some school problems. They also seem to demonstrate a lack of anxiety in stressful situations.

DR. PRICHARD: I think the children are a little different. The child with this syndrome is distractable. He can't fix his attention for long.

DR. ARELLANO: This same picture occurs in the monkeys; these animals do not pay attention to what you want them to do.

DR. PAMPIGLIONE: It appears that in the literature the definition of asphyxia is somewhat confusing. The early investigators considered "asphyxia neonatorum" as a period of apnea, from whatever cause, following birth, and this is quite a different definition from the one you use.

DR. PARMELEE: I would agree with this statement, because intra-uterine problems that could contribute to anoxia are lumped into this group as well. It is sometimes apparent that the acute episodes of anoxia are less traumatic in terms of sequelae. They cause many problems at the moment of birth with immediate consequences to the baby, but there is good recovery in terms of what we can pick up later on.

DR. DREYFUS-BRISAC: If we consider the group with asphyxia due only to neonatal apnea, it appears that below twenty minutes there are no important sequelae or asphyxia, but when the period of apnea is greater than twenty minutes one can expect neurologic sequelae.

DR. GLASER: Dr. Windle, if, as you say, the lesions are primarily confined to the afferent systems, to what do you attribute the motor components of the neurologic disturbances, especially spasticity, that these asphyxiated monkeys demonstrate?

DR. WINDLE: Of course there is some diffuse damage, but it would seem that the motor disturbances are primarily secondary to the damage to the afferent systems.

DR. KELLAWAY: What was the incidence of seizures in your group?

DR. WINDLE: The incidence was not high.

DR. KELLAWAY: It is necessary to distinguish two different types of situations, seizures which occur acutely and those which develop and remain in later life.

DR. WINDLE: Seizures were not commonly seen in later life, but we did note electrographic abnormalities.

DR. KELLAWAY: Yes, this is true of cerebral palsy. We find a tremendous number of silent foci as far as seizures are concerned in children with cerebral palsy, and the question is are these projected subcortical discharges rather than focal cortical abnormalities?

DR. PRICHARD: In our group we followed up almost 300 children who had seizures in the first month of life, and, of these, only quite a small number had seizures as older children.

DR. PARMELEE: In these cortical lesions that occur with respiratory distress, could one suggest that they precede the respiratory distress and are the cause of it?

DR. WINDLE: We are not sure, but it appears that cortical damage occurs just afterwards and I think for that reason it is related to the metabolic acidosis more than to the anoxia.

DR. KELLAWAY: As a working hypothesis, we have suggested the possibility that in many of these asphyxiated neonates we are dealing neurologically and electrographically with abnormalities which are primarily brain stem in origin but which give rise to changes of circulatory and respiratory function which may in turn compromise cortical elements and result in damage or dysfunction.

SOME EFFECTS OF CEREBRAL ISCHEMIA IN CHILDREN

G. PAMPIGLIONE

The Hospital for Sick Children, London, England

The importance of the blood supply to the brain has been recognized for a very long time, and the neurological phenomena that may follow severe blood loss and occlusion of major vessels were beautifully described by Kussmaul and Tenner (1859) over one hundred years ago. It would be difficult to improve on their clinical descriptions, and our contribution will cover only some neurophysiological studies carried out on infants and children during or after episodes of cerebral ischemia.

Our studies are related to those cerebral phenomena that may follow gross transitory alterations in the general circulation, including cardiac arrest. For practical purposes and in order to simplify the total number of possible variables, we shall consider the encephalon as if it were a single organ and the blood supply to it as if it were fairly uniform in various regions of the brain. Although many details about the origin of the electrical activity of the brain are still uncertain, we know, both empirically and experimentally, that the metabolic activity of the nervous tissue has considerable influence upon the type of electrical activity recorded from the scalp, whether in animal or man. We have learned from practical experience that the patterns of electrical activity of the brain may represent a sensitive index as to whether the cerebral biochemical mechanisms are working either within or outside their normal range. In our studies, therefore, we have been utilizing electroencephalography as one of the many physical signs in medicine, bearing in mind, however, that in particular conditions information as to the state of cerebral function may not be obtained through other physical signs.

The brain of an infant or child appears to withstand considerable transitory diminutions in oxygen supply and blood pressure without recognizable alteration of function. The individual variations are great, but there seems to be a particular level below which the cerebral circulation becomes "inadequate". Our ability to detect whether some alteration in cerebral function does occur usually determines our judgment of such "inadequacy of circulation". That is to say, the more sensitive our measurements become, the more efficient is our detective work.

Although minor clinical changes due to "inadequate" cerebral circulation may be easy to detect in a conscious and cooperative patient, appreciation of these changes when the patient is anesthetized or comatose may become very difficult, while the study of the electrical activity of the brain may still offer considerable help.

After a period of circulatory arrest, at normal body temperature, a series of changes develop in the central nervous system and function fails. After the re-establishment of an adequate circulation, another series of phenomena occur in the tissues, and a variety of clinical manifestations may appear. These phenomena are related to the duration of inadequate circulation in the central nervous system, to the pre-existing condition of the patient and of his brain, to the methods of resuscitation, and to several other factors not yet fully understood.

Through the kindness of my colleagues at Great Ormond Street, I was notified at any time of day or night as soon as a patient was in cardiocirculatory or respiratory distress. Over a period of six years, EEG data have been accumulated on sixty children and infants in whom a definite cardiac arrest had occurred either in the ward or in the anesthetic room and in whom resuscitation had been carried out with either direct or external cardiac massage. Fourteen other patients studied had periods of severe respiratory or circulatory difficulties without complete circulatory arrest. In addition, sixteen patients had either gross circulatory difficulty or an unwanted cardiac arrest during an operation on the heart and main vessels at a time when EEG studies were being carried out in the operating theater.

There seems little doubt that the best place to have a cardiac arrest is in the operating theater—if possible when the chest is open and when the body temperature is lower than usual—preferably with an experienced and alert surgeon nearby and, even better, when EEG and ECG changes can be recorded. This being a somewhat unusual combination of events, only a limited number of observations could be made (Fig. 1).

When allowance is made for the patient's age and pre-existing cerebral conditions, the EEG changes following a rapid fall in blood supply to the brain appear within 5 to 10 seconds if the patient's body temperature is not below 27–28°C. and if there is no gross venous engorgement (Schneider, 1961; Pampiglione and Waterston, 1961). An ingenious demonstration of this phenomenon had already been devised by Rossen, Kabat and Anderson (1943), who developed an inflatable pressure cuff to be placed around the neck of some 126 normal young male "volunteers". This cuff could be inflated within one-eighth of a second to a pressure of 600 mm/Hg., and loss of consciousness followed this maneuver in about 6.8 seconds, on the average, coinciding with the appearance of slow activity in the EEG.

In our experience, in exceptional cases when the ascending aorta had to be clamped for a short period during an operation, there was marked change in the EEG in a matter of 6 to 10 seconds with diminution of fast components and the appearance of large slow waves for a few seconds. This was followed by flattening of the traces upon which muscle action potentials appeared, while the patient had a mild tonic seizure (Fig. 2), probably modified by anesthetics and muscle relaxants. If the blood supply to the brain is immediately restored, the EEG will return to its previous appearance in a matter of a few seconds or minutes. In general, the return to the original pattern of activity may occur only if the adequate circulation is re-established within a couple of minutes at normal body temperature.

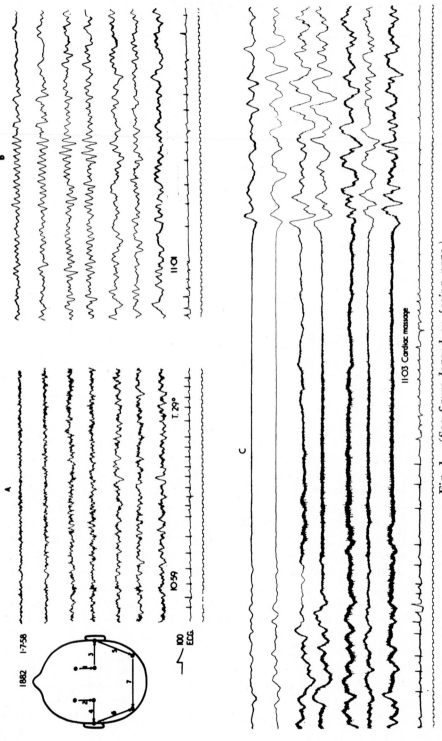

Fig. 1.—(See figure legend on facing page.)

When a patient is found pulseless in the ward, the nearest doctor is alerted, and he must promptly make up his mind whether or not to attempt to resuscitate the patient. Through a series of mechanical maneuvers, the heart beat may be re-established and, technically, the patient is again alive. Usually the patient remains unconscious or in a coma for a period of time, which may last a few hours or a few days or sometimes longer. During this period, the risk of further cardiocirculatory or respiratory difficulties, metabolic complications, and seizures is great. The efforts and attention of the resuscitation team are heavily tested, and it is difficult to predict from a clinical state that varies from minute to minute not only the chances of survival but even the chances of either good or poor survival.

Is this patient going to recover fully in a few hours? Is he going to remain alive with a gross mental and neurological impairment? Is he really alive or is he a decerebrate heart-lung preparation? Should any further fight against death cease? Is there any rapid way of evaluating whether a prolonged cardiac massage is doing any good? Is the continuing artificial respiration of any benefit to the patient? Are fits likely to occur, with further risk of circulatory distress?

With very few exceptions, the total duration of an episode of cerebral ischemia preceding successful resuscitation is not known. Any retrospective evaluation has proven quite unreliable, even when experienced people are involved, if they forgot to look at their watch. When less experienced observers attempt a guess, the range of error may be very great. From the few well timed cases we have studied, we know that, in general, the chances of full recovery of cerebral function fall rapidly when the circulatory arrest has lasted more than three minutes at normal body temperature. It has been stressed by Schneider (1961), among others, that if minimal residual circulation through the brain persists during an apparent cardiac arrest, the tolerance of the brain to relative ischemia may be prolonged.

From our observations, after a period of circulatory arrest of unknown duration, useful prognostic criteria could be derived from the EEG features seen between 2 and 24 hours after resuscitation. Carefully timed EEG studies may give precious information about the patient's cerebral condition, about his chances of survival from that episode, about the possible occurrence of seizures in the next few hours, and about the probable beneficial

---

Fig. 1. This boy, aged 5, during a chest operation with moderate extracorporeal cooling had some cardiocirculatory difficulties and then a cardiac arrest. Cardiac massage had to be carried out for nearly one-half hour. The EEG had been recorded throughout from the regions on the scalp indicated in the head diagram. The 8th channel records the electrocardiogram throughout. The time scale is in $\frac{1}{2}$ seconds. In A, the EEG and ECG are shown prior to the accident. In B, a diminution of the blood supply to the brain probably accompanied the cardiac irregularities. In C, the heart action had stopped, with gross increase in slow activity and appearance of muscle action potentials superimposed upon the EEG. Soon the cerebral activity disappeared altogether, to reappear, however, within 10 seconds from the beginning of cardiac massage.

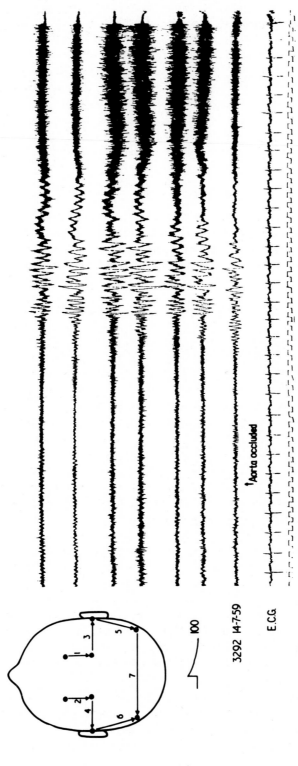

Fig. 2. Less than 8 seconds after the transitory occlusion of the ascending aorta there was a rapid increase in slow components in the EEG, followed by a disappearance of cerebral activity. Muscle action potential, however, became prominent at this stage, while the patient had a mild tonic spasm, probably modified by curarisation. No gross cardiac irregularity appeared. The time scale is in ½ seconds.

A
SURVIVAL - GOOD CEREBRAL FUNCTION

B
SURVIVAL - IMPAIRED CEREBRAL FUNCTION

C
"DEATH OF THE BRAIN" - NO SURVIVAL

D
GROSSLY DAMAGED CEREBRAL FUNCTION
DOUBTFUL SURVIVAL

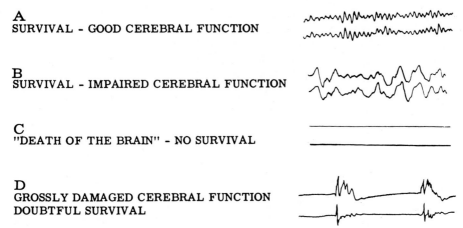

Fig. 3. Schematic and simplified comparison of the EEG features from 2 to 15 hours after cardiac arrest and resuscitation in children in relation to the final outcome at the end of a week. In the first hour or so after resuscitation these criteria have doubtful validity, apart from A. (From *Proc. Roy. Soc. Med.*, 1962, 55:653.)

effects of assisted respiration. In particular instances, the efficiency of cardiac massage may be evaluated utilizing the electrical activity of the brain as an indicator of the adequacy of artificially assisted cerebral circulation (Fig. 1). Some apparatus has been developed to transform the low frequency visual signals of the conventional EEG display into a simplified code of audio signals (Pampiglione and Picton-Robinson, 1960). Although this apparatus was devised primarily for use in the operating theater, particularly during cardio-thoracic operations, this approach might perhaps become a useful addition to the equipment of a resuscitation team, whose visual concentration is directed to tasks other than looking at an EEG. For example, in cases where prolonged cardiac massage must be carried out, an audio-monitoring of the EEG might represent a quick way of "listening" for whether some kind of cerebral activity has been re-established, whether the brain is "dead silent", or whether it is already producing grossly abnormal signals as a prodrome to more obvious clinical seizures.

A schematic prognostic guide was put forward in a previous paper (Pampiglione, 1962) based on the EEG features recorded about 2 to 24 hours after resuscitation, and it has become widely accepted (Fig. 3). It is important to remember, however, that no real rule exists, as each patient with cardiocirculatory difficulties affecting his brain is in a unique condition which may vary from moment to moment. He may even have the right to die, irrespective of the wishes or efforts of the resuscitator, although exceptional cases have been published of patients resuscitated over a dozen times or even one hundred times after repeated circulatory arrests.

A word of gratitude and encouragement to the resuscitation team should conclude our remarks. When a patient is found pulseless and apparently dead in the ward or elsewhere, there is no opportunity—and certainly no time —to assess either the chances of revival or those of good survival. If the resuscitator stops to evaluate the slender chances of success before acting, those chances rapidly vanish, as one minute may make all the difference. He has to act quickly. It is only later, and usually retrospectively, that a fuller evaluation of the rapid events can be made. It is at this later stage, probably a couple of hours or so after resuscitation, the careful and well timed clinical, biochemical, and neurophysiological studies might give the precious information as to whether or not it is worthwhile to continue the struggle against death.

REFERENCES

ARFEL, G., WEISS, J. and DU BOUCHET, N. EEG findings during open heart surgery with extra-corporeal circulation. In: H. GASTAUT and J. S. MEYER (Editors), Cerebral Anoxia and the Electroencephalogram. Charles C. Thomas, Springfield, Ill., 1961, pp. 231–249.

BRAZIER, M. A. B. The EEG in open-heart surgery and in surgery for aortic and cerebral aneurysms. In: H. GASTAUT and J. S. MEYER (Editors), Cerebral Anoxia and the Electroencephalogram. Charles C. Thomas, Springfield, Ill., 1961, pp. 256–267.

FISCHGOLD, H. and MATHIS, P. Ornubilations comas et stupeurs. Electroenceph. clin. Neurophysiol., 1959, suppl. 11, 124.

KUSSMAUL, A. and TENNER, A. On the nature of and origin of epileptiform convulsions after a profuse bleeding. The New Sydenham Society, 1859.

PAMPIGLIONE, G. Neurophysiological aspects of cerebral ischaemia. Proc. R. Soc. Med., 1960, 53:329–332.

PAMPIGLIONE, G. and PICTON-ROBINSON, N. Audio-monitoring of electroencephalography during surgery and anesthesia. Lancet, 1960, 2:352.

PAMPIGLIONE, G. and WATERSTON, D. J. EEG observations during changes in venous and arterial pressure. In: H. GASTAUT and J. S. MEYER (Editors),

Cerebral Anoxia and the Electroencephalogram. Charles C. Thomas, Springfield, Ill., 1961, pp. 250–255.

PAMPIGLIONE, G. Electroencephalographic studies after cardiorespiratory resuscitation. Proc. R. Soc. Med., 1962, 55:653–657.

ROSSEN, R., KABAT, H. and ANDERSON, J. P. Acute arrest of cerebral circulation in man. Arch. Neurol. Psychiat., 1943, 50:510–528.

SCHNEIDER, M. Survival and revival of the brain in anoxia and ischemia. In: H. GASTAUT and J. S. MEYER (Editors), Cerebral Anoxia and the Electroencephalogram. Charles C. Thomas, Springfield, Ill., 1961, pp. 137–172.

STORM VAN LEEUWEN, W., MECHELSE, K., KOK, L. and ZIERFUSS, E. EEG during heart operations with artificial circulation. In: H. GASTAUT and J. S. MEYER (Editors), Cerebral Anoxia and the Electroencephalogram. Charles C. Thomas, Springfield, Ill., 1961, pp. 268–278.

THIES-PUPPEL, H. and WIEMERS, K. Survival time and latency of recovery of EEG during heart surgery in hypothermia. In: H. GASTAUT and J. S. MEYER (Editors), Cerebral Anoxia and the Electroencephalogram. Charles C. Thomas, Springfield, Ill., 1961, pp. 279–291.

DISCUSSION

DR. PRICHARD: Dr. Pampiglione, I wonder if you have any data relating to the effect of hypothermia on the electrical activity of the brain?

DR. PAMPIGLIONE: Although systematic studies have not been done, we have not seen substantial changes in the EEG that we are able to recognize in relation to changes in body temperature down to 28°C.

DR. WINDLE: How long following cardiac arrest does cerebral activity continue, that is, how long does it take before the baseline is flat?

DR. PAMPIGLIONE: In cases of circulatory standstill, I would expect the tracing to be flat by the end of six to ten seconds.

DR. PRICHARD: Have you been able to relate the effects of various hemodynamic changes in cerebral circulation to these electrographic changes? That is to say, have you noted any relationship between say a decrease in arterial pressure or perhaps is it more a question of an increase in venous pressure?

DR. PAMPIGLIONE: It seems probable that the increase in venous pressure may be responsible for some particular EEG changes as well as the decrease in arterial pressure. What appears to be important in particular is the relative difference between the arterial and venous pressures within the skull at critical levels. I hope to give you some more data the next time we meet in two or three years time, perhaps sooner.

DR. KELLAWAY: Inferring from your data on operative material, wouldn't you say that knowing that there had been no other circulatory difficulties, that you could even shorten your evaluation time from two hours to maybe thirty minutes?

DR. PAMPIGLIONE: Not for the flattening of the traces and not for the slow activity.

DR. KELLAWAY: In other words, if you had thirty minutes of an iso-electric EEG would you believe that recovery could take place?

DR. PAMPIGLIONE: I would not be in a position to say that everything is going to be lost—because I have seen patients who had what I would call a total electrical silence for periods up to an hour and did make a good recovery. For a reasonably accurate prognosis I would have to wait for a longer period. I suppose one can be in doubt whether one hour or two hours and if one wants to be safe it's better to consider two hours after resuscitation.

DR. DREYFUS-BRISAC: Do you find a correlation between paroxysmal burst activity and the degree or rate of hypothermia?

DR. PAMPIGLIONE: We have not seen the appearance of paroxysmal activity at a temperature above 25°C. The fall in temperature has to reach a particular level and it has to reach that level at a particular speed.

DR. GOLDRING: The occurrence of paroxysmal activity in animals subjected to hypothermia is very well documented. In our studies in the cat and dog we have noted that it does not happen in every animal but a significant number develop spontaneous paroxysmal activity. Upon stimulation of the optic nerve with light flashes paroxysmal activity may be triggered in animals whose temperature is lowered. Blood pressure was continually monitored in these animals and no significant pressure change occurred at the time of seizure occurrence. Wherever studied (brain, cord) in the CNS an increased excitability occurs during moderate hypothermia.

DR. PURPURA: I think there is an important factor here in the hypothermia seizure-type activity which should be noted. In experiments we have performed on rapidly cooled hypothermic animals we have noted cardiac irregularities and secondary disturbances in circulation. These disturbances in circulation are sufficient to trigger off the seizure phenomena, and unless you are really looking carefully at what is happening in the peripheral circulation and in the cardiac circulation you are not going to see that your seizure activity is secondary to the circulatory insult.

TRANSIENT HYPOXIC CRISES IN CHILDREN

ROBERT MAULSBY AND PETER KELLAWAY

*Department of Physiology, Baylor University College of Medicine,
Houston, Texas*

Introduction

The term "transient hypoxic crisis" refers to a specific type of childhood seizure which consists of brief loss of consciouness, with or without convulsive movements, following an emotional or painful stimulus. Attacks of this type have been shown to be on the basis of acute cerebral hypoxia (Low *et al.,* Gastaut and Gastaut, 1958, Gauk *et al.,* 1963) and are thus analagous to certain forms of syncope seen in adults. Transient hypoxic crises are relatively common in otherwise normal children and can be diagnosed as such from the typical clinical history, provided that other conditions such as cerebral convulsive disorders be ruled out.

The purpose of this paper is to give a clinical and electroencephalographic description of the hypoxic crises and to discuss the theories regard'ng the pathophysiological mechanisms involved.

Material

Our observations are based upon study of a series of 332 childern (167 males, 165 females) who were subject to typical hypoxic crises. Detailed descriptions of their attacks, past history and relevant physical and neurological findings were available in all cases. Standard electroencephalograms, including waking and sleeping records, were obtained in 328 cases. An ocular compression test was performed in 89 cases during simultaneous recording of the electroencephalogram and the electrocardiogram.

Clinical Description

Two different clinical types of hypoxic crises may be recognized from the descriptions of the attacks. Both of these commonly occur in the same child.

Type I is a characteristic, easily recognized attack which has been called "breath-holding spell" for many years. It has received this appellation because a prominent feature of the attack is cessation of respiration which appears as if the child "holds his breath." This type of hypoxic crisis is always precipitated by a sudden painful or emotional stimulus which causes the child to cry. After one or more brief, but forceful cries, the child loses consciousness while maintaing the expiratory phase of the final cry. Often the child's face is flushed or sometimes noticeably cyanotic at the onset of loss of consciousness. The child then becomes limp with his eyes "rolled up," and, in the mildest attacks, he then regains consciousness after a few seconds, usually with resumption of crying. In more prolonged episodes, the primary limp phase is followed by a tonic or opisthotonic phase which is sometimes associated with a few, brief jerks of the upper extremities and occasionally by incontinence of urine and/or feces. This "convulsive phase," if present, is then followed by another brief limp or atonic phase before consciousness is regained. It is apparent from case histories that there is a functional continuum from simple breath holding without loss of consciousness to the full-blown pattern in which breath holding is followed by unconsciouness and a tonic-clonic seizure.

The total duration of the attack is usually quite brief, ranging from two to twenty seconds, but some may last one or more minutes. Parents tend to describe the attacks as having durations of several minutes, but this is usually a psychological exaggeration of time due to anxiety produced by the situation.

Upon recovery of consciousness the child is usually quite normal, but he sometimes appears weak and pale. Sleep commonly follows the more prolonged or severe episodes.

Type II hypoxic crises often occur in individuals who also have typical breath-holding spells. This variant of transient hypoxic crises has not been previously described in the literature or, at least, it has not been differentiated from the Type I hypoxic crisis (breath-holding spell). The Type II hypoxic crisis is precipitated almost exclusively by sudden, unexpected, painful stimuli such as a blow to the head. The child, without crying and without any apparent conscious acknowledgment of the insult, suddenly falls limply unconscious. He may then quickly regain consciousness or he may have an opisthotonic and clonic seizure followed by another atonic phase before consciousness is regained. Usually there is no cyanosis. Although it is often not obvious to the observer, the child usually does not breathe during the initial phase of the attack, the respiration being arrested in the expiratory position.

Comparing the clinical features of these two types of hypoxic crisis, it should be noted that Type I or breath-holding spell consists of a respiratory reaction to an emotional or painful stimulus followed by a typical episode of syncope, with or without convulsive features. The respiratory reaction consists of a forceful cry which is sustained in the expiratory phase until consciousness is lost. This feature of the attack has lead to the term "breath-holding spell" and is the chief clinical feature which distinguishes it from the Type II attack in which there is very little respiratory reaction to the stimulus. The syncopal episode in a Type II hypoxic crisis is indistinguishable from that seen in a breath-holding spell.

Electroencephalographic Correlates

If one observes the electroencephalogram during either the Type I or Type II hypoxic crisis, a typical pattern of acute cerebral hypoxia is seen as first described in detail by Gastaut and Gastaut (1957, 1958). There is first a generalized slowing with appearance of high voltage "hypersynchronous" very slow waves in all areas. The child usually loses consciousness within 3 to 5 seconds after hypersynchronous slow activity begins. In brief episodes the hypersynchronous pattern then slowly diminishes and the record returns

to resting waking status as the child regains consciousness. In more prolonged episodes, the hypersynchronous pattern abruptly ends after 5 to 8
seconds, the record becoming essentially iso-electric in all areas simultaneously.
If present for 4 or more seconds, this iso-electric phase is accompanied by
the convulsive phase of the attack, rigidity, opisthotonous and perhaps myoclonic jerks. This progression of EEG changes is reversed during the recovery
phase. The iso-electric pattern is replaced by another phase of hypersynchronous slow activity in all leads which gradually diminishes as the record
returns to the resting waking status and the child regains consciousness.

Between attacks the routine electroencephalogram is characteristically
normal. Of 328 children referred to our EEG laboratory for hypoxic crises,
289 or 88.2 per cent had a normal EEG. Of the remaining 39 (11.8 per cent)
with abnormal EEG's, six showed the fourteen and six per second positive
spike pattern, three showed an active focal abnormality and thirty showed
nonspecific dysrhythmias of various degrees.

Pathophysiological Mechanisms

The mechanisms involved in production of these transient cerebral hypoxic
episodes have not as yet been established and are still a matter of dispute
among authorities working in this field. Let us first review some of the
theories which have been proposed, pointing out the numerous factors which
could be involved.

The neurogenic theory. Strauss (1957) noted that the loss of consciousness
seen in breath-holding seizures appeared after only a few seconds of breath
holding—a period which he considered to be insufficient to produce asphyxia
or a disturbance of venous return. From this observation he concluded that
"patients with breath-holding spells have a faulty cerebral mechanism which
makes unconsciousness appear as a reflex reaction to a variety of stimuli."
In his theory, breath-holding seizures are compared to catalepsy induced by
anger. The breath holding seen in an attack is regarded as merely superimposing hypoxia upon that which is primarily a neurogenic disturbance. No
clinical or experimental evidence is offered to support his hypothesis.

The hypocalcemic theory. Lennox (1960) proposed that the phenomena
seen in breath-holding seizures could be explained on the basis of hypocalcemia. The hyperventilation of crying, he says, induces alkalosis which causes
a decrease in the serum level of ionized calcium. This leads to tetany of
sudden onset and a brief period of apnea. Carbon dioxide accumulation during the period of apnea reverses the process. This form of hyperventilation
syndrome in infancy, he says, is similar to that seen in adults in response to
emotional situations, but the clinical pattern differs in that apnea is produced. Lennox attributes this to a "a more sensitive and unstable" respiratory
center in infants. He admits, however, that he is at a loss to explain why
many attacks occur after only a few brief cries which are hardly sufficient to
produce hyperventilation.

Self-asphyxiation theory. The simplest theory is that breath-holding is a
voluntary or semi-voluntary motor act on the part of emotionally disturbed

children in response to certain stimuli. Consciousness is lost and a seizure occurs as a result of cerebral hypoxia produced by simple self-asphyxia. This theory is held by several authors including Hinman and Dicky (1956) and Gauk, Kidd and Prichard (1963). The latter group studied two children during spontaneous breath-holding spells, monitoring respiration, pulse rate, intra-arterial blood pressure, EEG, and ear oxymetry. During the breath-holding spell they found that the pulse rate and intra-arterial blood pressure were slightly elevated while oxygen saturation at the ear fell progressively over a 30 second period to below 40 per cent. They concluded that these observations indicate that asphyxiative hypoxia is the chief pathophysiological mechanism in breath-holding seizures, but examination of their published data reveals a possible objection to their conclusion: They imply that consciousness was lost within the first 10 to 15 seconds after respiration has ceased; during this time oxygen saturation at the ear was in the range of 75 to 90 per cent—levels which we believe to be insufficient to account for the initial loss of consciousness in the absence of other factors. Furthermore, EEG changes were present within 10 seconds, at which time oxygen saturation was 90 per cent or above according to their chart!

Cerebral ischemia theory. British authors, Sharpey-Schafer (1956) and Vulliamy (1956) suggested that the loss of consciousness in breath-holding spells is on the basis of acute reduction in cerebral blood flow caused by a sharply raised intrathoracic pressure or Valsalva-like maneuver associated with the breath holding in the expiratory phase. In their concept, the attacks are a self-induced syncopal phenomenon similar to the "fainting lark" trick (Howard *et al.*, 1951). The initial crying produces hypocapneic cerebral vasoconstriction due to hyperventilation and, when the breath is suddenly held, maintaining expiratory effort, intrathoracic pressure is sharply raised producing a decrease in effective perfusion pressure in the cerebral circuit by increasing jugular venous pressure and/or by decreasing carotid arterial pressure. Adequate demonstration that such a Valsalva maneuver does occur in breath-holding spells (such as monitoring esophageal pressure) has not been accomplished, but there is some indirect evidence in this regard which will be discussed later. Certainly, this mechanism could account for the rapid loss of consciousness when the breath is held for a period of time insufficient to produce asphyxiation.

The hypervagotonia theory. Gastaut and Gastaut (1957, 1958) demonstrated that "anoxic convulsions" similar to breath-holding seizures could be produced by ocular compression (the oculocardiac reflex). By simultaneously monitoring EKG, EEG and respiration, they obtained data which indicated to them that the loss of consciousness in these reflexly induced attacks was due to acute cerebral hypoxia secondary to: (a) vagal cardiac arrest, (b) respiratory arrest sufficient to produce asphyxia, or (c) a combination of cardiac and respiratory inhibition. They concluded that the basic underlying mechanism of the clinical attacks is a "familial hypervagotonia" which, spontaneously reinforced by extero- and interoceptive stimuli bombarding the vagal brain stem centers, produces respiratory and cardiac inhibition responsible for the loss of consciousness and convulsions.

Other syncopal mechanisms. Several other possible pathophysiological mechanisms have been mentioned by various authors but not considered seriously. These include vasodepression, individual hypersensitivity to brief periods of minor hypoxia and abnormal circulatory phenomena such as left-to-right shunts opening up during the attacks. Vasodepression is considered unlikely since measurements of systemic blood pressure by Gauk *et al.*, (1963) revealed a slight rise during the attacks. Individual sensitivity to hypoxia and transient abnormal circulatory phenomena have not been evaluated in children with breath-holding spells.

Contributory factors. Certain auxillary factors seem to be important in the clinical incidence of transient hypoxic crises. Of 224 cases seen in our laboratory, 64 or 28.6 per cent had a positive family history of breath-holding spells—thereby suggesting a familial predisposition.

Holowach and Thurston (1963) found a significant anemia (defined as hemoglobin of less than 7.9 Gm. per 100 ml.) in 23.5 per cent of 160 cases of breath-holding spells, and they suggest that anemia may be a predisposing factor in the occurrence of breath-holding spells. In our own group of cases, however, 75 received hemoglobin determinations and only 8 or 10.6 per cent were found to have a hemoglobin level below 7.9 Gm. per 100 ml.

Age of the patient is important; in Figure 1 the black bars represent the percentage of 332 patients having the onset of their attacks in each three month period from birth to 42 months of age. Note the peak incidence between 6 and 15 months of age. The cross-hatched bars represent the age distribution of the same group of patients when they were first referred to our laboratory.

Observations during the ocular compression test. Actual clinical hypoxic crises are rarely observed in the laboratory, but, as first reported by Bridge *et al.* (1943), it is relatively easy to produce "artificial" hypoxic crises in these children by means of the oculocardiac reflex; and the clinical and electroencephalographic features of the resultant hypoxic episodes are quite similar to actual clinical attacks occurring in response to painful or emotional stimuli.

We now employ the ocular compression test routinely in the EEG Laboratory whenever a child is referred for attacks which might be hypoxic crises. A positive response (defined as one which shows typical hypoxic changes in the EEG) tends to confirm a clinical diagnosis of transient hypoxic crises since our previous studies indicate that 40 per cent of children with known hypoxic crises show a positive response whereas less than 2 per cent of children in the normal group will show such a response.

In the majority of patients who show a marked response to ocular compression, it appears that vagal cardiac arrest in the chief factor in production of an acute cerebral hypoxic episode. After as little as 4 to 5 seconds of reflexly induced asystole, there is marked EEG slowing and hypersynchrony. A longer period of asystole, usually 8 to 10 seconds, must occur for production of the

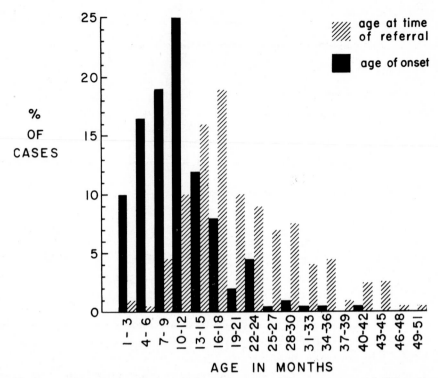

Fig. 1. Age incidence of transient hypoxic crises. The percentage of 332 patients having the onset of their attacks in each three month period from birth to 42 months of age is indicated by the black bars. Cross-hatched bars represent the age distribution of the same patients when they were first referred for electroencephalograms.

complete pattern with an iso-electric phase. More prolonged periods of asystole produce only longer iso-electric periods without altering the basic pattern. When normal heart beat is re-established, the typical EEG pattern begins to revert toward normal after a "lag" of abuot 6 to 9 seconds.

Figure 2 is a record of a typical EEG response to ocular compression. Note the period of asystole indicated by the EKG trace in channel 8.

It is interesting that one "escape" beat of the heart in a 6 to 8 second period of asystole seems to be enough to prevent the typical clinical and EEG changes which would otherwise occur in such a prolonged period of asystole. Figure 3A illustrates this phenomenon in a child 4½ years old. Older children and adults may have cardiac arrest for as long as 10 to 12 seconds without any change in the EEG. Figure 3B shows a 27 year old who had 7 seconds of asystole without even a hint of EEG change.

The cardiac arrest produced by ocular compression can, by itself, account for the acute cerebral hypoxia observed during this procedure. In the few clinical episodes of Type II hypoxic crisis observed in our laboratory which were provoked by an unexpected pinch or slap, a significant period of asystole was noted—suggesting that this reflex mechanism may be "hypersensitive"

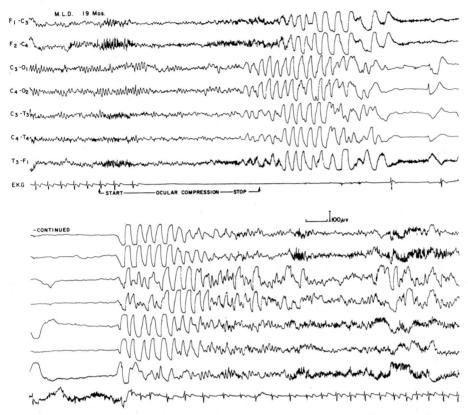

Fig. 2. Typical "positive" response to ocular compression.

and capable of initiation by painful stimuli in various parts of the body, particularly in the distribution of the trigeminal nerve as was originally suggested by Bridge *et al.* (1943) and later asserted by Gastaut and Gastaut (1958). Further support of this theory of the mechanism of Type II hypoxic crises is afforded by the observation that children who have easily reproducible hypoxic crises of this type may be rendered completely insensitive to the usual provocative stimuli by adequate atropinization.

Figure 4 is a record showing the EEG and EKG in a 26 month old child during a typical spontaneous breath-holding spell or Type I hypoxic crisis. Note that in this instance, as in most typical breath-holding spells, there is no cardiac arrest. This necessarily indicates that some mechanism other than vagal cardiac arrest must be involved in production of the cerebral hypoxia during a Type I hypoxic crisis. Assuming that one of the mechanisms reviewed above is operative in this instance and that Type I and Type II hypoxic crises have different pathophysiological mechanisms, we must still search for a common factor in order to account for the fact that both types of hypoxic crises usually occur in the same individual.

If one monitors respiration during ocular compression, a characteristic

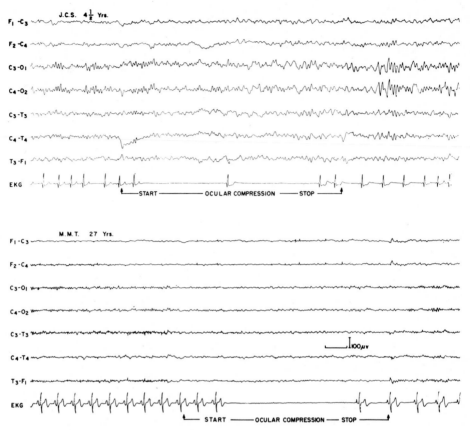

Fig. 3. "Negative" responses to ocular compression. *A* (top): One escape beat in a ten second period of asystole seems to prevent typical electroencephalographic changes. *B* (bottom): No change in electroencephalogram during a seven second period of asystole in an adult.

pattern is almost invariably observed. This consists of prolonged expiration, usually with an initial audible cry or "whine." The forced expiratory effort is usually begun simultaneously with cardiac arrest, and it is maintained during cardiac arrest into the phase of EEG hypersynchrony and iso-electric phase during which the child is otherwise unconscious, limp or convulsing—thus suggesting that this "breath-holding" is an involuntary, subcortical component of the reaction to ocular compression. The first inspiratory gasp, or relaxation of expiratory effort, usually occurs *after* EEG recovery has begun. These effects can be demonstrated indirectly by electromyographic studies of the abdominal expiratory muscles. Figures 5A and 5B are records from two typical cases during ocular compression. Although intra-esophageal pressure has not been monitored during this procedure, the prolonged contractions of the expiratory musculature suggests that a situation similar to the Valsalva maneuver may be present during ocular compression. The electromyographic

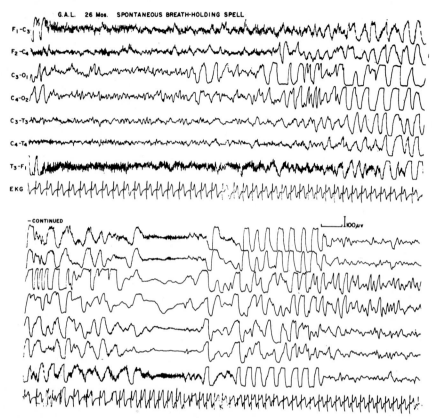

Fig. 4. Spontaneous breath-holding spell in a 26 month old child.

pattern of the abdominal expiratory muscles is quite similar during spontaneous breath-holding spells. This is illustrated in Figure 6A and B. The upper tracing is from a 25 month old child during ocular compression. The lower tracing illustrates the comparable abdominal EMG pattern obtained during a spontaneous breath-holding spell.

An hypothesis. Although fragmentary, these data suggest a possible common mechanism which might relate the two types of hypoxic crises: The cardiac arrest (seen during ocular compression and during Type II hypoxic crises) and the respiratory response (seen during ocular compression, but most prominent in Type I hypoxic crises or breath-holding spell) could be simply two variably associated responses which are elicitable by emotional or painful stimuli and are mediated by a common brain stem reflex pathway. In this concept, one or the other response pattern may predominate in any given situation. The respiratory response, prolonged forceful expiratory effort, appears to be the most constant expression of the "reflex." The cardiac response may or may not occur; when it does consciousness is more quickly lost as is evident from the description of Type II attacks. The end result is the same in both cases—syncope due to cerebral hypoxia.

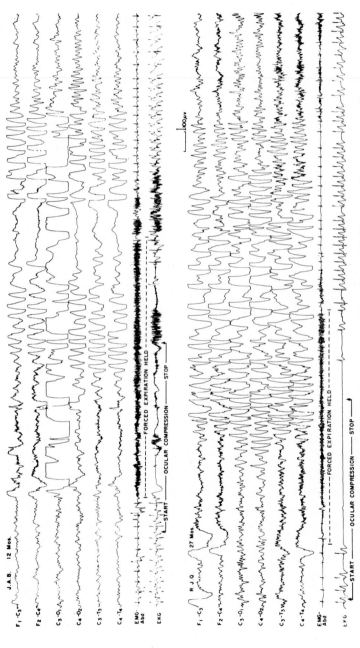

Fig. 5. **Responses to ocular compression.** Channel 7 of each tracing is the electromyogram from a pair of electrodes applied to the abdominal expiratory muscles. A (top): 12 month old child. B (bottom): 27 month old child.

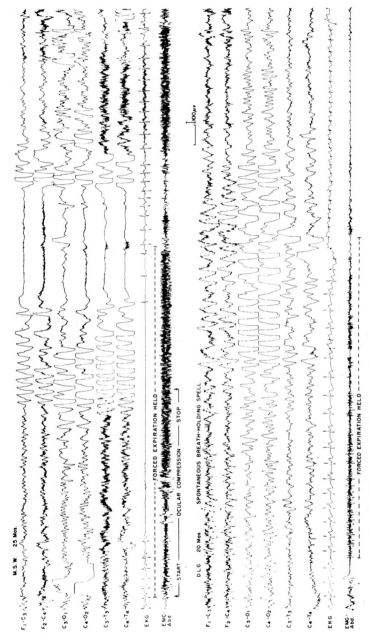

Fig. 6. Comparison between the response to ocular compression and a spontaneous breath-holding spell. Channel 8 of each tracing is the electromyogram from a pair of electrodes applied to the abdominal expiratory muscles. A (top): 25 month old child during ocular compression. B (bottom): 20 month old child during a spontaneous breath-holding spell.

REFERENCES

BRIDGE, E. M., LIVINGSTON, S. and TIETZE, C. Breath-holding spells. *J. Pediat.*, *1943*, 23:539–561.

GASTAUT, H. and GASTAUT, Y. Syncopes et convulsions. *Rev. Neurol.*, *1957*, 96:158–163.

GASTAUT, H. and GASTAUT, Y. Electroencephalographic and clinical study of anoxic convulsions in children. *Electroenceph. Clin. Neurophysiol.*, *1958*, 10: 607–620.

GAUK, E. W., KIDD, L. and PRICHARD, J. S. Mechanisms of seizures associated with breath-holding spells. *New Engl. J. Med.*, *1963*, 268:1436–1440.

HINMAN, A. and DICKEY, L. B. Breath-holding spells—A review of the literature and eleven additional cases. *A.M.A. J. Dis. Child.*, *1956*, 91:23–33.

HOLOWACH, J. and THURSTON, D. L. Breath-holding spells and anemia. *New Engl. J.*

Med., *1963*, 268:21–23.

HOWARD, P., LEATHART, G. L., DORNHORST, A. C. and SHARPEY-SCHAFER, E. P. The "mess trick" and the "fainting lark." *Brit. Med. J.*, *1951*, 2:382–384.

LENNOX, W. G. *Epilepsy and Related Disorders*, Little, Brown and Co., Boston, *1960*, pp. 389–392.

LOW, N. L., GIBBS, E. L. and GIBBS, F. A. Electroencephalographic findings in breath-holding spells. *Pediatrics*, *1955*, 15:595–599.

SHARPEY-SCHAFER, E. P. Emergencies in general practice: syncope. *Brit. Med. J.*, *1956*, 1:506–509.

STRAUSS, H. Electroencephalographic observations on the mechanism of breath-holding spells. *Electroenceph. and Clin. Neurophysiol.*, *1957*, 9:164.

VULLIAMY, D. G. Breath-holding attacks. *Practitioner*, *1956*, 177:517–519.

DISCUSSION

DR. PRICHARD: Do you think the slow activity is due to hypoxia or is it a central mechanism?

DR. MAULSBY: I think that both the slow activity and the period of electrical silence are purely hypoxic effects. Of course, the best way to prove this would be to measure oxygen availability in the cerebral tissue at the time these patterns appear. I have never seen this type of pattern produced neurogenically.

DR. PRICHARD: What do you think about ocular compression as a routine procedure? Put it this way, what's the longest cardiac arrest you have induced?

DR. KELLAWAY: There have been no complications in well over a thousand instances of ocular compression. The longest period of cardiac arrest was about 22 or 23 seconds. The only possibility that I could think of that the heart would stop permanently would be if there was some other complicating condition present.

DR. LOMBROSA: Did I understand that you were able to prevent both the EEG and clinical manifestations of these spells by atropine?

DR. KELLAWAY: We atropinized a group of patients in which these spells were easily elicited, not only by ocular compression but by some brief unpleasant stimulus and we found that the cardiac response and the clinical attacks were both blocked.

Index